THE GOLDEN AGE OF PLANT HUNTERS

By the same author :

THE COVERED GARDEN
GARDENING IN THE NORTH
COOL GREENHOUSE PLANTS
INDOOR PLANTS

Contributor to :

THE SHELL GARDENS BOOK

The
GOLDEN AGE
OF PLANT HUNTERS

Kenneth Lemmon

SOUTH BRUNSWICK
NEW YORK: A. S. BARNES AND COMPANY

THE GOLDEN AGE OF PLANT
HUNTERS. © Text, Kenneth Lemmon,
1968. First American edition published
1969 by A. S. Barnes and Company,
Inc., Cranbury, New Jersey 08512.

Library of Congress Catalogue Card Number: 73-81686

SBN 498 07395 5
Printed in the United States of America

Contents

Illustrations

✕⁘✕

COLOUR PLATES

All the colour plates are reproduced from William Curtis's *Botanical Magazine*, by kind permission of the Royal Horticultural Society.

BLACK AND WHITE PLATES

Preface

In this book I have attempted to pay some slight tribute to the backroom men of flora—the plant hunters, or 'botanical travellers' as Sir Joseph Banks preferred to call them, without whose almost superhuman efforts and great personal sacrifice our gardens would never have been the scenes of beauty they are today.

To tell only the stories of these men, most of them unchronicled, unhonoured and unsung, except in scattered letters, unpublished journals and odd corners of other people's books and writings, might well have seemed but a biographical tribute to their labours. But the seventy years or so of their endeavours, from Cook's first voyage of 1768 to John Gibson's return to Chatsworth in 1836, saw the hitherto insurmountable problems of plant transportation from foreign lands closely studied and finally conquered.

It is this which makes the period dealt with in this work so vitally important and, I venture to assert, of the greatest interest to British gardeners and gardens.

The same seventy years saw a great wealth of plants brought into this country despite the early difficulties—a wealth of floral treasure plucked from the heart of tropic and subtropic lands by men who would and did die for a flower.

I should like to think that the reader when he has laid down this book will go into his garden to find his heart quicken and his sympathies go out to the courageous adventurers, aware now of their intrepid exploits, as he sees the diversity and beauty of a herbaceous border, the nobility of the trees, the forms and colours of innumerable shrubs, the gay pelargoniums, the glories of autumn colour of the *rhus* and the acers, the glory of an orchid house and the strange but compelling beauty of the stove-house and greenhouse. He could well remember that not a single non-native plant he sees is there without the blood, sweat and tears of the botanical travellers.

I cannot conclude this preface without acknowledging with sincere thanks the help of many people—my wife for her patience and forbearance when research has taken so much of my time and left her in solitary state, Mr W. R. Elgie for hours of work, reading proofs and manuscript and for the thankless task of indexing, to Mr F. Beckwith, librarian of the Leeds Library, for drawing my attention to so many clues leading to profitable reading, to Mr Roy Woodlock for valuable help with the typing of manuscript and notes, to Mr A. Simmons and the staffs of the Royal Horticultural Society's Lindley Library and to my many gardening friends, both professional and amateur, who are always ready to lend an ear to an author's problems and give of their experience and knowledge.

KENNETH LEMMON

MORLEY,
    December 1967

1. Plant Hunting Started Early

THE first time primitive man tore a plant from the wild to grow near his rough homestead, instead of snatching at any edible leaf or fruit on his way through the forest, the first step to civilization was taken.

It was the first revolutionary and epoch-making act which changed man from a wild, nomadic hunter to a settler, a domesticated being. From this first step, in all probability a chance grasping of a wild plant, arose the first plant hunter.

And while the thousands of years passed which brought *Homo sapiens* from a being little above the animals he hunted to the man of the clearing, the settlement, and from that to the embryo village, to the town, the city, the state, the passage of time also gave him the opportunity to look around, to appreciate that there was more in his life than the sheer adventure and misadventure of snatching at an existence. The desire grew in him to surround himself, his home, his temples and his cities with vegetative treasures of usefulness and beauty.

The desire fired a covetous ambition which initially could often be satisfied only by marauding raids of people and tribes when, as an incidental of victory, trees and flowers were among the booty carried home by the conquerors. Sometimes, when the conquerors settled in the country of the vanquished, the traffic was two-way, for the conqueror settling in an alien country sighed for his familiar background of trees, fruit and flowers and, having them brought over as seeds or seedlings, he added the plants and trees of his country as exotics in the foreign one.

Later—much later—came the civilized plant hunters who went out into the mountains, the plains and the jungles of the world to distribute the natural beauties of the earth on a world-wide basis.

We first come across documented evidence of plant hunting in Egypt nearly five thousand years ago when Sankhkara, one of the pharaohs, sent ships down the Red Sea to the Gulf of Aden after cinnamon, and for cassia used in embalming the dead. Throughout the centuries of Egyptian civilization, by conquest and by travel, almost all the useful and beautiful natural products of the Middle East were brought to the Nile valley and naturalized there. There is a magnificent record of one of the first plant-hunting expeditions on the walls of the great temple at Karnak, where Queen Hatshepsut's great sea caravan to Punt (perhaps Somaliland/Abyssinia) to obtain growing specimens of the incense tree (*Commiphora myrrha*) is shown in vivid detail. Five great-sailed, many-oared ships are shown in harbour while slaves in pairs with carrying sticks on their shoulders take aboard growing trees, their roots and balls of earth strapped in woven baskets. Already the decks are full of the trees.

As history shows all too tragically, the most resplendent of civilizations totter into ruin, but fortunately for human development not before its conquerors or its beneficiaries inherit its treasures of mind and nature. So it was, ultimately, that the Greeks took over from the Egyptians and so in turn it was that to a dismal British landscape of birch scrub, oaks, Scots pine and holly the Romans brought variety, charm, colour and usefulness. Indirectly the finds of those earliest of plant hunters of the Nile, of the ancient biblical lands and of the Mediterranean seaboard, were now to become part of the British landscape so far as the climate would allow. For the Romans, as they settled in their forts and in their villas up and down the length of the country, planted their native vegetation.

What a wealth of natural beauty and utility they brought! The plane tree, the lime, the chestnut, the sorbus, the box, the elm, the pear, the cherry, the vine, the damson, the quince, the peach, the mulberry, the fig, the rose, the medlar, the hyacinth, rosemary, thyme, cabbage, leeks, onions, radishes, parsley and lettuce.

After the Romans left the country, for hundreds of years horticulture as an art almost totally disappeared, though of course, even when they ran into a wild state, many of the plants and trees that had been brought here grew and multiplied.

While it was a conqueror and a conquest which brought for us the first tremendous benefits of the plant hunters, it was the spread of Christianity which maintained and added to those benefits. As the monks came over from Europe to found and fill the monasteries, the first of which was founded in Britain in the sixth century, they brought with them the plants wherewith to fill the herb gardens which provided so integral a part of their diet. Here also they grew the madonna lily and the rose with which to decorate the high altar, and brought in from the wild or reimported from Europe, where the Byzantine Empire had kept the floral torch alight, almost all the present-day inhabitants of our herb gardens for flavouring and for making the necessary simples and medicines.

Over the hundreds of years of monastic life in Britain flower gardens were added to, orchards were planted, the vine was grown, trees were planted both for ornament and shelter. From the Continent came the iris (*germanica*), the paeony (*officinalis*) and the poppy (*rhoeas*).

Meanwhile, and up to the dissolution of the monasteries in 1539, gardens had broken the bounds of the purely herb gardens and the restricted confines of Norman castles, spilling out into the less formal gardens of manor houses and less fortified homes. From 1095 to 1270 the Crusades had taken volunteers from this country and Europe into Africa, the lands of the Near East generally, and right to the very doors of Asia at Constantinople.

There crusading Englishmen, often of high birth and vast property, and some-times educated, saw growing for the first time the fabulous spoils of the Arabs and Portuguese, the spoils of trade routes by land and sea which had led to far Cathay. They saw among many rarities the orange, the lemon, the pomegranate, anemones, tulips, the cedars of Lebanon, the soaring cypress, the squat ugly olives and the graceful myrtles. Some they tried to establish in their own country by way of seed, but the time was not yet ripe, no glasshouse tradition had arisen to cope with such rarities. But woven into the adventure and colour of the Crusades were the memories and legends of a glorious natural wealth unknown to British gardens. It was still herbs for the herbalist and physician which were all important, grown as handy as might be, so that the gardens to Elizabeth's day were invariably simple gardens belonging to the doctors or their suppliers.

Commerce and diplomacy between Britain and Europe with its royal houses and seat of the papal power saw to it that from the Crusades onwards Britain was very much a part of Europe, taking, as it were, its products, styles, manners, fashions, as well as its gardening practices and fruits as part of the background to aristocratic living; so when Wolsey, with his love of the Italianate, gardened, his model was some magnificent ducal villa of the Campagna. His king, Henry VIII, followed suit, and there arose a desire for the unusual and rare so that seeds and plants would often accompany state papers in the ornate wallets of courtier and statesmen diplomats of the day on their travels throughout Europe. The herb garden as such was facing its first competition.

But it is William Turner to whom we must now turn to learn at first hand about plant hunting. Turner, a native of Morpeth, had spent much of his early life in such botanical centres as Basle, Strasbourg, Bonn, Cologne, Padua (which had the first botanical garden in Europe) and at Bologna in the botanical garden there, looking at plants and learning about them.

In 1551 Turner was Doctor of Physics at Oxford and was given Sion House garden, hard by Kew, to look after. *Hortus Kewensis* gives a long list of plants first recorded or introduced by him, including *Laurus nobilis* from Italy, *Jasminum officinalis* from the East Indies, *artemisia*, the juniper, the walnut, *cistus*, lavender, *genista* and an antir-rhinum from Italy.

After the troubles of Henry and Mary, Elizabeth's reign brought expansion, trade and commerce with the world. British ships and men were anchoring in strange far-off harbours and, as said William Harrison, Dean of Windsor, in his *Description of England*, 1577: 'Strange herbs, plants and annual fruits are daily brought unto us from the Indies, America, Caprobane [Ceylon], Canary Isles and all parts of the world.' Indeed, the

story goes that Sir Walter Raleigh brought over the first orange pips to give to his
kinsman, Sir Francis Carew, to grow the first orange trees in England at Beddington in
Surrey. Sir Walter also brought the potato home, by way of his agent, Thomas Heriot.

There was now growing up a race of gardeners in their own right, men who could
take over the gardening ambitions of the great nobles, men with gardening connections
in many lands. L'Obel from Lille, who had lived in Antwerp and who had the horticultural knowledge of the Low Countries at his finger-tips, gardened for Lord Zouche
at Hackney. He described many new plants, including the yucca, and grew plants
brought from abroad by his master. There was the thorn apple (*datura*), the 'small
candy mustard', the dog's tooth violet, *Lychnis chalcedonica*, from Constantinople, and
Vitex agnus castus.

Contemporary with L'Obel was Nicholas Lete, a London merchant trading with the
Levant, a great lover of gardening who plant-hunted in France. He was responsible for
the introduction of the Persian fritillary, Parkinson saying of it: 'It was first brought
from Persia into Constantinople and from thence sent to us by the means of divers
turkie merchants and in especial by the procurement of Mr Nicholas Lete.' He sent
another London gardener, John Gerard, the Turks-cap lily and in return John wrote of
him that he was so 'greatly in love with rare and fair floures and plants, he doth carefully send into Syria having a servant there at Allepo and in many other countries for
the which my selfe and likewise the whole land are much bound unto him'. Gerard
lists a cabbage of Lete's introduction 'with crincly leaves of a blewish green' and 'a
yellow gillyflower from Persia'.

The pen of John Gerard (1545–1612) singled out many plant hunters who sent their
spoils to grow at his famous physic garden at Holborn or to that of his master, Lord
Burleigh. His introductions from abroad were many as the result of his fame as a
'green-fingered' gardener and because of his aristocratic connections. He grew many
tulips, which arrived in England about 1578 after the bulbs had been filched from
Suleiman the Magnificent by Busbecq, ambassador from Vienna in 1554, and found
their way by devious and clandestine routes. From Padua he received *helichrysum* (the
everlasting flower), Solomon's seal from Charles de L'Ecluse, the famous Flemish
botanist and author. Gerard's own collector in the Mediterranean brought him seeds
and plants of the prickly pear. Jean Robin, gardener and botanist to Henry II of
France, sent Gerard many rare seeds from his Paris garden, including *Epimedium
alpinum*. Lord Zouche sent seeds from Crete, Italy and Spain, while Lord Hunsdon,
Elizabeth's envoy to France, sent him 'other rarities from the farthest points of the
world'. And thus there was an ever-increasing number of exotics which could be seen
growing in the garden at Holborn: *Clematis pedicellata* from Majorca, *Cistus incanus* from
the south of Europe, roses from France and Germany, *Hibiscus syriacus* from Syria,
Lonicera alpigina from Switzerland, *Cornus mas* from Austria, *Philadelphus coronarius*
from Europe, viburnums, phlomis and *Daphne gnidium* from Spain and a host of others.
Loudon put the number of plants introduced into this country during the sixteenth
century at eighty-four, a vast difference indeed from the dark floral ages of the past.

In direct line of descent from the Gerards and Letes of the gardening world were the Tradescants, gardeners and plant hunters extraordinary to the royal house and to the gentry.

The Tradescants, father and son, must be recorded as among the very first British plant hunters. John, the father, travelled much in Europe, the son in Virginia. While John Tradescant's hunting was of a nature much more mercenary than romantic, the two of them did introduce a remarkable variety and novelty to the English gardening scene. These included the first lilac, gladioli, lupins, the pomegranate, the *hypericum* and many crocuses.

Some of the early bargaining experiences of the elder Tradescant in the European markets, principally stocked by the Dutch from their overseas possessions at the Cape and in the East Indies, are still extant in the Hatfield correspondence, for he bought some of these early plants for the first Earl of Salisbury. From Lady Amherst's researches into the original papers can be noted what was available and what was the cost of those early rarities.

For instance, on 3rd January 1611 he paid £3 at Leyden in Holland 'for roots of flowers of roasses and shrubs of strong and rare'. From Harlem he bought 'rathe ripe cherry trees, 32 at 4/– the peece £6/8/–; for flowers called anemones, 5/– for 16 Province roses, 8/– for two mulberry trees, 6/– for the great red currants, six plants; for two arbor vitae trees 1/–, 40 frittelarias at 3 pence the peece 10/–'.

He bought fruit in Brussels and in Paris bought 'eight pots of orange trees of on[e] years growthe grafted at 10/– the peece, £4' and 200 'sypris trees' for £10.

John Tradescant's bill for plants came to £110 8s. 9d. and travelling expenses were additional. For transporting this European treasure he used baskets and hampers and bought padlocks to keep thieving hands out.

In 1618 he went farther, but still within the temperate zone, when he travelled to Russia with his neighbour, Sir Dudley Digges, exploring for plants on the islands of the delta of the Dvina and round about Archangel, from where he brought the first list ever made of Russian plants. Landing at Archangel he found the yellow cranberry in fruit, dried the berries and sent the seed to Jean Robin at the Jardin des Plantes in Paris. On the banks of the Dvina he found a 'single rose wonderous sweet with many other things I mean to bring with me'.

He also carefully took shoots of bird cherry and dogwood loaded with berries, but, like so many plant hunters after him, fell foul of the sailors, for the ship's boy ate all but a few and gave the plants salt water instead of fresh so that many withered away.

It was but two years afterwards that Tradescant joined an expedition, ostensibly as a gentleman adventurer to harry the pirates on the Corsair coast, sailing in a merchant-man of twenty-four guns, but on his landfalls he collected plants not pirates, bringing back with him the Algerian apricot, no doubt as a handful of stones.

The son, also John Tradescant, travelled in Virginia, America, in 1637, 1642 and 1654, from where his introductions included the michaelmas daisy (*Aster tradescantia*), monarda (*Monarda fistulosa*), *Rhus cotinus*, the American plane tree (*Platanus occidentalis*), the tulip tree (*Liriodendron tulipifera*), the American walnut, the grape vine, *Vitis vulpina* and *V. labrusca*, the red maple (*Acer rubrum*), the deciduous cypress (*Taxodium distichum*), the acacia (*Robinia pseudo-acacia*), the daffodil called *plenissimus* and the spiderworts (*Tradescantia*) named after this great family of early plant hunters. Whether the introductions were by means of plants or seed there is no record.

When early attempts were made to collect plants from the New World and the Indies, difficulties, disappointments quite other than climatic and portative befraught the would-be importers. John Evelyn writing in 1681 to William London in Barbados bemoaned the fact that the 'Hollanders' in the East Indies would not let an exotic or economic plant out of their 'graspe'. 'Concerning nutmegs, cinnamon, cloves and those other aromatics you so reasonably covet I feare it will be a very difficult province to obtain such of them from the East Indies, they being mostly in possession of Hollanders who are (you know) a jealous people and as I have been informed make it capital to transport as much as a single nutmeg (I meane such a one as being set would produce a tree) out of their countrie; the late Sir John Cox who had often been at Nova Batavia told me he could not procure one handful but such as were effete and deprived of their sprouting principles, upon any termes, much less could he obtain a plant.'

He went on to tell his correspondent that he himself had grown and given to others to grow 'some forraine and exotic seedes' but with very little success. He wondered whether some 'subtil and industrious person might not smuggle a seed or two from the plantations (and why not?)' he asked, 'as that countrie man of ours, who some years since brought home the first heads of saffron out of Greece (whence it was death to transport) in the hollow head or top of his pilgrim staff'.

'After all,' he concluded, 'our western climate has already benefited from the importing of sugar, ginger, indigo and other beneficial spices and drougs.'

And the real enthusiasts did try, for Evelyn was advising the Earl of Sandwich, who was then (1688) ambassador at the Court of Spain, to bring home 'seedes, such especially as we may not have common only in our countrie'. He inquired also whether the noble earl could not bring over 'some of those quince and cherry trees which Your Lordship so celebrates'. The earl had been writing earlier to Evelyn in high praise of these trees and John was envious of them: 'Why', he asked, 'could not the plants be secured in barrils or packed up as they transport other rarities from far countries?'

Some eighteen years later he was importuning his friend Samuel Pepys, secretary of the Admiralty Board, for seeds and plants by way of a Captain Nicholson, whom both of them had entertained to dinner just before he sailed out to New England on duty.

Evelyn writes: 'The ingenuity and extraordinary industrie of the Gent. by what I both learned from the character you gave him, and what I myself could observe on so short a time, together with your interest in him makes me not willing to omitt so favourable an opportunitie of putting this note into his hands, through yours; and that it may comply with his diversion, when he is in the countrie, to collect any of these (or other) natural productions of the vegetable kingdome; you (who were first pleased to recommend me to him) will give him leave that they may be sent consigned under your auspicious name to, Sir, your most humble and continually obliged servant, J. Evelyn.' From New England he wanted seeds of the white cedar, seeds and plants of larch, lime, hemlock and poplar and tulip tree; also nuts and plants of the filbert tree, seeds of all kinds of 'firrs' and 'Nutts of pines and wall nutts of all kinds'. He wanted both seed and plants of all sorts of plums and plants only of the sarsaparilla. From Virginia he asked for seeds and plants of 'the benjamin [*Ficus benjamina*], gumme and sugargras [*Acer saccharinum*] trees, stones and plants of the date palm, seedes and plants of the pappaw tree, nutts and plants of the chinquapine, plants of the sumac tree (three kinds) seedes of the cedar of Virginia and seedes and plants and acorns and plants of the maple tree bearing keys of crimson colour, the peacock taile tree and oakes of six kinds'.

The advice accompanying the plant list is particularly detailed and shows quite clearly the means of seed and plant preservation in use at the time. Evelyn writes: 'The seedes are best preserved in papers; their names written on them and put in a box. The nutts in barrils of dry sand; each kind wrapped in papers written on.

'The trees in barrils their rootes wraped about mosse; the smaller the plants and trees the better; or they will do well packed up in matts; but the barril is best, and a small vessel will contain enough of all kinds, labells of paper tyed to every sort with ye name. . . .

'Some are of the opinion that plants or rootes that come from abroad will be better preserved if they are rubbed over with honey before they are covered with mosse, pretending that the honey has a styptic quality to hinder the moisting that is in the plants from perspiring. But if they are to come by a short journey of eight days or thereabouts honey would not then be necessary and covering them with mosse a little would suffice without.

''Tis thus layers and slips are transported from parts beyond the sea, or else you take a piece of potter's earth as big as your fist, temper it with honey and thrust into it four or five layers or slips and after having wrapped them up in wet mosse you lay them in boxes which you must likewise fill with the same mosse if there be occasion for it, and these sorts of plants being thus ordered and packed up will be able to undergo a long voyage without damage.'

One of the outstanding figures of the seventeenth-century gardening scene, an amateur to oust all amateurs, was Dr Henry Compton, Bishop of London from 1675 to 1713, who made his Fulham Palace garden a mecca for visiting botanists, lovers of the curious, and all with an eye for a new plant from foreign parts. Switzer wrote of 'a thousand species of exotick plants in his stoves and gardens' and Ray lists among these the tulip tree, the magnolia, the sassafras tree, the tree angelica (*Aralia spinosa*), the hickory, the box elder, the liquidambar, *Atriplex, Cornus, Rhus, Arbutus unedo*, Virginian red cedar and *Cupressus sempervirens*.

It will be noted that many of the 'exoticks' of Fulham were trees, and many were

certainly seen there for the first time in England. 'It would be interesting to know',
writes Loudon, 'the means by which Bishop Compton procured his trees and shrubs
from America and who were the botanical collectors of that day.'

But it seems that the botanical bishop did more than carefully tend his rarities; his
episcopal diligence was all-embracing and extended in his missionary work to plant
collecting. To the virgin woods of the New World and their native heathen Indians he
sent a young parson, the Reverend John Banister, as missionary, who along with his
theological requisites for conversion must have carried a fair knowledge of conservation. Whether on Christian or botanical duties the records are not explicit, but before
he travelled to the American continent the Reverend John had spent some time in the
West Indies where he had certainly noted the plant life, for a list of the plants written up
by him can still be seen at the Oxford Botanic Garden.

But it was to the North American flora that he devoted most of his missionary-cum-
botanical life. He is noted as the first English plant hunter there and in 1681 sent a plant
list of his finds to his patron. He did much more than write, however, for it is almost
certain that many of the good bishop's introductions were from Banister's North
American seeds and small trees sent directly to Fulham, including *Crataegus coccinea,
Cornus sericea, Baccharis halimifolia, Laurus benzoin, Liquidambar styraciflua, Magnolia
glauca, M. longifolia, Negundo fraxinifolium, Spiraea opalifolia, Rhus copallina, Aralia
spinosa, Menispermum canadense, Quercus coccinea, Ostyra virginica, Abies balsamifera,
Gleditschia triacanthos, Abies alba* and *Abies nigra.* The Reverend John Banister served
his master and the goddess Flora well, and to the bitter end, for he was one of the many
botanical martyrs who gave their lives for green treasure. In 1692 he fell from a rock on
one of his Virginian explorations and was killed.

Banister's introductions, either by way of seed or infant trees packed in moss in
casks and boxes, must have been under the watchful care of sympathetic sea captains,
who would be much more amenable and sensible to a parson's plea for the safe conduct
of the precious cargo and a bishop's blessings on their safe arrival than to the appeals
of an ordinary gardener. This must have been so or Bishop Compton's garden would
never have been the showplace it was. Unfortunately, details of his seed and plant
preserving methods do not accompany the contemporary plant lists, and it would seem
a practical assumption that they were similar to those used later by the celebrated North
American plant hunter, John Bartram, the honest God-fearing Quaker, who from 1735
until 1768 supplied hundreds of plants and thousands of seeds from North America
with recorded success, albeit with many failures too, to Peter Collinson, a fellow
Quaker and London woollen draper.

Bartram's methods, evolved out of practical hit-or-miss experiments, also owed
much to Collinson's instructions which he himself contrived as a result of handling the
seeds and plants sent over in London river and, later, in his own garden and stoves, as
well as those of the many patrons he served.

It was the patrons who made this early plant commerce possible, for their financing
of the project at ten guineas a year triggered off Bartram's long and arduous journeys on

foot and by pack-horse through the Indian-held and Indian-ridden forest lands of North America from Philadelphia to Lake Ontario. In the many letters between Bartram and Collinson, still in existence, we are able to get fascinating glimpses of plant hunting, plant discovery and plant transport.

Two trumpet-shaped leaves of *Sarracenia*, wrapped in moss, from Bartram, which subsequently were forwarded to Linnaeus, were accompanied by a plant hunter's excitement at the discovery and a plantsman's love of natural treasure in the wild. 'If you could only see', reads the letter, 'how the many leaves grow around the centre bud which makes a pretty appearance with the mouth open to catch rains and dews; many poor insects lose their lives by being drowned in these cisterns.'

One method of preserving new and uncommon seedlings on their long forest trek which was suggested by Collinson was to get ox bladders, cut off the neck as high as possible and hang them on a saddle pommel. Then when Bartram came across his new plant he could carefully dig it from its bed, and with some of its native earth still around its roots he could put it into the bladder, add a little more soil and a modicum of water, then tie up the neck close around the stock of the plant, leaving leaves and flowers to bloom freely in the air. Paper sent out from London, probably in the vessels in which Collinson sent cloth for the New Englanders, was made up by Bartram into bags, small, middle-sized and big, to hold newly gathered seeds, which were then put into the basket-work panniers he had slung one on each side of his saddle. He speaks at one time of having collected fifty different seeds of North American wild flowers which he had carefully dried before sending to London. Later he speaks of choosing the right time of the year to collect cones of rose laurel, white pine, seeds of sassafras and other berries and balm seed. Failures were reported by Collinson often; for instance, on one occasion the plant cases had been put on deck with pipe staves on top of them and rats had eaten both the roots and the branches so that only one solitary stump remained of a North American rarity. Bartram was also taken to task for making his cases too big, too heavy and too stout; one weighed 300 pounds, forcing Collinson to complain and advise more and smaller packing cases. A quite successful method, cheating the rats, with reasonable handling on the voyage and a quick customs clearance at London docks, Collinson persuaded, was to lift the young plants or the infant trees, still growing in a fair-sized sod; and what a delightful bonus this method often paid, for Collinson would occasionally find the grass full of little seedling wild plants, sometimes even orchis, growing all around the initial seedling tree or shrub.

'Why not just lift sods from the wild, boggy places?' asked Collinson, for that was where most of the rare and odd plants thrived. He asked too that seeds be put into bottles filled with earth or sand the better for them to withstand the journey and the vermin. Bartram's introductions were indeed extensive and outstanding; he sent, it is calculated, some 320 species of North American plants to this country, or, as John himself put it: 'I have sent seeds of almost every tree and shrub from Nova Scotia to Carolina.'

These seeds and plants distributed by Collinson to the many noble patrons and by them to their friends must have had an ever-growing effect on the gardeners of the country, whose horizons must have been widened considerably, and their envy aroused and their acquisitiveness put on edge.

The matter and the plates too, in Mark Catesby's eye-opening *Natural History of Carolina, Florida and the Bahama Islands*, the first section of which was published in 1731, with its beautifully figured plates of North American trees new to Britain, created a furore. Later Loudon said of it: 'The appearance of such figures for the first time in England must have greatly contributed to induce the wealthy to procure the introduction of the trees they represented to this country.' Subsequent history proved just that.

George London and Henry Wise, who translated *Le Jardinier Solitaire* from the French of François Gentil and Louis Liger in 1706, had already exhorted the gardeners of their day to look wider afield. 'A florist's curiosity', they said, 'is not to be confined to his own country nor to such flowers as he can find there; he should seek abroad and deal with neighbouring nations for what he has not of his own.

'To succeed in this commission he ought to address his correspondence with some one in those parts he means to trade in and whether he has seeds or bulbous roots sent him they are always to be put up separate in boxes to the end that being packed up they may be better preserved and last the longer.'

They further advised that such separate sort of seed or bulbs should be wrapped up individually and labelled so they could be easily distinguished on unpacking and there would be no mixing of names or plants.

'Likewise,' they continued, 'after they have been thus packed up we must remember to put up a good store of moss with them and to take care that the moss in which the plants are packed do not take wet for if it should the plants would be in danger and be spoiled by it. Then we cord up the boxes very well and by our seal on divers places and so direct them to the several persons they are to be consigned to. If you find these roots by coming a great way and being longer than ordinary on the voyage have contracted any mouldiness or become anyways damaged you must immediately take off from them their coats that are damnifyed.'

Sir Hans Sloane in the preface to that noble work on the natural history of Jamaica spoke of eight hundred herbarium species which he had shown very freely 'to all lovers of such curiosities among whom was Sir Arthur Rawdon', who went off home post haste and dispatched his gardener, James Harlow, to Jamaica. Harlow had had previous experience of collecting in Virginia for Mr Watts of the Chelsea Physic Garden, but that record does not speak of live plants—seeds and dried herbarium species maybe. But Sir Hans states that Harlow was sent 'to bring the plants themselves alive to him [Sir Arthur Rawdon] for his garden at Moira in Ireland'. This was in the mid 1600s.

He brought back almost a shipload, recorded Sir Hans, and added that the vessel was 'laden with cases of trees and herbs planted and growing in earth. Many of Mr Harlow's plants were spread about the country and were grown by Mr Petiver and Dr John

Fothergill'; but, said Sloane, none were better grown than those at Badminton by the Duchess of Beaufort 'by means of stoves and infirmaries'.

A reading of the natural history of Jamaica and Sir Hans Sloane's list would appear to make many of the eight hundred (over a hundred were ferns of various kinds) economic plants such as gingers and cinnamons, in other words more woody tree and shrub-like plants than actual herbaceous or beautiful covered-garden plants.

His successes in the field have been doubted, for we have G. S. Jenman, F.L.S., writing in the *Journal of Botany* of 1884 that 'if the statement is true that Harlow brought back living plants then not only in period of time, but in actual accomplishment he is a long way ahead of the most enterprising of his modern successors'.

Indeed Sir Arthur's gardener had collected many seeds, sown them in mould, and was hopeful they would germinate on the long journey home. Those that did must have done so only after considerable tending and nursing and by James Harlow's daily ministrations of airings, waterings, sunnings and protection from sundry blastings, saltings and the rollicking of horny-handed tars who could have had but little sympathy for a gardener and his tender nurslings while they carried out their arduous duties on the windjammers of those days.

So that while the Sloanes, Petres, Millers, Fothergills and the Sherards of mid eighteenth-century days wrote and talked proudly of their tender greens, their curious exotics from foreign parts, they were making orchids out of onions! They were right to be proud of these rarities, for rarities they were, many being seen in Britain for the first time ever, but their roomsteads, their curiously contrived stoves and greenhouses could only have been repositories for little seedlings struggling to live after quite incredibly long and climatically mixed sea and land treks.

This is not to belittle the efforts of these early lovers of the unusual and foreign—for their triumphs were historic and their failures were gallant—but an attempt to put the matter into its proper perspective; to show that the early growing of flora from lands other than those of the north temperate zone was not of spectacular quality or quantity.

And, of course, the reasons were obvious, and the difficulties for many years insurmountable despite the most ingenious and inventive minds which gave time and study to the problem. Ingenious too were the methods and the ideas when applied to the transportation of viable seeds from the New World, the West and East Indies and the Dutch possessions.

There was also the stark fact that in the seventeenth century flowers as such were thought little of, being relegated to the distaff side of gardening, where the tending of what flowers there were was a desultory occupation for ladies. Thus we have Sir William Temple in 1685 saying of flowers: 'I will not enter upon any account of flowers having only pleased myself with seeing or smelling them and not troubled myself with the care which is more the ladies' part than the men's. . . .' And Evelyn was just as cursory, leaving the ladies to look after the flowers while the men looked after the most important subjects such as oranges, myrtles, laurustinus, vines, peaches, nectarines, cherries and pears.

The great Linnaeus, although more concerned with herbarium species, had given much thought to the safe delivery of living seed from far-off countries to his university garden at Upsala in Sweden; and who should know better in the whole of Europe than this dedicated man whose correspondents covered most parts of the world and who was in almost daily receipt of plant material, seeds, dried specimens and long, detailed letters on all aspects of plant life?

In December 1758 he wrote to John Ellis, a London merchant much concerned, as we shall see later, in promoting horticultural commerce between this country and the American colonies, claiming to have discovered a perfect, never-failing remedy for the carrying of seeds from their native haunts to whatever gardener or botanist desired them, wherever they might be.

'Seeds', said Linnaeus, 'may be brought from abroad in a growing state if we attend to the following method. Put your seeds into a cylindrical glass bottle and fill up the interstices with dry sand to prevent their lying too close together and that they may perspire freely thro the sand. Then cork the bottle or tie a bladder over the mouth of it. Prepare a glass vessel so much larger than that which contains the seeds, that when it is suspended in it there may be a vacant space on all sides of about 2 inches distance between both glasses for the following mixture: 4 parts of nitre, one-fifth part in equal parts of common salt and sal ammoniac. These must be well pounded and mixed together and the space all around between the outward and inward glass well filled with it. This saline mass, which should be rather moist, will always be so cold that the seeds in the inner glass will never suffer during the voyage from the heat of the air. This experiment has been tried and not failed.'

John Ellis himself carried out many experiments, particularly with acorns and with chestnuts, conveying his results proudly to the Fellows of the Royal Society.

In January 1759 Ellis got hold of some acorns of the cork-bearing oak (most probably *Quercus suber*) and put them in sand for their Atlantic journey, but these rotted because, he surmised, 'of the confined air in the hold of the ship which occasioned hot and penetrating steams and caused seeds in common packages to sweat and ferment and finally putrefy'. He next advised packing seeds in casks tightly fastened to keep out sea-water, for these casks were to be placed on or near the deck so as to have the benefit of free circulating air. This was not successful either, so then he tried acorns 'smeared several times in a strong solution of gum arabic'. After they had been dried in a window they were folded in paper and put into a deal box where they lay from October to the following January, but on the acorns being cut open they were 'hard, dry and inclining to black, being quite petrified'.

Then he tried soaking the paper in a strong solution of gum arabic, but, alas, while the acorns were somewhat softer on being unwrapped, on being opened up they were decayed.

Another batch was smeared well with gum seneca and put in paper. On opening 'the kernels were shrivelled up and grown quite dry and hard like horn'.

The patient Mr Ellis rolled another portion of seed in 'a mixture of pitch, rosin and beeswax called "mummy" by the gardeners', and shipped them to Georgia in a box filled with dry sand well flattened down, the box then being put into a tight cask among papers and wearing apparel stowed in the upper part of the ship's hold.

Other acorns for the same destination travelled in different ways, for instance a batch of ten were first rolled in beeswax before being put into the brewer's loam which had been moistened with a thick solution of gum arabic. Another ten were each covered with fuller's earth made into a paste with a stiff solution of gum arabic. Seven batches in all were put into a chip box filled with dry sand and the box placed in a tight cask, which arrived in Georgia after a five-month voyage on the high seas. Of the seven parcels one only had survived, the one covered with beeswax and put into the brewer's loam cake moistened with gum arabic. The others had 'putrified by excessive perspiration'.

As, said Mr Ellis, the chestnut was one of the most difficult seeds to preserve on long voyages, he had carried out another extensive series of trials of various methods with an eye on the transportation of seeds to and from the East Indies. One trial using mutton fat and beeswax in which to wrap the nuts had proved successful.

Subsequently some of the sound nuts were planted 'in two garden pots and placed in a very spacious conservatory belonging to my worthy friend, Philip Carteret, F.R.S., at his seat near Godalming in Surrey'. When they germinated it proved, said Mr Ellis, that beeswax and mutton fat were the proper larger seed preservative for the 'gentlemen that go to China and other parts of the East Indies to preserve many kinds of valuable seeds in a state of vegetation during the voyage of a whole year till they arrive here and probably till they are carried to our settlements in the American colonies'.

It only remained for the East Indies and China travellers to put their beeswax and mutton-fat filled jars in the coolest part of the ship to prevent the mixture being affected by the heat of those parts which far exceeded ours.

Small seeds in their pods, Mr Ellis said, could be preserved by placing them thinly on pieces of paper, cotton or linen cloth that had been dipped in wax, then rolled up tight and well secured from air by a further covering of wax.

Now Mr Ellis felt he could give instructions to the would-be collectors and outlined a method in which the seeds to be collected had first of all to be free of all blemishes and wounds and condensed perspiration. Then the collector had to put melted beeswax into a shallow plate about half an inch deep, and let it cool so that it could be cut out in wedges. These, he advised, should be rolled round in the hands to make a malleable ball. The seed to be carried was then popped into a chip box 7 inches long, $4\frac{1}{2}$ inches broad and $3\frac{1}{2}$ inches deep into which wax had been poured to the depth of $1\frac{1}{2}$ inches. When the collector could bear his finger on this false bottom he laid out the balled acorns or nuts in close rows one on top of the other until the box was full. Then he poured melted beeswax over the lot and cooled the mass off in front of an open window. On cooling he filled up any chinks which might have occurred and pressed the top surface perfectly flat before covering the box with a tight lid, after which he put the box in a closet on a shelf and left it; of course the collector would find some cool place on the ship.

As a result of his experiments Mr Ellis proudly announced that his instructions 'if properly followed may in a few years put us in possession of the most rare and valuable seeds in a vegetating state from the remotest parts of the world'.

These difficulties of plant portage were well understood by the botanists and gardeners in England, who wished to study in detail and grow in abundance the strange new inhabitants of the plant world they had seen as pale ghosts in the herbariums. And though these difficulties acted as a brake on the enthusiasm and the consummation of these ambitions until more efficient methods were worked out by Joseph Banks, who had studied and experienced them on Captain Cook's voyage round the world, the longest since Drake's, progress was made, for throughout the eighteenth century the import of plants increased.

This numerical progression must, for its proper understanding, however, be put against the rapidly changing social and political background of the period.

At the most elementary stage of this study it can be said unequivocally that a nation and people without riches cannot afford the luxury of plant hunting and introduction. Nor when a nation is embroiled in war and bloodshed do its tastes tend towards the aesthetics of living. The very basic requirements for any nation to concern itself with explorative botanizing on the one hand, and highly technical conservatory gardening skills allied to the desire for scientific knowledge of plants on the other, are a rich aristocracy with leisure and money to spare for purely non-mercenary interests in the natural sciences. There must be freedom, either by conquest or agreement, to sail the seven seas and explore foreign lands without let or hindrance. There must be more than friendly, there must be actively interested and helpful people, not only at ports but associated all along the long tortuous lines of communication from plant habitat to the dissecting bench or greenhouse stage thousands of miles away. Lastly, there must be a persuasive urge not to be denied, to search diligently and as painstakingly reveal the secrets of nature not for self-glory but for the glory of an active Christian faith as real as it is compulsive.

For it is no coincidence that the first systematic pioneers in both the seventeenth and eighteenth centuries were men of God, many of the Quaker faith, whose love of nature was part of their love of God and all His works. And it must always be upon this sure and solid foundation of man's religious love of nature, this devout feeling of oneness with God and His natural creations, that the later eighteenth-century botanizing and plant hunting must be put.

An eighteenth-century man could identify his love for natural philosophy with his religion, consciously, without doubt or subtlety or any appeal to a classical pantheism.

England in the eighteenth century fulfilled most of these basic essentials most of the time, so that there was running through the whole hundred years an unbroken chain of botanical discovery.

Horticultural traffic before the third decade of the 1700s was largely in seeds, in some hardy, woody plants and, of course, in the specimens carefully dried and pressed in paper for the many great herbariums being stocked throughout Europe by the enthusiastic and ever-demanding natural philosophers. To these people the old herbals with their absolute insistence on plants for the *materia medica* were becoming too restrictive and, with the then state of knowledge of the natural flora of the world, too narrow in their scope, omitting so much that was desirable for its aesthetic attraction and charm.

The eighteenth century too was notable for the change, revolutionary albeit slow, which took place in British gardens, from the formal garden with its long avenues radiating from a point marked by obelisk or statuary, clipped hedge formality, geometric parterres and overall artificiality, to the return to nature and the desire to exchange geometric line and compass style for a freehand sketch of gardening.

The swing from formalism, the revolt from artificiality, was led by the great literary figures of Addison, Steele, Pope, Whately and Horace Walpole; the work of transformation being carried out by artistic landscape gardeners of the calibre of Capability Brown, Bridgeman, William Kent and Switzer. And as the French-fashioned, stately home garden of martial and regimented horticulture was torn out of its strait-jacket, a softer lawn, shrubbery and rolling parkland scenery arose in its place. This took place through most of the first half of the century, so that when the newly rich of the Industrial Revolution came on to the scene in the latter half, wishing to display their newly acquired wealth to attain a higher social status, they bought land and mansions in the country and gardened in the fashion of the day with an ostentatious flourish of shrubs and flowers rather than with a sober march of avenued wood.

This change brought the desire for new shrubs, new ornamental trees, new and colourful flowers, not only for the stocking of the great conservatories that began to rise but also for the shrubberies and to dot the spacious lawns that were being planned to grace the surroundings of the mansion—not to delineate it, to fix it in a closed hedge like a spider in a web. It was a more gracious feeling for nature that brought with it the *Jardin anglais* and gave plant hunting a compulsion and an aim beyond that of the merely botanic and scientific.

In the first half of the nineteenth century, as early as 1825, J. C. Loudon said we grew 13,000 species and botanist's varieties, nearly the fourth part of the estimated flora of the whole world. The plant introduction figures for the century as worked out by Loudon show the pattern well enough, and if we remember the historic background to the years it will be apparent how the graph rises and falls with the nation's fortunes.

Figures for the eighteenth century compared with those for the seventeenth century illustrate the overall progress which was made, for during the many-sovereigned years of Elizabeth, the two Jameses, the two Charleses, Cromwell and William and Mary there were troubled rules, troubled people and troubled times, as the plant-introduction graph shows plainly, with the seventeenth-century figure of 940 as against a grand total of 8,938 for the Georgian and comparatively untroubled era of the eighteenth century.

That era—the eighteenth century—was one bursting at the seams with an intellectual vitality which searched and probed at the natural world and empirically attempted to drag forth the secrets of the universe. At the outset, while Anne was queen, for the first decade Britain was still primarily an agricultural country with an agricultural economy based solidly on the land and its products. The wars of Marlborough gave us Gibraltar, by its culmination the Treaty of Utrecht gave us the freedom to trade in the Spanish Empire (the Indies), in Central and South America, while in the New World we got Nova Scotia, our rights recognized in Newfoundland, and a vast territory was handed over to the Hudson's Bay Company. During this time we were able to introduce some 230 new plants, largely from the West and East Indies.

In the following reign began the Georgian era, which will always be notable in botanical history for the exciting influx of new plants from all parts of the world. Yet introductions during the reign of the first George were small, Loudon noting only 182, but he listed 1,770 during George II's reign when Walpole brought peace and prosperity to the country, and 6,765 during the reign of George III, reflecting Britain's increasing influence and power in New South Wales, the East Indies, the Cape of Good Hope and India.

An amazing collection of new material came to us from the Cape, which we took over from the Dutch in 1795, for in 1800 Loudon noted 336 heaths besides proteas, pelargoniums and bulbous plants.

At the outset of this golden reign of botany it was said in 1763 that there was twice the number of plants in the country that there was in 1731 and 'considerably above half of the number of exotics now in our gardens', says Loudon, 'were brought here during the reign of George III', Lord Bute, William Aiton and Sir Joseph Banks being the prime movers, with Kew as a collecting house to which the new foreign flora flowed.

And it is to Joseph Banks we should now turn, for it was he who reconnoitred the uncharted seas of flora scientifically, painstakingly, and with youthful enthusiasm backed with great wealth.

Yet even the meticulously planned expedition of Banks was still up against the difficulty of getting live plants to this country; Banks and his companions had to content themselves with a botanical reconnaissance of samples—they brought back enough drawings and herbarium species to fire the imagination of the botanical and gardening world, but no flourishing plants in flower and leaf to show the glories of the South Seas and the newly discovered Pacific world.

But his was the key which opened the floodgates to the greatest outpouring of horticultural riches the world had ever seen and the doors to a floral El Dorado unbelievably rich and rare.

2. *The Botanical Reconnaissance*

NEVER had a scientific expedition been so lavishly mounted, never had one set sail with so thorough a preparation or so extensive in its objectives—to seek out all that was new in botany, zoology, ornithology, horology, climatology, entomology and astronomy—as when Joseph Banks and his specially hand-picked team set out from Plymouth with Captain Cook in the *Endeavour* on that August day in 1768.

The cost to Banks was at least £10,000, his personal assistants numbered nine, comprising Dr Daniel Carl Solander, the Swedish naturalist and favourite pupil of Linnaeus, Sydney Parkinson, artist and botanical draughtsman, Alexander Buchan, chosen for his skill at 'landskip and figure'; Herman Sporing, another native of Sweden, as assistant naturalist, James Roberts and Peter Briscoe, Banks's personal servants from his home at Revesby Abbey in Lincolnshire, Thomas Richmond and George Dorlton, two Negro servants of Banks's, and one John Reynolds, who although listed in the ship's muster roll as servant to Charles Green, the astronomer, is listed as artist on Banks's staff in Banks's journal of the voyage.

And the equipment—let a contemporary list the details: 'I must now inform you', wrote John Ellis, the Quaker doctor and Royal Society man, in a letter to Linnaeus, 'that Joseph Banks, Esq., a gentleman of £6,000 per annum estate, has prevailed on your pupil Dr Solander to accompany him in the ship that carries the English astronomer to the new discovered country [the Society Islands] in the South Sea . . . where they are to collect all the natural curiosities of the place and, after the astronomers have finished their observations on the transit of Venus, they are to proceed under the direction of Mr Banks, by order of the Lords of the Admiralty, on further discoveries.

... No people ever went to sea better fitted out for the purpose of natural history, nor more elegantly. They have got a fine library of natural history; they have all sorts of machines for catching and preserving insects; all kinds of nets, trawls, drags and hooks for coral fishing; they have even a curious contrivance of a telescope by which, put under water, you can see the bottom at a great depth, where it is clear. They have many cases of bottles with ground stoppers, of several sizes, to preserve animals in spirits. They have the several sorts of salts to surround the seeds, and wax, both bees' wax and that of the Myrica; besides, there are many people whose sole business is to attend them for this very purpose. They have two painters and draughtsmen, several volunteers who have a tolerable notion of natural history; in short Solander assured me this expedition would cost Mr Banks £10,000. ...'

When at Plymouth on 25th August 1768 Banks stepped aboard *Endeavour*, the epoch-making voyage embarked on was, to his fellow Royal Society friends, the many natural philosophers of the day and to London society in general, very much Banks's voyage, not Captain Cook's, for Joseph Banks at twenty-five was already a figure in influential aristocratic, scientific and high social circles, while James Cook, as befits the silent service, was but a sailor whose qualities were known only to his discerning masters at the Admiralty. Banks had been made a Fellow of the Royal Society at the early age of twenty-three and had already sailed to Newfoundland with his friend Lieutenant Constantine John Phipps (later Lord Mulgrave) and written the first plant list for that country. He had behind him schooling at both Eton and Harrow and was a gentleman commoner of Christ Church, Oxford; his friendships were with the squire-archy and the ruling classes and included Lord Sandwich, who was at the time First Lord of the Admiralty.

Yet it was at the best a most uncomfortable, unpredictable and dangerous prospect which faced this young philosopher as *Endeavour* set sail. It was probably coincidental, but certainly on the ship he already had friendly ties and associations to override the vexations, the petty annoyances, the boredom and irritability which must arise when ninety-six men were destined for three years to live chock-a-block, literally rubbing shoulders on a ship of 368 tons, which overall was only 166 feet in length—less than three cricket pitches—and at its greatest breadth was 29 feet 3 inches, a ship rammed tight from prow to stern with stores of all descriptions and a farmyard of animals, hens, cattle, dogs, cats and even a goat. The restriction imposed on an active young man like Banks by the very lack of deck space on which to take a turn must have been irksome in the extreme. His work was obviously done in the Great Cabin shared by Captain Cook, Dr Solander and the party's draughtsmen and artists, for his bedspace just opposite the captain's across the lobby entrance to the cabin was only a small one, so that both sailors and naturalists would share unusually crowded quarters doing many different kinds of work, much of which had precious little to do with the ship's day or her navigation and administration; yet despite this there is no record of anything but the happiest and most harmonious relations between the two principals.

Could this have been due to the very strong north country, if not Yorkshire, flavour there was in the ship and her company? In the Banks' family tree drawn up by Banks himself, and found among his papers on his death, he was proud to claim descent from the family of Banke of Banke Newton, near Skipton in the Yorkshire Dales, and where, in Gargrave parish church, can still be seen the Banke arms; whereas James Cook himself, though of Scots extraction, was a native of Marton in Cleveland, had run away to sea from Staithes, and had been apprenticed to the merchant service at Whitby near where, a little higher up the coast, is Mulgrave Castle; here lived Lieutenant Phipps, Banks's friend and companion on his Newfoundland voyage, at whose house he had stayed.

The *Endeavour* herself, a flat-bottomed, shallow-draught coaster, had been built at Whitby as the *Earl of Pembroke*, an east coast cat in the coal trade, with bluff wide bows and broad in the beam so that she could sail inshore, and was the sort of boat Banks must often have seen when staying at Mulgrave only a step away from the port.

Then there was Charles Green, chosen by the Royal Society to carry out the ostensible purpose of the voyage, to observe the transit of Venus from Tahiti, although Cook's secret instructions from the Admiralty ordered him to sail southwards in search of 'a continent or land of great extent', the Terra Australis of the old sea stories; Green was the son of a Yorkshire farmer. Richard Pickering, master's mate and later master, an excellent surveyor and maker of charts, was from West Tanfield, a Yorkshire village near Ripon. The Second Lieutenant, Zachariah Hicks, had been pressed into the Navy from Ripon.

Once *Endeavour* was under sail and away, however, there was no time for boredom or worry. By the second day out Banks had observed and was making a natural history note about porpoises, and from that time forward not a day passed but he and his party, with rum for sailors who helped, were busy with casting nets, trawls, drag nets, harpoons, hooks, hoop trawls, drag lines, landing nets or the fizgig, a rough kind of harpoon. On many days he would put his own personal pinnace overboard and, rowing round the ship, collect fish, seaweed and minute sea animals to be brought aboard, dissected, classified and sketched; or he would be in the main chains with the hoave, which he enjoyed: 'I stayed in the main chains from eight till 12 dipping for them [insects] with the hoave and took vast numbers'; or he would be casting a line from one of the stern windows of the Great Cabin. He shot birds by the hundred throughout those long days at sea, all to be named, drawn in colour and catalogued. At the close of day when the midnight oil was burned in fluttering lamps—candles would not keep alight with the cabin windows open, and they had to have these open to benefit from the fresh sea air at all times—they examined minutely and discussed scientifically the hundreds of natural objects they culled from sea and sky.

Endeavour's first port of call was Madeira, where Solander and Banks made their first acquaintance with a subtropic flora. Banks, who was sponsored by both the Royal Society and the Admiralty, could now carry out his instructions from no less a person than the Earl of Morton, President of the Society, who asked that where new plants were found 'the variation of the compass at that particular place should be specified'.

Also the latitude under which the plant grew and whether to the south or the north of the equator; '... the latitudes in which seeds are collected might also be noted with the nature of the soils in which they grew; and if earths could be brought in boxes, it might tend to promote natural knowledge'.

Five days in Madeira were spent by Banks and Solander from early to late on trips round and about Funchal looking for plants. They collected 299, which were taken aboard, laid out in the Great Cabin, catalogued, and those that were novel and unknown were given to Parkinson to draw, although the rarities were few.

Off to sea again, the days were filled once more with catching fish, birds and even a shark which 'we made shift to have a part of him for dinner and very good meat he was ...' said Banks in his journal.

Several times the party went out in the boat again as marine zoologists to collect the swarming population of the warm seas, although two *Balistes monoceros* 'were taken under the stern; they were following a shirt which was towing and showed not the least signs of fear, so that they were taken with a landing net without the smallest difficulty'.

Despite his time spent in shooting and fishing and the subsequent work on the catches, he was finding the confines of the ship by now somewhat irksome and had two ropes fixed in his cabin on which he exercised, one day taking a nasty tumble on his head which left him sick and bruised for the next few days. On 25th October they crossed the equator, although Banks paid in bottles of brandy for Solander's and his (Banks's) greyhounds' exemption from the usual ducking, which he watched and described. The rest of the ship's company who had not crossed the line before were itemized down to ducks, hens, cats and dogs. 'A block was made fast', wrote Banks, 'to the end of the main yard and a long line reved through it to which three pieces of wood were fastened, one of which was put between the legs of the man who was to be ducked and to this he was tied very fast, another was for him to hold in his hands. ... When he was fastened on this machine, the boatswain gave the command by his whistle and the man was hoisted up as high as the cross piece (the third piece of wood) would allow, when another signal was made and immediately the rope was let go and his own weight carried him down, he was then immediately hoisted up again and three times served in this manner. ...'

Now having crossed the line Banks came into first-hand contact with the mildews and the moulds caused by the humid tropic air which proved so damning to plants and were the principal obstacle to their transportation. 'All kinds of leather became mouldy, portfolios and trunks covered with black leather were almost white. Soon afterwards this mould adhered to almost everything; all the books in my library became mouldy,' the journal said.

On 13th November they entered the harbour of Rio de Janeiro and faced their first disappointment, for here, where all manner of botanical treasures could be found, the Brazilian authorities would not let them go ashore. But, as Sydney Parkinson showed, a determined botanist like Banks was not to be robbed of this unique occasion for plant discovery; 'Mr Banks and Dr Solander', wrote Parkinson, 'appeared much chagrined at this disappointment; but notwithstanding all the Viceroy's precautions we determined to gratify our curiosity in some measure and having obtained a sufficient knowledge of the river and harbour by the surveys we had made of the country we frequently, unknown to the centinel [put on board by the Viceroy], stole out of the cabin window at midnight, letting ourselves down into a boat by a rope, and, driving away with the tide till we were out of hearing, we then rowed to some unfrequented part of the shore where we landed and made excursions up into the country. . . .'

The floral picture that met their eyes was indeed worth the clandestine trip; even the hedges were so full of curious bloom that Parkinson loaded himself with them. Banks himself listed 316 plants collected and enthused about 'the parasitic plants, especially Renealmioe [renealmia syn. tillandsia] for I was not fortunate enough to see one epidendrum, and the different species of bromelia, many not before described. Karratas [*Karatas nidularium fulgens*] I saw here growing on the decayed branch of a tree 60 feet high at least which it had so entirely covered that the whole seemed to be a tree of karratas. The growth of rhizophora [mangrove tree] also pleased me . . . add to this that the whole country was covered with the beautiful blossoms of malpighioe [malpighia], Bannisterioe [Banisteria], passiflora not forgetting poinciana and Mimosa sensitiva and a beautiful species of clusia of which I saw great plenty, in short the wildest spots here were varied with a greater quantity of flowers as well as more beautiful ones than our best devised gardens; a sight infinitely pleasing for a short time, though no doubt the eye would soon tire of a continuity of it'.

But that did not deter the flower hunters, for they bribed the sailors allowed ashore for provisions to collect everything growing they could see and, says Parkinson: 'We found also many curious plants in the sallading [salads] that was sent to us.'

Course was set for Tierra del Fuego on 2nd December and reached on 15th January 1769, Christmas having been celebrated in the meantime, with a note from Banks: 'All good christians, that is to say all good hands, got abominably drunk so that all thro' the night there was scarce a sober man in the ship.'

On the 14th the plant hunters went ashore on Staten Island off the coast of Tierra del Fuego, and in only four hours on shore Banks wrote: 'I found about a hundred plants. . . . Of these I may say every one was new and entirely different from that either of us had before seen.' Captain Cook's dry comment on this short botanical excursion was: 'At 9 they returned on board bringing with them several plants, flowers, etc., most of them unknown in Europe and in that alone consisted their whole value. . . .' Next day they anchored in the Bay of Good Success, and Banks and Solander had their first experience of this uninviting coast, with its miserable natives streaked with red and black, wearing seal-skin capes and scratching the barest of livings from inhospitable terrain—but at least they were not hostile. The following day they mounted a big expedition to climb, if possible, from the shore to the high lands they could see, to look for alpine plants. There were Dr Solander, Banks of course, Buchan the artist, Green the astronomer, Monkhouse the surgeon, Peter Briscoe, Banks's personal manservant, the two black servants and four sailors to carry the equipment. The party set out at first through pathless thickets going uphill all the way, thinking they would meet with easier going, but instead they hit a scrub of 'low bushes of birches reaching to about a man's middle. They were so stubborn that they could not be bent out of the way, but at every step the leg must be lifted over them; on being placed again on the ground it was almost sure to sink above the ankle in bog. No travelling could possibly be worse than this . . .' wrote Banks. About two-thirds of the way to the alpine pastures Buchan, who was an epileptic, had a fit and after a fire had been kindled he was left with a servant. A snowstorm now set in, so Banks, Solander, Green and Monkhouse with their servants, after pushing farther inland, made their way back to poor Buchan and all of them set out for some rising ground in the woodland where, night coming on, they would have to stop, pitch the 'wigwam', and make their way back to *Endeavour* in the morning light.

'We got about half way very well,' wrote Banks, 'when the cold seemed at once to have an effect infinitely beyond anything I have ever experienced.' Dr Solander was the first to feel it; he said he could not go any farther but must lie down though the ground was covered with snow, 'and down he lay, notwithstanding all I could say to the contrary. Richmond, a black servant, now also lay down and was in much the same way as the Dr.'.

Banks continued to drive the rest of the party on to some shelter and sent five in advance to light a fire at the first convenient place. Then he persuaded Solander and Richmond to exert themselves and got through most of the birch scrub when Solander said he must sleep, and did, for quarter of an hour. At the same time Richmond sat down and could not be persuaded to move, although Banks told him if he did sit down he would freeze to death. George Dorlton, the other Negro, was with the party, and he and one of the sailors were left to look after Richmond, while Banks and Solander, who had heard the news that the rest of the party had managed to build a fire about a quarter of a mile ahead, drove on to get help, although Solander still needed all the urging Banks could bring to bear to get him to warmth and comparative safety.

After all had enjoyed the warmth of the fire two men set off through the woodland to bring help and succour to the three left behind, but these two unfortunate men returned to the main party after half an hour's thrashing about in the blizzard to say they could find no trace nor hear any sounds of their companions. The horrible truth now dawned on Banks; they had left a knapsack with a bottle of rum in it, and the three must have taken this for warmth in such quantities that they had fallen insensible in the snow.

'For two hours now', chronicled Banks, 'it had snowed almost incessantly, so that we had little hopes of seeing any of the three alive; about midnight, however, to our great joy, we heard a shouting, on which I and four others went out immediately, and found it to be the seaman, who had walked, almost starved to death, from where he lay. I sent him back to the fire and proceeded by his directions to find the other two. Richmond was upon his legs, but not able to walk; the other [George Dorlton] lay on the ground as insensible as a stone. We immediately called all hands from the fire and

Gardenia radicans. William Kerr introduced this gardenia from Canton in 1804. *Kerria japonica* was named for him.

Aitonia capensis. One of the many exotics sent from the Cape by Francis Masson, Kew's first plant hunter.

attempted by all the means we could contrive to bring them down, but found it absolutely impossible. The road was so bad, and the night so dark, we could scarcely ourselves get on, nor did we without many falls. We would then have lit a fire upon the spot, but the snow on the ground, as well as that which continually fell rendered this plan as impracticable as the other, and to bring fire from the other place was also impossible from the quantity of snow which fell every moment from the branches of the trees.

'We were thus obliged to content ourselves with laying out our unfortunate companions upon a bed of boughs and covering them over with boughs as thickly as possible, and thus we left them, hopeless of ever seeing them again alive, which indeed we never did.

'In this employment we had spent an hour and a half, exposed to the most penetrating cold I ever felt as well as to continual snow. Peter Briscoe, another servant of mine, began now to complain and before we came to the fire became very ill, but got there at last almost dead with cold.

'Now might our situation be called terrible; of 12, our original number, two were already past all hopes; one more was so ill, that although he was with us, I had little hope of his being able to walk in the morning, and another seemed very likely to relapse into his fits, either before we set out or in the course of the journey. We were distant from the ship, we did not know how far; we knew only that we had spent the greater part of a day in walking through pathless woods, provision we had none but one vulture which had been shot on the way, and at the shortest allowance could not furnish half a meal; and, to complete our misfortunes, we were caught in a snowstorm in a climate we were utterly unacquainted with, but which we had reason to believe was as inhospitable as any in the world. . . .'

Fortunately next morning, with snow still falling but with the sun coming up, after each man had been given a tenth of the vulture to cook himself, the party set off, with Briscoe able to walk and Buchan not too ill. After a march of three hours they made the beach and the ship, where Cook was infinitely relieved to have them aboard safe and well, although both Buchan and Briscoe took several days to get over their ordeal.

With their keeping-boxes full of the 125 plants they had collected and described by Banks as 'truly the most extraordinary I can imagine . . . to speak of them botanically, probably no botanist has ever enjoyed more pleasure in the contemplation of his favourite pursuit than did Dr Solander and I among these plants', Endeavour made for Tahiti and her appointment with the transit of Venus.

After weighing anchor on 21st June, and having stowed lumber and guns between decks in preparation for the violent storms they fully expected would accompany their attempt to round the Horn, they were tremendously relieved to find their rounding was as little trouble as if they were going round the North Foreland. For many days out, however, Banks and his party had been too busy to notice the weather, for before the plants collected could lose their fresh colours and form, and while others were being prepared for preserving and dried in the keeping-papers, the artists were busy at work from first light to last lamp transcribing in colour the flowers and plants into the floral albums so vitally important to the botanical record of this historic and epoch-making voyage.

Banks, after the botanical record was safely taken, lost no time to be out with a gun on deck, again shooting both on the wing and in the yards several different albatross, and 'Mother Carey's chickens'. He was bilious for a day but perked up enough to eat one of the albatross, which, he said, was preferable to the pork on the table. A dead cuttle-fish floating by, torn about by the birds, was hauled on board, cooked, and hailed by Banks as 'one of the best soups I ever ate'.

This was a long run from the Cape to Tahiti, and shipboard conditions began to tell on them. A young marine accused of theft threw himself overboard, and Banks had inflammation of the throat and swollen glands, so decided to try the anti-scurvy concoction put up for him in hogsheads by Dr Hulme. He made himself a punch of the mixture, which contained one-fifth brandy and four-fifths lemon juice. This did the trick.

Not until 4th April did they sight land. The glass was used continually for the botanical party to describe vegetative and human inhabitants, for *Endeavour* had no time to anchor for a closer inspection if a camp was to be prepared on the Tahitian shore in which to set up the instruments for the observing of the transit. The island was made on 13th April, *Endeavour* having been at sea eighty-three days. They were welcomed by canoes round the ship full of friendly natives and saw their first examples ever of 'tattowing'.

Almost immediately they went ashore, the captain and Banks, for Cook had great confidence in the young naturalist, and from that first day he was appointed unofficial trader, ambassador and mediator to the native people. It was he, said Parkinson, who was more disturbed than anyone of the ship's company when a native, trying to make off with a musket, was shot and killed, and exclaimed angrily on being told: 'If we quarrelled with these Indians we should not agree with angels.'

He too gave the native chiefs classical names—Ajax, Hercules, Lycurgus and Epicurus. Tragedy overtook Banks's own personal party once more after only five days when Buchan, the 'landskip' painter, died and was buried at sea, an irretrievable loss: 'My airy dreams of entertaining my friends in England with the scenes that I am to see have vanished,' wrote Banks. But the ebullience of the young naturalist soon returned, and his excursions with his own people and with Captain Cook and his officers to all parts of the island, noting the scenery, the flora and the fauna, the native customs, dress, language, religion and traditions, occupied his time to the full.

It was his tent which was first to be pitched on shore while the fort was being built by the ship's crew to house the transit instruments and the personnel who were to use them. He was the first to taste roasted dog and pronounced it as good as any meal he had tasted, and he sampled fried rats for breakfast. Breadfruit had already become almost a staple diet. The fair ladies of the island were also sampled, Banks leaving his place by a Tahitian queen at a meal put on in their honour for 'a very pretty girl with fire in her eyes that I had not before seen in the country'. Banks loaded her with beads and presents and, says Parkinson, who called the girl Otea Tea, after some trouble as to who should sleep in whose tent, 'Mr Monks and Mr Banks came to an *éclaircissement* some time after; had very high words and I expected they would have decided it by a duel which, however, they prudently avoided'.

Then in his journal Banks writes of wrestling matches arranged for their entertainment and of surf-riding and swimming, in which the natives, in surf more dreadful than he had ever seen, caught a roller making shoreward at tremendous speed by putting an old canoe on the very crest of it and were carried to the shore with incredible swiftness. How they ever survived in such crashing, tearing seas he could not imagine.

Much of the botanist's time was taken up with tracing and arranging for the return of innumerable pieces of equipment, including part of Mr Green's vital transit quadrant, from the almost daily thieving natives, who looked on the 'invasion' as a jolly opportunity to collect loot of all kinds.

While Banks was using so much time acting as ship's agent his artists—under mosquito-nets, for the flies ate the colours off the canvas as soon as they were put on— drew from life, plants, animals, fishes, boats, the native costumes and implements.

The three months at Tahiti passed quickly enough until nearly time for sailing, when Banks decided to take home with him Tupia, a native chief and priest. Writing of the scheme, he said: 'I do not know why I may not keep him as a curiosity, as well as some of my neighbours do lions and tigers'; but there was much more to it than that, as they found, for Tupia became interpreter on innumerable occasions and eased their way round the Pacific Islands as no one else could have done.

So on 13th July they took their leave from Tahiti, calling as they sailed to survey and to botanize at Huahine, Tahaa and Raiatea in the Society Group. At Tahaa, Banks again took on the post of agent and bought three hogs, twenty-one fowls and as many yams and plantains as the ship's boat would hold, the last-named being boiled and served as bread, the ship's variety, Banks wrote, being so full of vermin that he had seen 'thousands shaken out of a single biscuit' and had taken as many as twenty in his mouth at one time, tasting hot as mustard.

The 9th of August was a memorable day for *Endeavour*, for on that day she left the Society Islands Group to seek the 'great continent to the Southwards'. Five days out Banks and Tupia in the pinnace tried to land on Rurutu (Tubuai Islands) but, finding the natives hostile, they had to shoot at them with musket fire as they attempted to seize the boat and haul it on shore.

They had by them the Tasman chart of 1642, showing a meagre strip of coastline not connected to a country; it could have been the shores of Terra Australis or maybe the Southern Continent itself. A hazardous prospect lay before them. It was a long haul to any prospective landfall; in fact they found it was a run of fifty-seven days.

In his journal Banks found time to tell of the ship's food and how provisions were going. They had North American apples for apple-pie given to them by Dr John Fothergill, '17 sheep, four or five fowls, as many South Sea hogs, four or five Muscovy

ducks and an English boar and sow with a litter of pigs'. They had small beer and
potatoes and salted cabbage as well as 'sour crout', while both the ship's company and
Banks's party took boiled wheat for breakfast as an anti-scorbutic.

Heavy seas were encountered on this stage of the voyage, *Endeavour* dipping her
bowsprit in the troughs and rolling in the swell so much that there was no rest for
anyone, so difficult was it to keep in a bunk. Although Tasman's Land was their target
on the chart, on 8th October, three months after leaving Tahiti, they dropped anchor
in Poverty Bay, New Zealand.

Here was a botanical paradise for Banks and Solander: a new botanical world where
the plant life was completely strange to them. Every tree, shrub and flower was a fresh
surprise, for here, for the first time, a trained botanist was seeing a remarkable flora
which included the largest buttercup in the world, a forget-me-not with leaves as big as
those of rhubarb, a speedwell forty feet in height, the smallest member of the pine-tree
family, tree-like daisies, arborescent lilies, plants of the carrot family with stiff leaves as
sharp as bayonets, mosses more than a foot tall, and a vegetable sheep (*Raoulia eximia*)
which Banks saw through glasses, and tree-ferns which graced the shores and deeply
wooded ravines.

Hostile natives were again troublesome, and Banks once again was first to land with
Captain Cook and Solander. They were met by about a hundred natives, all grotesquely
tattooed, brandishing long lances, and threatening in their attitudes. The party were
hardly ashore before they had to hurry back to the ship's boat, left in the charge of four
of the ship's boys, which was being attacked by a large, war-whooping mob. Muskets
were fired again to get out of an ugly situation, a native being killed.

Next day similar trouble arose when the ship's boat tried to intercept a canoe, the
occupants of which put up such a fight that muskets were used again and four natives
killed. This slaughter upset Banks, who wrote at the end of the day: 'Thus ended the
most disagreeable day my life has yet seen, black be the mark for it and heaven send that
such may never return to embitter future reflection.'

Yet, in the midst of all this active hostility, Banks managed to collect about forty
species of plants in the keeping-boxes before leaving Poverty Bay on the 11th,
Endeavour taking an inshore course, southward at first, hostile natives in canoes
stopping all ship's boat or pinnace work for Banks and his party.

On the 21st they landed at a bay Cook named Hawke's and found many plants.
Fortunately the natives were friendly here, and one day, when they stayed so late in the
country that the ship's boat had left them, they asked the natives to take them aboard
by canoe; they all overturned in the pounding surf before they reached *Endeavour*, wet
but safe. Another two days were spent plant hunting with success before anchor was
weighed and they continued their passage northwards, calling in turn at Tolaga Bay,
Anaura, round the cape Cook named East, Mercury Bay, where they explored a river
and where Banks and Solander sailed for a league upcountry and shot and ate shags
which were nesting on the flats.

A few days later they rowed up a river Cook named the Thames and saw magnificent timber 19 feet 8 inches in circumference and 89 feet high before the first branch. The thickness was carried right to the top, Banks noted. Green plants were collected in quantity for the artists to draw and the botanists to catalogue and name. Before they left the east coast, and after a day's hunting for plants, they found themselves adrift in a row-boat unable to make the ship and had to lay to at anchor, sleeping in the bottom of the craft all night.

Endeavour continued her inshore passage of the coast, Cook naming bays, promontories and mountains as she went, and in December 1769, while she was rounding North Cape, Banks was able to satisfy himself that the rumour was true that the natives practised cannibalism, for ashore he saw, in a basket by the side of some natives cooking a dog, some human bones with meat still adhering to them, which the family told him was the remains of seven enemy warriors whom they had killed a few days before; and a day or so later a native in a canoe brought to the ship 'heads of four people which were preserved with the flesh and hair on, I suppose as trophies. . . .' He bought one. Banks was assured that the natives ate only their enemies who were killed in battle.

Christmas Day of that year was livened by a goose party, the geese for which were shot by Banks from the ship's boat.

By mid January they found and named Cook's Straits and realized that they had circumnavigated an island; whether to the southward was the shore of a great continent remained to be seen. From 9th February 1770 until 1st April they circumnavigated South Island and realized that New Zealand was divided into two islands separated by a strait. *Endeavour* had sailed and mapped 2,400 miles of coastline.

Unfortunately for Banks, who would have dearly loved to botanize and explore, they had little time to land until they turned into Queen Charlotte's Sound again and anchored at Admiralty Bay, which was unfortunate, for Banks could see through his glass fertile well-wooded country and the vegetable sheep in the foothills.

In all, Banks had collected 360 specimens of seeds, plants and ferns, and of these about 200 drawings were made by Parkinson. In his journal Banks wrote that, of the 400 species seen, all except a dozen or so had never before been described by any botanist.

The 31st of March found Cook, Banks, Solander and the officers in the Great Cabin. They were there to take a momentous decision—they were to turn homewards now, but which way were they to turn? By Cape Horn in the high latitudes and maybe find a southern continent? Steer to the southward of Tasmania and direct to the Cape of Good Hope? Or stand to westward and hope to fall in with some coastline of New Holland and follow that northward so far as it went and return by the East Indies?

The last course was chosen as being the only one appropriate to the state of the *Endeavour*; her sailcloth was almost in ribbons, she had no stores, and her crew and her provisions were showing signs of wear and tear. This was a disappointment to Banks, who believed in a southern continent, and despite his long time at sea would still have been happy to go on into the unknown before they took a homeward course; but Cook had more to think about than sheer adventure—he had men and a ship to get home safely.

On 31st March they sailed out to sea again, and by this time, being well south of the trade winds, *Endeavour* was able to take a direct western route towards the other scrap of coast on Tasman's chart which was in fact the southern portion of Tasmania. During this course Banks was out fishing and bird shooting most days, still adding to his now quite staggering collection of natural history specimens, both fish and fowl. *Endeavour* never managed to hit the Tasmanian coast, however, for southerly winds drove her northwards until she hove in sight of the southern tip of Australia's east coast, a part of that great continent never seen before.

She struck the coast just south of Cape Howe, almost the extreme point of the east coast. The missing by Cook of Van Diemen's Land (Tasmania) left to Bass the resolving of the blank on the charts, nor, until Bass's voyage, was Cook or any other navigator sure whether or not Tasmania was part of the Australian continent.

This country's coastline proved to have quite a new and vastly different race of natives for *Endeavour* to deal with (all 'Indians' to Banks)—'black, stark naked, with bones through their noses, armed with sharp pikes and a wooden weapon made like a short scimitar' (a boomerang). Banks noted too the curious painting of their bodies, 'painted with white, their faces seemingly only dusted over with it, their bodies painted with broad strokes drawn over their breasts and backs, resembling much a soldier's cross belt, and their legs and thighs also with broad strokes round them, like broad garters or bracelets'.

The keen-eyed Banks through his glass had observed much of the natives, their habits and customs, before he landed in the first boat on the 28th. He had 'plainly discerned that the women did not copy our Mother Eve even in the fig leaf'. He had noticed, too, a throwing stick the natives carried and fishing spears, as well as details of native canoes.

They were not to find these black, naked Australians at all friendly, the first encounter being anything but happy as they stepped ashore on 28th April 1770 at Sting Ray Bay, later to be named Botany Bay by Banks because of the unusual number of plants he found and dried on the beach there.

Two natives put up a very spirited defence of their territory, and muskets had to be fired before the ship's boat could be beached and the party landed, but they could stir little from the shore until they felt they knew the natives better; they explored their houses and looked at the wooden weapons the natives had left behind, apprehensively watching out for attack all the time. But by 1st May they felt emboldened enough, with a ten-musket escort, to go upcountry and spent the whole day ashore, seeing only one native but plenty of strange and unusual vegetation—the *epacris*, those beautiful heath-like plants of all colours, the acacias in all their grace of leaf and variety of form, the gums (first called gums by Banks), the crimson flowered waratah (*Telopea speciosissima*) and the luxuriant, ornamental flame tree (*Brachychiton acerifolia*), whose scarlet flowers in coral-like racemes lit up the swamps like a forest fire. Then the banksias, the Australian honeysuckles and the giant fig trees, the palms, the tree-ferns, so graceful and so different, in the swamps, too, the terrestrial ferns and the beautiful amaryllis and flowers of the lily tribes. It was a botanical birthday, and next day's rain found both Banks and Solander well content to find an excuse for staying on board to examine their precious finds until after lunch when 'we returned to our old occupation of collecting in which we had our usual good success'. Above and in and out of this botanical uniqueness were flying the gaudy-coloured, screaming cockatoos, parrots and, as Banks called them, 'loryquets'.

On the 3rd Banks wrote: 'Our collection of plants was now grown so immensely large that it was necessary that some extraordinary care should be taken of them lest they should spoil in the books. I therefore devoted this day to that business and carried ashore all the drying-papers, nearly 200 quires, of which the larger part was full, and spreading them upon a sail in the sun, kept them in this manner exposed the whole day, often turning them and sometimes turning the quires, in which were plants, inside out. By this means they came aboard at night in very good condition'—and hence Botany Bay.

They were to spend eight days here, going on shore most days and exploring as far as they might in the day. They often walked till they were too tired to walk farther. For two men like Banks and Solander this was indeed a wonderland. The vegetation which met their sight and was eagerly torn from its native heath for the drying quires was being seen for the first time by civilized man. Almost all were new and almost all were in full bloom. The trees, 'yielding a gum' and most of them exceedingly tall, were so unusual with their willow-like leaves, redolent of a pharmacist's shelves; then those strange but royally beautiful tree-ferns (*Livistona australis*). Numerous flowers of uncommon shades of colour resembling giant heaths (the *epacris*) were everywhere in the hinterland once they got away from the mangrove swamp shores into the open forest and scrub country where the feathery fronds of the wattle (the mimosas) held sway, each a sunlight spray of yellow; to be examined with surprise were the curious family of *proteas*, the unique grass tree (*Xanthorrhoea arborea*), a peculiar feature of the landscape with its tufts of drooping wiry foliage enfolding a huge bulrush-like florescence, all stemming from a bare rugged stem up to twelve feet high. They found their days, too, full of pleasant odours from the aromatic wattles, eucalyptus and a general flora whose scent gave the characteristic Australian bush smell.

The *grevillea* family, too, was a botanical find, with its unusually shaped, highly coloured flowers and stark, rigid foliage. Really New World were the callistemons, the bottle brushes, with their startling scarlet stamens rising from the long thin pokers of stem and leaves. Startlingly hued crotons were numerous by the shores and there were palm trees, some with leaves 'plaited like a fan', another bearing pinnate leaves like those of a coconut, while another (*Cycas media*), never more than ten feet high, had small pinnate leaves like those of a small fern. Evincing both comment and wonder, as well as trouble to the botanists in their searches, were the fourteen-foot-high grasses between the trees and the shrubs through which they had to push their way almost as if in a miniature jungle.

This was a unique picture of Australian flora and physical scenery which Banks was never to forget, and although his first impressions of New South Wales—as they called the north-east country (later to be divided into New South Wales and Queensland) which he and Cook discovered and which the captain claimed for his king on Possession Island off Cape York—were that the country was 'barren', he obviously had second thoughts. Probably at the time both Banks and the captain were disappointed at the lack of edible vegetables to be found; the aborigines did not need to cultivate the ground—they managed with what animals they killed, the fish they caught and a few leaves and roots with which they relieved their diet.

It must have been later, turning over his experiences, as they made their long way home, that he thought again about Botany Bay, and probably recalled the beautiful range of the Blue Mountains like a frieze to the Antipodean scene he saw from the ship, and those densely wooded ravines he could see through his glass as they skirted the coast, for later it was his enthusiasm and persuasion that brought the first settlement of British people to Australia and this same Botany Bay where he first landed, although Governor Philips moved a few days later to Port Jackson, a mere seven miles northwards. Banks, being the man he was, would never have dispatched a single one of his fellow countrymen to eke out an existence on both a barren and a strange foreign shore.

Closely skirting the shore after eight days at Botany Bay, *Endeavour* sailed northwards to tropic coasts. Banks observed through his glass the vegetation changing. Now he saw the palm-nut tree (*Pandanus tectorus*)—a convincingly tropic sight—and how shifting sands were engulfing trees, but very few natives were sighted at all. On the 23rd they anchored and landed near the mouth of a large lagoon (this was named Bustard Bay and is now part of South Queensland). Here Banks reported a great variety of plants, some the same as they had seen in the tropic islands and some they knew from East Indian herbaria. They found stinging caterpillars too, and on the hillsides gum trees, differing from those at Botany Bay in that these had longer leaves hanging down like those of a weeping willow; a brilliant gamboge-coloured gum exuded from their bark. Many figs and a great number of these new-style gums were noted in the diary, as well as Banks's prowess with the gun when a bustard was shot for dinner, making an excellent meal.

It was only a short stay here and *Endeavour* weighed anchor on the 24th to face the most hazardous stretch of coastline known to any navigator in the seven seas. Cook could not have known nor Banks guessed as they saw breakers ahead that they were now entering and steering directly between the mainland coast and the coral dangers of the Great Barrier Reef. Away it stretched in front of *Endeavour*'s course for 1,200 surf-girt miles, hugging the east coast and keeping within its flanking coral, which lay sometimes but ten miles or so away, sometimes ninety, some of the most dangerous shallows, sandbanks, wicked currents, flat and mountainous islands, and coral spurs, hidden and menacing and unnavigable channels ever set to catch the unwary navigator. Yet all *Endeavour* had to warn her were breakers ahead and the constant vigilance of the man heaving the lead. Very soon Cook found his water shoaling—one minute he had 100 fathoms under him, the next it had shoaled to a few feet. Immediately the boats were got out to sound ahead as rough water and sandy seas gave some indication of conditions. *Endeavour* made a painful way up the Queensland coast. To make matters worse, poor Mr Orton, the captain's clerk, who had stumbled into his bunk drunk the night before, was found next morning with the clothes cut off his back and both ears severed.

A few days later, on 24th May, they were glad to drop anchor as a respite from their hazardous passage in Broad Sound where, although Cook reported neither fresh water, greens nor any meat, Banks reported having gone ashore 'and found several plants we had not seen before, among them, however, were still more East Indian plants than in the last harbour, one kind of grass [*Heteropogon contortus*] which we had also seen there was very troublesome to us. Its sharp seeds were bearded backwards and whenever they stuck into our clothes these beards pushed forwards until they got into the flesh. This grass was so plentiful that it was hardly possible to avoid it and with the mosquitoes that were likewise innumerable made walking almost intolerable.

'We were not to be repulsed, but proceeded far into the country. The gum trees were like those in the last bay, both in leaf and in producing a very small proportion of gum —insects in general were plentiful, butterflies especially . . . the air for the space of three or four acres was crowded to a wonderful degree; the eye could not be turned in any direction without seeing millions and yet every branch and twig was almost covered with those that sat still, of these we took as many as we chose, knocking them down with our caps or anything that came to hand.'

Still the same shoal-filled sea made progress slow and nerve-racking as *Endeavour* steered her northward way. The monotonous but so necessary call of the leadsman accompanied them day and night as first she found a navigable channel and then shoal water or sunken coral. On 7th June Banks, Solander and Hicks landed on Palm Island, hoping the trees they had seen were coconut—for coconut milk would have meant so much to a ship whose water supplies were running down, and what water was left had a noticeably unpleasant taste—but they were disappointed.

At this stage in her coast-skirting track *Endeavour* ran into even greater danger without any warning for either her navigators or her captain, for here, near Family Islands, the Barrier Reef draws its coral teeth nearer to the mainland, multiplying a hundredfold the navigational hazards.

At the next short anchorage on the 9th Cook went along with Banks and Solander to explore Green Island (all the islands as they came across them were charted and named by Cook), and to look for fresh water, but mangrove swamp, surf and rocks did not endear these shores to them and *Endeavour* drove on until the night of the 11th. 'Scarcely were we in our beds,' wrote Banks, 'when we were called up with the alarming news of the ship being fast upon a rock, of which she in a few minutes convinced us by beating very violently against it. Our situation became now greatly alarming, we had stood off shore three hours and a half in a pleasant breeze so we knew we could not be very near it. We were little less than certain that we were upon sunken coral rocks, the most dreadful of all on account of their sharp points and grinding quality which cut through a ship's bottom almost immediately. All this time she continued to beat very much so that we could hardly keep our legs on the quarter-deck. By the light of the moon we could see her sheathing boards, etc. floating thickly around her and about 12 her false keel came away. . . .

'For our comfort, however, the ship, as the tide ebbed, settled to the rocks and did not beat nearly so much as she had done. A rock, however, under our starboard bow kept grating her bottom, making a noise very plainly to be heard in the fore store room, these we doubted not would make a hole; we only hoped that it might not let in more water than we could clear with our pumps.'

When day broke, fortunately the wind dropped, but daylight disclosed to the *Endeavour*'s company just what a perilous plight they were in—eight leagues from the shore stranded, with not a sand bank, not a rock on which they could put a foot. All around him Banks, from his vantage point on the quarter-deck, could see feverish activity. Stores, ballast and hundreds of movable goods and chattels were being carried in great haste from the hold and hauled overboard, while other sailors unlashed six heavy deck guns and let these roll over the side; another party lugged old stones, staves, hoops, casks, oil jars, almost anything they could easily lay their hands on and all that was not essential to life they tossed overboard—50 tons of material was thrown in the sea in an attempt to lighten the ship. The pumps were started and all hands from the captain downwards, including Banks, Solander and all their party, took quarter-hour shifts turn about; in spite of this, water in the hold gained on them. Banks could not help but comment that although this ship's crew knew every oath that ever was heard under the jack he never heard a complaint, 'everyone working with surprising cheerfulness'.

No grumbling or growling was to be heard in any part of the ship, though hopes fell when, as night came and the tide rose, the ship budged not an inch on the higher water and the sea poured in, so that the three pumps could not keep up with it, and the fourth pump was found to be useless.

Banks's mood changed with the circumstances and now he wrote pessimistically of the prospect before him:

'Now in my opinion I entirely gave up the ship and packing up what I thought I might save prepared for the worst.

'The most critical part of our distress now approached; the ship was almost afloat and everything ready to get her into deep water but she leaked so fast that with all our pumps we could only just keep her free. If (as was probable) she should make more water when hauled off (she was being winched from anchors laid about the ship) she must sink and we well knew that our boats were not capable of carrying us all ashore so that some, probably most of us, must be drowned. A better fate, maybe, than those would have who got ashore without arms to defend themselves from the Indians or provide themselves with food in a country where we had not the least reason to hope for subsistence so barren had we always found it, and had they ever met with good usage from the natives and food to support them, debarred from the hope of ever seeing again their native country or conversing with any but savages, perhaps the most uncivilized in the world. The dreadful time now approached and the anxiety in every-body's countenance was visible enough.'

But the tide and Cook's seamanship with anchors and winches and desperate men at the capstans and at the oars floated *Endeavour* off her coral grave and 'the people who had been 24 hours at extremely hard work now began to flag. I myself', wrote Banks, 'was much fatigued and had laid down to take a little rest (many fell to the deck as they left their spell at the pumps and lay there until they were roughly hauled to their feet to take over again) when I was awakened about 12 with the alarming news of the water having gained so much upon the pumps that the ship had four feet of water in the hold. Add to this that a regular land breeze blew off the coast so that all hope of running her ashore was totally cut off. This, however, acted upon everyone like a charm, rest was not more thought of but the pumps went with unwearied vigour till the water was all out . . .'.

Then it was found that the carpenter had made a mistake in his sounding of the hold water-level and they were better off than they had ever dared to hope. It was at this time that Mr Monkhouse, one of the midshipmen, came up with an idea—that of fothering the ship; he had seen it done before with success. You got a sail, stitched on it in close rows tufts of finely chopped oakum and wool. Then the sail was sunk under the ship, the theory being that the suction of the water through the leak would draw in the oakum- and wool-stitched sail and would stop up the hole.

Endeavour was got under way by dint of tugging and towing by every boat on board and by manful, desperate hands at the oars; she was stood in for land, and within a quarter of an hour of the sail being handled into place the pumps drained her dry.

On the 14th Cook and Banks went ashore in a cove to find any harbour where the ship could be beached and her keel repaired, if that was possible. They found an ideal situation in the mouth of a river (later to be called Endeavour River by Cook). The ship was handled close to the river bank so that when the tide fell she would stand with her bow on dry land and the carpenters could get at her keel. In no time a landing platform was rigged between the ship and shore and the men worked like blacks to empty her of all movables. A tented camp was set up ashore and as the tide fell and *Endeavour*'s keel was exposed it was seen that providence had been with them in their disaster, for in the middle of the keel was a hole 'big enough to have sunk a ship with twice our pumps', but the coral had wedged itself in the hole and acted as a plug. The coral had cut a hole and taken away the planking as if clean cut with an axe. The fothering, it could be seen, had been drawn in round the coral and wood and finished off the plugging.

Before the ship was tied up, for it was a slow process to handle her to her temporary 'dry dock', Banks and Solander were ashore and plant hunting. It was a very ill wind that didn't blow this botanist an opportunity to pursue his work, and here at Endeavour River he was to have fifty days in which to pursue it. He found a nymphaea with blue and white petals, many gum trees, palms, figs, two sorts of fruit like pears, a small-leaved plant that smelt like lemon and orange peel and made an agreeable substitute for tea; plantains, the stately Moreton Bay pines, the red cedars, the yellow woods, the tulip woods and the silky oaks he found in the woodlands on the sides of the river as he went upcountry on excursions. He spent days in gathering plants and drying them in the sand. He also reported having seen 'the beast so much talked of' (this was the first kangaroo ever seen by a white man). 'He is not only like a greyhound in size and running but has a tail as long as any greyhound's. . . .' Later, he observed: 'Instead of going on all fours the animal went only upon two legs making vast bounds.' Subsequently Lieutenant Hicks shot one, a 78-lb. specimen, and Banks spoke highly of it next day at dinner as a stew.

One day while the ship was hove up the river bank at a crazy angle Banks went aboard to find the water in the hold had run backwards and flooded the bread room, where he had stored his precious plants. He started to work immediately and had all the plants moved ashore to be sorted out and dried in the sand. Many were saved but many were entirely spoiled. To make up for this loss, as many as possible were gathered again at Endeavour River; and to help his people to collect and preserve them better, large baskets were made of plantain leaves, for it was found they were unable to preserve them in a good natural state in this type of country without them.

Banks found the native sand not too good for drying and had recourse to his paper-drying books and saw that 'one person is entirely employed in attending them. He lifts them all once a day, exposes the quires in which they are to the greatest heat of the sun and at night covers them most carefully up from any damp, always being careful also not to bring them out too soon in the morning or leave them too late in the evening'.

Seeing that this stay was obviously to be protracted Banks took the opportunity of making two- and three-day trips away from the base upriver, across the river mouth; on these botanizing foragings he found many plants he had not seen before in New Holland, for here were tropical plants not found at Botany Bay; once, through the mangrove swamps which stretched inland for about a mile and the long grasses which grew from three to four feet high, including the kangaroo grass (*Themada australis*), he found many representatives of the beautiful, graceful and stately family of palms, the pandanus and calamus. In the higher reaches the steep banks of the river were covered with trees of many sorts; the cotton tree (*Hibiscus tiliaceus*) broke through the mangrove fringe, which later gave way to open eucalyptus forest with many acacias, and the glorious remains (for this was the dry season) of many flowering trees and shrubs: capparis, clerodendron, grevilleas and melaleucas. Not far away from the river in the gullies on the slopes of the hill they called Grassy were tropical rain forests with vines, pittosporums, barringtonias, bombax and the glorious tree-ferns later to become such a feature of our tropical conservatories and palm-houses. Mosquitoes proved most troublesome when they camped under the stars at night, compelling the party to lie in the smoke of their fires in an attempt to keep them off.

It was the following day as they dropped downriver to the *Endeavour* camp that they came across the natives for the first time. They were difficult to get to know and had to be persuaded by Tupia in a long harangue with many signs to lay down their fierce-looking pikes. For several days the natives continued to visit the camp, but acted warily, suspicion on both sides making friendly intercourse difficult. But gifts were exchanged and finally black men with bones through their noses were persuaded to cross the gangplank on to *Endeavour*'s deck. It was evident why very soon: all they wanted was one of the turtles the crew had caught for victualling; several times they laid hold on one and dragged it to the side of the ship, each time being restrained from pushing it overboard. Banks took part in the restraining but was pushed so violently by one of the would-be turtle stealers that, leaving the commotion on deck to sort itself out, he went on shore to tidy up his botanical collections; and while still collecting his equipment together, the baulked natives tumbled off the ship, picked up their arms they had laid on the banks and immediately set fire to the four-foot high grass and under-growth 'which, as dry as stubble, burned with vast fury'. 'A tent of mine which I had put up for Tupia when he was sick, was the only thing of any consequence in the way of it, so I leaped into a boat to fetch some people from the ship in order to save it and quickly returning hauled it down to the beach just in time.'

Now the *Endeavour* was as seaworthy as she could be made, and after the carpenters had done their best under difficult conditions it was time to think of pushing north-wards to find what other perils and dangers lay ahead. It was Cook and Banks who climbed together the nearest high ground to see what was the prospect for making the open sea again. Imagine their disappointment and apprehension when as far as the eye could see it was shoals, breakers, reefs and small colonies of islets threaded by serpentine channels in all directions. It was still the Great Barrier Reef, though they had no knowledge of this, which stretched its tortuous passage before them. Again it was only Cook's clear head, good seamanship and careful pre-plotting of his course that got *Endeavour* through. It was 3rd August when, with the pinnace ahead sounding the way, *Endeavour* made her way slowly and with much difficulty down the river to the sea. High winds, and the fact that Cook had to make a decision whether to beat back the way he had come and try to make the open sea on the other side of Bustard Bay or push on northwards, delayed them until the 6th, when Cook decided on a north-east course, only to meet immediately with gales and shoals, breakers and high surf visible on all sides so that Cook was forced to note in the log: 'I was quite at a loss which way to steer.'

It was Mr Banks whom the captain chose when he was forced to anchor and go ashore to climb high land once more in an attempt to find a channel. The view they took in was dismal indeed, all shoal, reefs and breakers again, and next morning, with Banks for company and confidences, Captain Cook went ashore to an island they named Lizard and saw from the high rocks the outer reef, but also noticed several channels, through one of which they determined to make, leaving the coast and taking to the open sea once more. On this island, Banks, never losing an opportunity, filled in time while waiting for the ship's boat by plant hunting, about which he wrote: 'On it I found some few plants which I had not before seen.'

During this time the master had found a passage which he himself could not get through for the swell but judged with a mariner's eye that *Endeavour* could.

So on 4th August they plunged through the Great Barrier Reef and 'for the first time for three months', Banks wrote, 'we were this day out of sight of land to our no small satisfaction'. *Endeavour* had sailed about 360 leagues by the lead, indeed the leadsman had never been out of the chains either day or night for a moment all the time that the ship was under sail, 'a circumstance', Cook related, 'that perhaps never happened to a ship before'.

It was early days to be self-congratulatory, as Banks and Cook soon found out to their chagrin, for on the 16th their ship was in a dangerous plight once more: becalmed with a strong shoreward swell they found themselves being taken towards a reef where the breakers could be seen and heard crashing and roaring upon the vertical fence of coral, which they knew reached down for thousands of ocean feet.

The yawl, the pinnace and the longboat were got out over the side, cables were paid out and desperate men rowed madly, trying to turn the ship's head or to tow her bodily away from disaster. Ship and boats were relentlessly drawn towards the reef when, forty yards from inevitable destruction, a 'light air' from the shore sprang up and, with the added frantic exertions of all the boats, *Endeavour* turned slantingly away from the reef. But in less than ten minutes the light breeze faded away as quietly as it had come and *Endeavour* was at the mercy of the breakers once more, and Cook and Banks saw the whole drama being played all over again. Then a sharp-eyed sailor noticed a narrow channel in the reef about as wide as the ship's length. Cook decided to chance everything and crash his way through, but the ebb-tide racing out caught the ship and carried her two miles out to sea, helpless in a strong current. Again the look-out saw another narrow opening, and in the capable hands of the captain the tossing bark was steered straight at the passage and, catching the tide, was carried through as by a mill race at a tremendous pace and once more was among the relatively calm waters of the shallow, coral-locked seas.

Their subsequent coast-skirting progress northward through these shallow, rock-strewn, islet-studded seas was once more heralded by the monotonous call of the leadsman. His call would show soundings rising from twenty fathoms to ten or twelve and to within a few feet under the ship's bottom, which Banks had been told in the open sea still let in enough water to keep one pump manned all the time.

With her small craft well to the fore, *Endeavour* plunged her hazardous passage through the many perilous sea-miles up the side of Cape York until on 21st August the ship's company realized they had sailed the entire length of the east coast of New Holland, and on an island he named Possession Cook and Banks stood by the jack run up on a temporary pole while the captain claimed New South Wales for his king.

Stored in the bread-room and in the mounting presses in the Great Cabin and in Banks's and Solander's cabins near by were 331 Australian plants never before seen by a white man, including species of acacias, banksias, gardenias, correas, xanthora, orchids and eucalyptus.

Through Endeavour Strait and Torres Strait the brave but battered ship was now at last headed for home, Banks noting that he was now able to prove that New Holland and New Guinea were not joined but were two separate islands.

On 29th August Banks recorded sighting the coast of New Guinea and smelling a fragrance blowing off the land like that of gum benjamin, but it was 3rd September before Cook, Banks, Solander and Banks's servants, a party of twelve in all, stood in for the new shore, one fringed, as they could see through the glasses, with coconut palms. It was a gently shelving beach on which they set foot, which gave them a 200-yard wade to dry land. Close, thick palm groves came down to within 200 yards of the water's edge so that the party were very much on their guard, not knowing what manner of 'Indians' would appear to defend their native shore; but this anticipated danger did not deter either Banks or Solander from searching for plants on the edge of the wood while the rest of the party strolled along the beach. They were wondering how they could secure some coconuts growing high up in the trees when, with a hideous shout, three 'Indians' suddenly rushed out of the wood and 'running towards us the foremost threw something out of his hand which flew on one side of him and burned exactly like gunpowder. The other two immediately threw two darts at us at which we fired'. A third dart was thrown and the party fired again before the naked savages ran away and the captain decided to go aboard and leave New Guinea to the New Guineans. Almost immediately a yelling, aggressively gesturing mob of a hundred black men rushed down the beach throwing fire. Muskets were fired again and a volley had to be resorted to before the sailors could man the oars and pull back to *Endeavour* and safety, where, said Banks, people had just about reached the end of their tether. 'The disease called nostalgia' had hit them all except Cook and Banks, who had so many problems and interests to keep them going, but the 'others were far gone with the longing for home'.

Scarcity of provisions, certainly lack of variety of them, was now hitting the ship's company too. From the captain downward all were rationed to an amount of food which just managed to keep body and soul together. They passed Timor and the island of Roti, and on 17th of September anchored in the sheltered harbour of Savu, with now a desperate need for meat and any fresh provisions the natives could be persuaded to part with. Banks, as usual, acted as quartermaster in some irritating and protracted negotiations for buying buffaloes, sheep, hogs and greens with gold and muskets, about all they had left for barter. It was an on-off sort of business, with natives and Dutch officials blowing hot and cold, provisions being offered and then withdrawn, but finally Banks concluded his bargaining, and with fresh meat and some greens on board they set course for Batavia, anchoring in the roads there on 9th October when the 'rosy and plump' *Endeavour* crew jeered at the white-faced, spectre-like sailors who came alongside. But Banks's comment was much more to the point. 'No good omen of the healthiness of the country we had arrived at,' he remarked.

No time was lost by anyone who could to get ashore, and the morning after they had anchored Banks and Solander had rented a house and arranged to set up an establishment for the time it would take the Dutch and native shipwrights to patch up the

Endeavour in dry dock. Within a month, although Banks had been warned of the unwholesome climate but chose to think that their many vicissitudes, many changes of climate and country had rendered them immune to almost any ill, he found that the natives spoke the truth. Sickness hit them. Monkhouse, the surgeon, died first, on 6th November. Tupia, who had sailed with them all the way from Tahiti, went into a decline, until the death of his native boy Tayeto was too much for him, and Tupia was the third to die. Next it was Banks's two faithful retainers, John Reynolds and James Roberts, who were both taken ill, and Reynolds died on 18th December.

Both Banks and Solander were taken with the ague and the fever. All around them the seamen fell ill so quickly that the tents ashore were full of sick people and, with Monkhouse dead, very little attention could be given to them. Cook himself was confined to his own cabin but cured himself, while at that time Banks was so ill as to be deprived of his senses. Indeed both he and his Swedish companion were so ill that they could do nothing whatsoever for themselves, and were at the mercy of Malayan servants who cared little and knew less of the art of sick-nursing. The only remedy Banks could see was to leave the low, disease-ridden town and move inland to higher ground. This he did, renting a cottage about two miles out and open to the sea breezes.

Meanwhile *Endeavour* was in repair dock, where the full damage to her bottom could be seen. Planks were coral-rubbed and cut to such an extent that only a bare three-eighths of an inch of board remained. The worm had played terrible havoc too—the ship's false keel had completely gone and her main keel planks were badly damaged. All was ultimately repaired to Cook's and the carpenter's satisfaction by Boxing Day, 1770, when *Endeavour* left Batavia roads, men never having hauled up the anchor with more pleasure or alacrity, for they had left seven of their company buried ashore, all taken by what they had come to call the 'bloody flux'.

Every single member of the crew, excepting an old sailmaker, had been laid low with the fever, so that all on board were well pleased to be on the high seas making for the Cape of Good Hope and home with high hopes. But it was not to be. The 'bloody flux', as Cook called it, or the tertian malaria and dysentery, as it was described by Banks, had got into the ship and into the men and was not to be blown away by the fiercest of Indian Ocean gales. It now became extremely difficult to work the ship with forty sailors sick. She made a short call at Princes Island to buy turtle and provisions. On her course again, *Endeavour* entered a new year which was to bring her an appalling toll of death, Cook himself writing of the ship as nothing but a hospital.

He treated the water with lime, washed all between the decks with vinegar, but the flux had the upper hand, and in his journal Banks talked of nothing else but purging fevers, distempers, blood-lettings and excruciating pains, both to himself and to his comrades about him. On 23rd January and for the next seven days Banks recorded a death a day, and this was in a ship which was unique in not having lost a single man from scurvy. Herman Sporing, his Swedish assistant, was the first to go, then Sydney Parkinson, his devoted and conscientious botanical draughtsman, Charles Green, his Yorkshire friend and ship's astronomer, and sailors like flies. On the last day of the

Top: Sydney Parkinson's impressions, from the deck of the *Endeavour*, of the West coast of New Zealand's North Island showing Cape and Mount Egmont. *Centre:* A richly decorated Maori war canoe, from Parkinson's *Voyage to the South Seas*. *Bottom:* Venus Fort, erected by the crew of the *Endeavour* 'to secure themselves' during the observation of the transit of Venus at 'Otaheiti' (Tahiti).

A Maori Chief, the face 'curiously tataov
or marked according to their manner'; a
Parkinson drawing.

Sir Joseph Banks, who, from 1768,
when he went as naturalist on Cook's
first voyage, to shortly before his
death in 1820, was the moving
spirit behind the dispatch of
British plant hunters to all parts of
the world.

month Banks managed to struggle out of his bunk and make his way on deck to chronicle the fact that not more than eight or nine men could keep the deck, and that only four could be had at one time to man the watches. February started off with death's dismal numberings. Some days two died, others three. During the night of 4th March Fate relented a little when, after heavy seas and a gale blowing on shore had almost tossed them on the shores of 'Tierra de Natal' and four hours in heavy seas were 'spent in the vicissitudes of hope and fear', Banks said, they sailed out of danger and on the 12th sighted the Cape. Their total of deaths in the course of sixty days' sailing was twenty-three men died and buried at sea. Since she had anchored at Batavia in October *Endeavour* had lost thirty men.

So ill were the members of the crew remaining that one of Cook's first tasks at the Cape was to get a house ashore where his sick could be nursed back to strength. In harbour on 3rd April Banks reported the last death, bringing the grim total to thirty-one, although the total for the voyage was forty-two.

Solander was taken seriously ill with the flux for a second time, but fully recovered after fifteen days in bed.

Banks took the opportunity of *Endeavour*'s stay at Cape Town to look into the productions, climate, means of transport, disease, vegetation, native customs and habits, and made a searching survey of the Dutch East India Company's gardens, particularly the botanical section. He noticed the ground around the Cape covered with heaths, like the moors of Derbyshire and Yorkshire.

The Dutch told him they had settled the country two hundred miles inland, the journey being made by ox-wagon, 'the oxen being more nimble than ours at home, some of them driving 8 miles an hour'. There were no inns, he was told, so all travellers carried their own provisions, and oxen had to live off the country on ling or heath by the wayside.

On 14th April *Endeavour* sailed from the Cape, Banks having made an extensive reconnaissance that was two years later to set Francis Masson, the first gardener-botanical-traveller, out of Kew on his long trek for Cape heaths, pelargoniums and bulbous plants to delight the conservatories of the British well-to-do. The 28th saw Banks crossing 'our first meridian and completing the circumnavigation of the globe'.

From 1st to 14th May the ship anchored off St Helena, and here again Banks spent an extremely busy time surveying this twelve-mile-long, seven-mile-broad piece of land in the middle of the Atlantic Ocean. He botanized in all parts of the island, not finding many plants but noting the potential fertility of the soil, and the climate, which he noticed enjoyed a variety hardly to be imagined. His descriptions and his thoughts on the island made it a stopping-off point for later travellers and their plants from all parts of the east, a place where weak and sickly plants were taken from their cribbed and cabined quarters on board ship for an airing and pick-me-up on dry, firm land, as Robert Fortune was to note some thirty years later.

Although the Great Cabin and all his sleeping quarters, as well as many odd spaces on the ship, must have been full of natural history treasures, when *Endeavour* left St

Helena for home Banks still carried on with his work of shooting and fishing, to add to his collections.

By 12th June 1771 *Endeavour* had completed her great voyage of circumnavigation, and at three o'clock on that day Banks and Cook stepped ashore at Deal after three years at sea. Of Banks's original party of ten but four remained; himself, Solander, James Roberts and Peter Briscoe, his personal servants.

The botanical treasures of a then unknown world were quickly to be shown both to the learned and to the curious, for, shortly after Banks had spoken to the king about his natural history discoveries, Solander and he put into order the tremendous number of herbarium specimens so that this magnificent collection could be on view at Soho Square, Banks's London home, as soon as possible.

It was an outstanding collection which Banks and Solander assembled in the 'Solander cases' and the handsome folios in the Soho Square library, representing three thousand specimens of plants, one thousand of which were completely new to botanists. In those exciting cabinets the visiting botanists were able to handle rarities from beyond the seas, including specimens of the varieties of abutilon, acacia, calceolaria, callicarpa, callistemon, celosia, clerodendron, correa, crotalaria, dendrobium, drosera, epacris, erythrina, euphorbia, glycine, grevillea, helichrysum, hibiscus, hoya, ipomoea, ixora, jasmine, justicia, leptospermum, leucopogon, lobelia, loranthus, lotus, melaleuca, mimulus, olearia, passiflora, philadelphia, phormium, pittosporum, polygaea, polygonum, protea, santolina, stapelia, tournefortia, utricularia and viola.

Faithful, drawn-on-the-spot copies in Parkinson's skilled botanical hand had been made of 955 plants, from which he had later drawn 675 sketches and 280 completely finished drawings in colour and of such excellence that the dried specimens in the cases lived again as the various botanists handled the works.

The Australian collections were represented by 412 sheets of herbarium species, from which 365 finished drawings had been prepared and later 340 plates engraved. New Zealand's unusual botanical treasures were to be seen in 173 sketches and 205 finished drawings, the Friendly Isles were represented by 14 sketches and 144 completed portraits. Tierra del Fuego's fatal adventures showed a botanical return of one sketch and 79 drawings, Java provided 72 sketches and 44 finished drawings, while Madeira's flora could be seen in two sketches and 72 drawings. All this richly rewarding botanical work made up a canon, representing three years' voyaging and three years' botanizing, of 675 sketches and 863 final drawings, from which Banks had made 742 copper plates, to be used much later in James Britten's British Museum catalogue of the discoveries, published in 1900.

Quite apart from his botanical prowess and the high honour in which he was now held by botanists and natural philosophers alike for his unique contribution to the natural sciences, Banks, the man, as the companion to Cook on his nation-honouring, awe-inspiring voyage round the world, was a name to conjure with. Here was a socialite, as we should call him today, a tenderly nurtured young man of the best possible social and cultural background, of the best schools and clubs, who could, had he chosen, have led the normal country squire and high London season life of ease and luxury, befitting both his social position and his income. But instead, for three long years he had cast himself off from his country, his estates, his family and his friends to undergo incredible hardship, unheard-of privations and unpredictable dangers in every sea-mile of the most spectacular voyage made by a Briton for over a hundred years. Linnaeus, writing to a friend, summed up the popular feeling when he said: 'I cannot sufficiently admire Mr Banks who has exposed himself to so many dangers—surely none but an Englishman would have the spirit to do what he has done.'

Banks, although his stories of his voyage and adventures were the rage of London society and court circles, was not to publish his own journal, nor was it published until 1896, and then not in its entirety, but its contents were handed over to Hawkesworth, the author of *Cook's Voyages*, who used material from it freely without acknowledgment. Reference to the Oxford University Press edition of *Cook's First Voyage* will show, on comparison of Cook's journal with Banks's, that the sailor was indebted to the botanist for much of the detailed description of natural history, anthropological and ethnological observations as well as for much of its general background as distinct from the strictly nautical. This work was published, soon after the *Endeavour* had returned, in 1773. Sydney Parkinson's account, published by his brother, was on sale in the same year. A pirated edition was on sale as early as 1771, probably written from some diary kept by a member of the crew which had escaped confiscation by the captain. Wharton's fuller and clearer edition of Cook's journal came out in 1893.

So it was that the fame of 'Mr Banks's voyage', as it was known in the country's social circles, and his amazingly varied and startlingly new and strange botanical collection from the other side of the world, spread as quickly as an Australian grass fire. 'The native shrubs, ferns and palms which grew around Sydney soon became known and were more sought after in England than those of the Cape', it was said, and Labillardière, the French botanist, remarked that the old adage, *Semper aliquid novi ex Africa*, was forgotten in the more striking novelties brought back from Australia.

The floral wonders of a new continent were now in the hands and the minds of people of influence, people of knowledge, and their wonder spread to stimulate the imagination and the acquisitiveness of a widespread British and European gardening coterie.

3. Kew sends out its first Hunter

HARDLY had Solander and Banks had time to get their great collection in order and Banks his journal handed over to Hawkesworth, than the young philosopher threw himself with all his youthful vigour and enthusiasm into plans and arrangements for a second voyage with Cook.

The First Lord of the Admiralty, the Admiralty Board, all the people who could pull the proper and appropriate strings were seen, written to and given Banks's advice on what sort of ship was needed, the accommodation he and his party would want, some advice on what officers should be chosen, and what hand-picked people he himself would wish to take to make the voyage a success. There were naturalists, scientists, draughtsmen, artists and servants—a bigger and better party than ever before. At one time the First Lord was convinced that Mr Banks was in no possible doubt whatever that the Admiralty, the king and the country were fitting out Captain Cook, two crews and two ships for a Banks natural history survey of the South Seas and polar regions.

It certainly appeared like this, as Cook, at Deptford, his spirits downcast, saw his chosen Whitby collier, *Resolution*, fit successor to *Endeavour*, being torn apart and altered almost out of recognition for Mr Banks's convenience. The captain had been unceremoniously bundled out of his own Great Cabin—which had been extended for Mr Banks and 'his people' to make a naturalist's workshop, bigger now than the normal accommodation for an Admiral of the Fleet—and had been relegated to a round-house built above on the poop. Above the original main deck had been built another deck under which there were separate cabins made for Banks's party; officers

42

were dismissed to quarters in the dark, low between-decks, 'stored as close as herrings in a barrel', said Lord Sandwich.

Banks, to give him his due, was not asking the Admiralty to do all this alteration work for him at the taxpayers' cost; he spent £5,000 of his own money on it. But his demands were becoming overbearing. Lord Sandwich, the First Lord, fell out of favour with him. Pallister at the Admiralty Board was from the beginning against the drastic alterations to *Resolution* and now, on 9th April, Cook sailed her up to Woolwich to find her already many feet more in draught than she should be without stores or guns and moving as sluggishly as a snail.

At Woolwich, on 2nd May 1772, despite the coolness now being shown towards him, Banks entertained Lord Sandwich and a large party of distinguished people on board. Here was Mr Banks, literally strutting the quarter-deck, celebrating the start of a second Mr Banks's exploit.

All the fuss over, the *Resolution* weighed and struggled to Sheerness, nearly heeled over and drowned her crew on the way and was 'so crank' that Cook declared he could proceed no farther with this top-heavy, one-knot ship.

On 18th May the First Lord and the Board made a momentous decision. Soon the Navy Yard men were swarming over Cook's new ship, anchored off Sheerness, tearing out her ill-advised upper works and bringing her in the shortest possible time back to her original state.

By 13th June, when *Resolution* set sail for the southern ice-bound world, Mr Banks and his party were no longer of the company. He had taken out his tremendous assortment of stores and equipment, already calculated to have cost £10,000, and had gone back to Soho Square in high dudgeon. If he could not have his way about accommodation or another ship then that was it—he wanted none of it.

Yet a few days before *Resolution* sailed with a new company of natural scientists and artists chosen by the Admiralty, the Royal Society and the Board of Longitude, a thirty-one year old Scot had been taken on board on Admiralty orders for passage to the Cape. The two Forsters, father and son, German botanists, were also of the ship and all three were nominees of Banks. Soho Square was still the operational headquarters for the botanical survey of Cook's second voyage.

The Scot, an under-gardener from Aberdeen who had been working for several years at Kew, and the first of a long line of heroic Scottish and northern botanical travellers, was Francis Masson, chosen by William Aiton, superintendent at Kew, as the first ever King's Botanist, to collect seeds and living plants. And behind this appointment was Banks, for since Princess Augusta of Wales had died in 1772, Banks had replaced the Earl of Bute in that year as director of Kew. Banks had been to the Cape, he knew the works of Hermann, Commelin, Bormann, Breynius and others who had shown in print the richness and the uniqueness of the Cape flora; he knew that for close on a century botanists had spoken of the Cape as a mine of floral riches, but few actual plants, and these by way of Holland, had ever reached British gardens or greenhouses.

Although the actual letter to the king entreating him to send Masson to the Cape was penned by Sir John Pringle, the predecessor of Banks as president of the Royal Society, it was Banks who pulled the strings and who was the moving spirit behind this initial adventure, for it was to Banks at Kew that Masson addressed his letters, his bills for expenses and his parcels of Cape flowers, seeds and bulbs for many years to come.

The fact that Cape flowers, hundreds of pelargoniums, gladioli, ixias, heaths, the strange succulents, the unusual proteas, became so popular in British gardens either under glass or in frames was probably another piece of clever botanical reasoning by Banks. He had realized the futility of trying to bring home under the then conditions living specimens of tropical and subtropical flora, but he knew that the entirely different climatic conditions in Cape Province, with its high temperatures, often high but infrequent rainfall, its arid soils, its absence of forest cover and the mountainous terrain characterized by high, rock-strewn, sandy plateaus—the Karoo—had brought into being a hardy, woody, not easily killed type of vegetation which would travel under the conditions as he knew them—months under sail, barrels full of sand for bulbs, boxes full of sandy soil for the cacti and succulents, which under natural growing conditions forgo water for months, and the planted-up boxes of ericas and pelargoniums, two genera which could withstand rough treatment and lack of water for a comparatively long spell.

Masson then, as a protégé of Banks, was on the high seas and was to prove a sterling example of the long line of gardener-travellers who, from their severely restricted *milieu* of bothy, potting-shed and walled mansion or botanical garden, were sped by their botanical or merely acquisitive masters to the ends of the earth.

Lacking anything but the barest of educational background, unsophisticated, and with the dirt and sweat of toil still deep-stained on their strong gardening hands, how they ever managed to surmount their innumerable, incredible and unheard-of hazards without languages, without any previous experience of travel, without any training in the delicate art, which Banks well knew, of danger-fraught negotiations with the natives, must remain one of the mysteries of the early plant hunting and hunters.

Most of them, by dint of the most extraordinary hard labour and burning of the midnight oil long after hard-working, physically tiring days, managed to acquire a smattering of botanical Latin and, though none of them were long experienced as gardeners, a most exhaustive knowledge of plants and plant identification as well, coupled with a knowledge of preserving plant life in climates and conditions totally unknown and undreamed of by them.

The very first steps on their voyages must have been frightening enough, shot, as they were, from the relative comfort of the bothy, torn from the bosom of their comfortable, easy-going gardener comrades into the hell-hole mess of a British naval ship crewed by press-ganging the scum of the seaports—fierce, hostile men with a grudge. Imprisoned aboard their ships like so many convicts (for, given leave, they would have run), they were kept under discipline and orders only by the harshest of regulations and by the ever-present threat of the lash or cat-o'nine-tails, to which even the most humane captains, such as Captain Cook, had recourse many times on long voyages to assert his authority over such rascally, ruffian crews.

With such men the slow, easy-going, ruddy-cheeked countrymen gardeners were confined for months as their ships wallowed their tedious way through the seven seas from British ports in search of plants for their masters; sent out like bees from a hive, Banks's bees, to bring back floral honey for a Kew or gentleman gardener.

Masson was the pioneer, this young Aberdonian was the guinea-pig. How it was possible to select from a plethora of plodding under-gardeners those who would make their names or their masters' names, and find on strange, unaccommodating foreign strands the flowers, the plants which would grow and flower in an English garden, would be a secret which a modern university-trained personnel officer might well wish to know.

Certainly Masson, who was to travel thousands of miles in his master's and Flora's service before he died, was the wisest of choices, richly rewarding the trust Banks and Aiton put in him; adding to the floral calendar accessions which were to change the very landscape of the garden.

Masson was to spend some ten years at the Cape in two separate periods, during which time hundreds of seeds, bulbs and plants were sent home, to bloom strikingly and startlingly vivid in British greenhouses.

His account of his first stay at the Cape is, unfortunately, the only first-hand, detailed description we have of his travels and the many adventures and privations he experienced.

The story of the rest of his botanical travels, and they were almost unheard of in extent for both the man and his time, can only be picked up here and there through the medium of occasional letters to his patrons and his friends.

At the Cape then, and very much in the hands of the Dutch East India Company whose province it was, Masson landed on 30th October 1772 when the *Resolution* dropped anchor in Table Bay, and he stepped ashore to spring weather. Even for a sophisticated and experienced traveller such a vastly changed scene needed some little time to get attuned to, and to Masson, the raw garden hand, the translation from Kew Gardens to the Cape certainly needed some time to digest. He took until December of that year to settle in, getting the feel of the vastly changed climatic conditions—a year with the seasons opposite—getting acquainted with foreign people, both native Hottentots, among whom he would have to travel, and the Dutch, under whose sufferance he was there at all. He sought and found how to get himself into the hinterland by ox-wagon on rugged cart tracks, many of them impassable when the rains came; he learned that there were no inviting inns by the roadside to succour and feed the weary traveller or his beasts of burden, and saw on every hand that every journey would mean the long haul up the Cape mountains, those rugged bastions to a delectable botanical paradise beyond. He knew that all arrangements for any extended inland journey would be entirely his responsibility.

But first he had to cut his botanical teeth, to savour the thrill of a new plant creation on a small scale, to pick his daisies before his orchids. And there, on his very doorstep, was the Aladdin's Cave of the Cape Peninsula where, in an area about the size of the

Isle of Wight, is 'perhaps the most interesting botanical area of the world' (as a recent traveller wrote), containing more species than the whole of Britain. What a paradise for Masson, what a gargantuan aperitif to the rest of the Province!

Here, on the slopes facing the South Atlantic, he could see the last pink spires of *Watsonia pyramidatus*; the scarlet bells of probably the first Cape heath to be seen, *Erica cerinthoides*; the brilliant yellow ixia; the flashy coloured tritonias; the low, gentian-like rose bells of *Romulea rosea*; and the wax-like trumpets of the gladioli. The rocky kloofs he climbed down excitedly were carpeted with the rich purple of pelargoniums, *capitatum* being most prominent.

On Table Mountain itself, which reared its precipitous 3,800-foot rock wall behind his lodgings, Masson's scrambles brought him face to face with that exciting family of *proteaceae*, South Africa's most famous floral family, while silver trees and *Leucospermum conocarpum* splashed the lower slopes with sunshine yellow.

It was while on one of these near-home excursions on Table Mountain that he met with one of the first of his many dangerous adventures. He searched so zealously and so long during the day that he lost his way, although he had been told that a desperate gang of escaped slaves were in the same territory. Ultimately he stumbled into a shepherd's hut. He was unable to lock or bar the broken-down door, so, with the knowledge of wild beasts prowling near, desperate escapees on the run and his only weapon against them a clasp-knife, he took this from his pocket and slept with it under the knapsack he used as a pillow.

His apprenticeship over, he acquired a covered trek-wagon, big enough to carry stores and provisions for his whole party, some eight yoke of oxen and a native guide and driver. Although he was entirely inexperienced, a tenderfoot on such a man-sized expedition, by 10th December he was away for a relatively short reconnaissance eastwards, some 400 miles, on a roundabout route to Swellendam, across the sandy, windswept country of Cape Flats.

His companions on the journey were a Swede, Franz Per Oldenburg, a soldier of fortune, and a Hottentot to drive the wagon.

Because as yet Francis Masson, from Aberdeen and Kew, was not quite accustomed to the South African temperature, which in December at Cape Town can reach over 100 degrees in the shade, they travelled through the night 'over a large sandy plain', and after stopping a day or so to hunt antelope, traversed 'the plain again, the soil of which being a pure white sand blown by the S.E. wind from the shores of False Bay often formed large hillocks. It is nevertheless overgrown with an infinite variety of plants peculiar to this country'. This was Masson's first reaction to the flower-enamelled veld, to a floral brilliance of colour as brilliant as the sun itself—sunflowers indeed. On he went, past the Tygerberg and the Paardeberg, the road rising only gently as yet, although around him were the massively rugged peaks growing in splendour as his gaze was drawn into the blue haze of their far-off majesty.

The party had their first experience of the ever-present danger of fording the Cape rivers when, later in the month, they came to cross the Berg River and crossed by its sandy, treacherous, rock-strewn bed into the Drakenstein valley, barriered by the fantastic peaks of the Drakenstein range on one side and the towering twin peaks of the Paarl Berg on the other. Masson and his Swedish companion climbed the 2,000-odd feet of the Paarl Berg, where they spent a whole day on the summit in search of plants which Masson could see were so vastly different from those he knew; particularly did he note the Cape heathers, or heaths, in masses of colour splashing the sun-baked earth with an even richer purple than his own Scottish moorlands.

He stayed at Paarl, then a small village called Peral, before pushing on south-westwards to take the road at the base of the Klein Drakenstein leading to Fransch Hoek valley watered by the Great Berg River, on whose banks Masson noted 'a great variety of uncommon trees'.

Christmas had come and gone by now, with no mention by Masson of either its celebration or its passing, and on 4th January 1773 he was rumbling into Stellenbosch, then 'a small village of about 30 houses' and some thirty miles from Cape Town, their general direction being exactly opposite to that of their December trek. On the 5th they left, travelling along the foot of the Stellenbosch Mountains towards the Hottentot Holland range and next day 'ascended the mountain by an exceedingly steep, rugged path which the peasants call Hollands Kloof, and after much labour and fatigue gained the summit where we entered a spacious plain interspersed with an infinite number of large fragments of rock visibly decayed by the force of the S.E. wind which blows here during the summer with very great force. Some appear like church steeples and some pierced'.

The wind might well blow, for they were above 4,000 feet, with the whole sweep of False Bay spread out before them. 'These mountains', remarked Masson, 'abound with a great number of curious plants and are, I believe, the richest mountains in Africa for a botanist.

'We then passed the Palmiet river, so called by the peasants from a plant [*schoernis serratus*] which almost covers the water, the leaves of which greatly resemble that of the ananas or pineapple, but the flowers are like those of a reed.'

Another fording, this time of the Bot River, where he 'lodged at a mean cottage and the Dutch and the Hottentots lived almost promiscuously together, their beds consisting only of sheep skins'.

Now they came to Caledon, where a natural spring was even then used by the Dutch for curative purposes. Masson wrote: 'We came to a hot bath situated on the east side of a large mountain called Zwart Berg. The water is scalding hot when it springs out of the earth, but after being conveyed about ten or twelve paces to the bath it becomes more temperate.'

The 10th January saw them fording the River Zonderend, and at night 'we came to Sweet Milk Valley where there is a good house belonging to the overseer of the company's woods who received us with great civility and kept us with him five days'. From this base, after the rest that the gardener traveller must have so obviously needed, on the fourth day he climbed into the thick evergreen woodland, which clothed the mountain-side near by, accompanied by the overseer and eight rough dogs which startled two wolves (jackals or hyenas) and began an hour's fight, which was not left off until the two 'wolves' were killed.

'We afterwards', he wrote, 'climbed many dreadful precipices until we arrived at the dark and gloomy woods with trees 80 to 100 feet high interspersed with climbing shrubs of various kinds. Trees were often growing out of perpendicular rock and among these the water sometimes fell in cascades over rock 200 feet perpendicular with an awful noise.'

When the day was over and he was back in his comfortable overseer's lodging, this Aberdeen gardener, who had never travelled but a few miles from his bothy, sat down and wrote of the effect of the day's scenes upon him: 'I endured the day with much fatigue, and the sequestered and unfrequented woods, with a mixture of horror and admiration.' The greater part of the trees, he managed to remark, were unknown to botany. Some he found in flower, but others, which were not, had to be left for later trips.

It was now 16th January and his horizons were widening quickly, for on that day they came to a Hottentot kraal. 'I saw women and children build huts; very low circular huts made of slender poles to make an arch covered with mats made of reeds with a round hole in the middle of the floor for a fire which the family sat around. There was no hole in the roof for the smoke', but in view of the irritating attention of hordes of flies attacking Masson and his party this was no great fault.

Now they crossed the Breede River where the Zonderend joined it and made for Swellendam—200 miles north-east from the Cape—a good first effort. They spent two days there, 'but finding the season too far spent for making any considerable collections I returned back to the Cape upon the same way that I had come'.

He reached Cape Town towards the end of January, a 400-mile journey in just over a month in entirely strange country.

'It was upon this journey that I collected seed of so many beautiful species of erica which have succeeded so well in the Royal Gardens at Kew,' he proudly boasted in a letter to Sir John Pringle at the Royal Society some months later.

So ended the first botanical reconnaissance of the first botanical traveller in the service of a British king, and on it, for the delectation of George III and for his chief gardener, Joseph Banks, Masson saw a wonderland of botanical treasure within his grasp. His first journey was but a whetting of the appetite, an aperitif to the glories that were there for the picking. Here were natural rarities to suit the greenhouse connoisseurs; the gloriously varied heaths, the startlingly coloured pelargoniums, the other-world-like strangeness of the proteas, the vastly diversified, highly colourful family of Cape bulbs, the unique, weird and wonderful conglomeration of the succulents and cacti in incredible shapes and sizes and in floral colour to baffle the imagination, all soon to become more widely grown, more widely loved than the discoveries of Banks had ever been.

Masson knew that Banks had been right in choosing the Cape for his travels, for although this was a region of tropical and subtropical vegetation, it was the habitat of sun-dried, woody, shrubby plants which in both seed and plant form would travel without much complicated packing or any other method of conservation beyond parcelling up in strong boxes or barrels to be stored in the holds of H.M. ships which called regularly at the Cape on their way from their Indian and Far Eastern ports of call.

Today some of the terrain through which Masson's ox-wagon wound its painful, rugged way is still known as a botanical paradise. The St Loury Pass district is known as the national home of the Cape heaths, of which today 350 varieties can be counted, blanketing the mountains and the passes. Caledon has a wild-flower reserve rich in everlasting flowers, proteas, heaths, the orchid (*Disa grandiflora*), the red nerine and the Caledon bluebell. The Garden Route beyond Mossel Bay is probably one of the best-known floral and scenic motor-car routes in the world.

While Masson had no such survey to guide him he knew enough to realize that new and exciting botanical finds awaited him whichever way he chose to leave the Cape. He did not hurry back into the hinterland, but until September carefully laid his plans. He became acquainted with the Dutch farmers who came to the Cape to transact their government business, and with the curators and gardeners at the Dutch Company's botanical garden there, and he learned all he could about the natural floral history of Cape Province. After extensive inquiries from the Dutch he made arrangements for a route which would serve him and his master best and bring the richest reward.

In the meantime he had met and become friendly with Carl Per Thunberg, the Swedish botanist, trained in the Linnaean School of Botany at Upsala and one of the favourite pupils of the great Linnaeus himself. This was a most fortunate meeting for the Kew under-gardener with a smattering of botany, a keen, observing eye and a trained hand for drawing what he saw, and he was to gain much from it. He was a quick, eager pupil, and when he set out on his second journey on 11th September 1773 it was Thunberg who accompanied him. Masson had, said Thunberg, a good wagon tilted with sailcloth, a European servant and three Hottentots for drivers and general servants. This time both Masson and Thunberg had horses, so they could leave the slow, lumbering wagons to reconnoitre botanically the kopjes, the mountain tops, the spruits and the desert plains on either side of the wagon track. In the ox-wagon as they set out from Cape Town was a full supply of boxes and bags for collecting roots and seeds, cartridge-paper for the drying of specimen plants, a good supply of shoe leather (for, as Masson had found, the sharp, rocky roads played havoc with footwear), fire-arms, gunpowder, ball and a necessary supply of tobacco, mirrors, beads and other such trinkets for placating or pleasing the hostile or friendly natives they would meet on their way.

From the Cape they took the north-west coast route to the Blaauwberg, where days and nights of rain and fog caused them much trouble, and where for one miserable night they lost their way completely and had to camp in the middle of a plain. Rain and fog accompanied them for the first six or seven days out, so that they were glad to reach Groene Kloof, then a Dutch East Indies station, where they stayed for a few days and, despite the rain still being with them, 'made several excursions along the sides of the hills and also over a large sandy desert towards the sea where we found a great variety of beautiful plants and several animals peculiar to this climate, ostriches, antelopes and plovers'.

The little party now entered 'a large barren country called Zwaart Land' (now the Malmesbury-Darling district), where they found miles upon miles of grey sandy soil covered with low shrubs, over which their way was made with great fatigue until they reached Saldanha Bay on 22nd September, where Masson noted an amaryllis from the bulb of which the Hottentots made poison for their arrow tips. Still hugging the coast they came across 'packs of wild dogs as large as foxhounds' and then climbed the Witte Klip 'from the top of which we had a view of the coast back to the Cape of Good Hope'.

This new terrain at this time of the year at the peak of the flowering season called out the poet in the dour Aberdonian. 'The whole country', he wrote, 'affords a fine field for the botanist, being enamelled with the greatest number of flowers I ever saw of exquisite beauty and fragrance.' This was the veld which to the plant hunter is a veritable natural paradise, and where in one square foot one can count no fewer than eleven different species in flower, and, as Masson came to know them better with Thunberg's help, he could speak of his finds, the dimorphothecas, ixias, lachenalias, gazanias, romuleas, the white arum lily (*Zantedeschia aethiopica*) and the now well-known chincherinchees (*Ornithogalum thyrsoides*).

Flooding at the mouth of the Berg River caused some delay in leaving the St Helena Bay district, and travelling four days upcountry through marshland inhabited by hippo the party found wagon travel difficult owing to deep, loose sand and brackish water.

Botanically the area was not much use to Masson, for he recorded that the soil was too salty to grow anything worth while, but at the ferry his botanical fortunes turned as he collected and recorded ixias, irises and gladioli. It was a significant turn of events, for at this stage in his own account of this journey Masson starts to use botanical names for his plant finds, which betokens patently the influence of Thunberg, the trained botanist, on the under-gardener with his smattering of botanical Latin and nomenclature.

Making the crossing of the Berg they came to the 24 River District to find, in refreshing contrast to the salt marshes, a glorious prospect of vines, oranges and lemons. Now, making inland, they experienced the dangers and difficulties of mountain-trekking, for having left the coast they faced and started to climb the fringe of Blue Mountain which buttressed the apparently bare but, after rain, incredibly beautiful 3,000-foot high plateau—much of it Karoo land—from the coastal plains. 'We climbed over the mountain', wrote Masson of this first memorable ascent, 'by a passage called Kartouw, the most difficult in the Cape Province, we being obliged to lead our horses for three hours amidst incessant rain which made the road so slippy that the horses stumbling among the loose stones had their legs almost stripped of skin. And the precipices were so steep that we were often afraid to turn our eyes to either side. Towards sunset with great labour and anxiety we got safe to the other side where we found a miserable cottage belonging to a Dutchman but, however cold and wet as we were, we were glad of anything.'

As for the wagon, a hand's breadth only out of the track was enough to send the stumbling cattle, wagon drivers and invaluable stores crashing down the abyss on their left. So the Dutchman's hovel had to do. 'There was only one room,' said Masson, 'and the Dutchman gave us one corner to sleep in. He hung a reed mat and he and his wife slept there in the other corner. Just beyond a number of Hottentots lay promiscuously together.'

On 10th October they forded Olifants River, having crossed the Olifants River range, and were 120 miles north of the Cape in the river valley, bounded on either side by the almost precipitous walls and fantastic weathered turrets and peaks of the Olifants range and the Cold Bokkeveld. Because there was good pasturage for both oxen and horses Masson and Thunberg kept to the banks of the river to Citrusdal, and from there attempted to cross, with horses and wagon, the high range of the Cold Bokkeveld on the east side. But the road and the pass were impassable. The wagon overturned on the side of a precipice, a shaft was broken and other damage was so great that, with a make-shift rope repair, it made its slow way back to a peasant's house which they had passed earlier. Here the Hottentots were told to repair the wagon and to make their way over Grey's Pass to Rood Land, the present Tulbagh valley. Taking their horses, Masson and Thunberg then pushed on through Cold Bokkeveld 'to Elans Kloof, a narrow winding passage through a high chain of mountains north-east of Olifants River. This road is rugged beyond description, consisting of broken and shattered rock, rugged precipices encompassed on each side with horrid impassable mountains covered with huge rocks that have tumbled down from the summit'. He did note *Protea grandiflora*, however, while every minute expecting rocks to hurtle down the mountain on to him. It was tremendously hot, and as a respite they stayed at a peasant's home for a day, as they entered the Cold Bokkeveld, where not so much as a shrub was to be seen and the high mountains on each side were without vegetation.

But in the apparent starkness and aridity of the countryside Masson was to find the renowned Cape succulents, the stapelias and that strange genus Thunberg was to name for him, the Massonia. It might well have been, as modern field workers maintain, that where plant life appears scantiest it is there that it becomes of the most absorbing interest to the true botanist, yet Masson found the terrain had a melancholy effect on him and he was glad to descend from the plateau by a very steep path into the Warm Bokkeveld encompassed on all sides as this way was by 'horrid high mountains', where they found sour wine and fruit but herbage up to the horses' bellies and, growing among it, more ixias, gladioli and irises.

'We had another high chain of mountains to pass', Masson chronicled, 'before we met up with our wagon and inquired the way of a native woman with whom we had lodged the previous night and who told us that with no guide and only one pass [Mosterts Hoek], which was very dangerous, we should run the risk of losing our lives, having a rapid river [Breede River] to cross several times by fords which were dangerous by late rains. We were a little intimidated by this information but fortifying ourselves with resolution we proceeded and in an hour arrived at the first precipice which we looked down with horror at the river which formed several cataracts inconceivably wild and romantic. This passage, which took us three hours, is at the broadest a quarter of a mile, but generally not more than one-eighth. The mountains on each side rise to steep, perpendicular heights and are now snow-covered. We crossed the river four times. The fords were exceedingly rough, the beds being filled with huge stones tumbled down from the mountain, and though this was laborious and difficult we were repaid by a large number of plants. The banks of the river were covered with a great variety of evergreen trees and the precipices are ornamented with erica and other mountain plants described before.' Many strongly but freshly smelling pelargoniums tumbled down the river banks, a riot of reds and yellows shouted from the proteas and the stabbing linearality of the aloes, huge and commanding, added form to the landscape with their fierce arrow-heads of florescence.

Now the party were in the Roodeland District, but, being fatigued, they took a day for rest and for examining and preparing the plants they had already collected.

On 24th October 'we went mountain climbing again on Winter Hoek, known as the highest mountain [6,818 feet] in this part of Africa. The top was snow-covered and we expected to find plants which would endure the severity of our climates, but at the top we found nothing but grasses, restiaceae and algae. It was a day's journey, very rugged and difficult to mount'.

On the 28th and 29th they continued along the banks of the Breede River, where they found many curious plants growing, and on the 30th they crossed the Hex River and trekked on to Koaree River 'where many new plants were found, particularly geraniums, stapelia and one of the liliaceous kind with a long spike of pendulous flowers of a greenish azure colour [*Ixia viridiflora*] which among the long grasses had an unusual effect', and whose soft pea-green flowers created a sensation at Kew when seen for the first time. *Ixia bulbifera*, so called by Thunberg, hereabouts covered the distant landscape like a red carpet, while the gay red, shouting oranges and yellows of the gazanias were calmed by the pervading mauves and olive green of the mesembryanthemums. It was rewarding country, for apart from the sun-drawn chromatic hues of flowers, the very rock and soils of the landscape were a poem of russets and browns, of reds and blues.

But it was difficult going, hilly with many ridges lying across their pass to Kogman's Kloof, near present-day Montagu, where the Kogman's River tore its way through the mountain wall of curious vertical strata bedecked with brilliant lichens which, after rain, made the pass walls shimmer with light and colour.

Mimosa nilotica was also very prevalent and noted by Masson as they made their way now through comforting greensward and level plains to Swellendam where, by the side of the Buffel Jakt River, they set up camp, rested, gave the oxen a well-earned holiday and—good fortune—had a new set given to them by the captain of the Dutch East India Company fort there, for the two men were determined to push on much farther than nearby Swellendam, a mere 200 miles from the Cape, although Masson's circuitous trek had already taken him well over 300 miles of mountain valley and road.

Strelitzia regina, the Bird of Paradise Flower, probably one of the most exciting of Masson's introductions from South Africa. Named for George II's queen, Caroline, of the House of Mecklenburg-Strelitz.

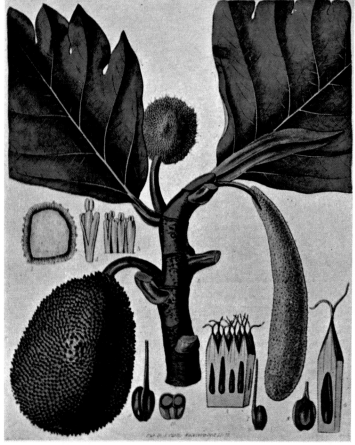

Breadfruit. David Nelson was the gardener to whom Sir Joseph Banks entrusted the transporting, by the *Bounty*, of the breadfruit from the Pacific to the West Indies.

The 10th November, as they set out, refreshed, to Duivenhok River, was nearly a day of mourning, for Masson almost lost his companion while fording. 'Thunberg without making inquiry', wrote Masson, 'took horse and suddenly disappeared. He and his horse plunged head over heels into a pit made by a hippo, deep and steep on all sides, and for a few minutes I thought he might be dead but his horse managed to get a foothold and scrambled out.' Thunberg soon dried out and boasted of his nerve and prowess at staying on his horse, and the party enjoyed the comparatively lush levels of the coastal strip as they journeyed 'across hill and dale through long coarse grass', the journal reads, 'and in the declivities of the hills grew large clumps of *Aloe socotonna* [*socotorina*] five and six foot high'. Indeed here the aloes covered the hills and sides of the mountains and at a distance gave the appearance of a vast army, for their gaunt, bare stalks, a man's height, were crowned with fleshy leaves. All manner of differing forms and colourings of these stately plants were found and recorded, as many an English garden and greenhouse was to show.

There was another river to cross, the Gouritz, which, for 100 yards, they forded carefully, with the water coming up to the seat of their saddles. They were heading for the botanical paradise of the Little Karoo, and Masson, in his excitement, before they reached Mossell Bay for a short rest, anticipated his coming enjoyment of a bountiful but bizarre nature, writing: 'Now on each side of this land lies an extraordinary tract of land, in Hottentot language, carro. It is a dry, burning soil of a reddish colour intermixed with rotten rock and entirely divested of grass, but enriched with an interesting number of evergreen shrubs, both frutescent and succulent, crassula, cotyledon, euphorbia, portulaca and mesembryanthemum. On the way we visited the seashore at Mossell Bay and on the way to the sea spent the night with a Swedish Pomeranian, a refuge in a mud hut with no beds, although he had several hundred oxen and thousands of sheep. The Hottentots around kept a fire burning all night to keep off wolves and tigers.[1] On the 16th we came to Mossell Bay. The shore was covered with shrubs, many unknown to us but not in flower. To the north-east is a woody country called Houtniquas [Outeniquas] Land whose woods intercepted by rivers and precipices are so large that their extent is not perfectly known. Wild elephant and buffaloes render travel difficult. We now directed our course northwards [and inland] to the great chain of mountains which we had again to cross by a hard day's march from side to side over Hattaquas Kloof [Attaquas Pass, a climb of over 2,000 feet] and continued our journey through dismal country where we saw neither man nor beast but our labour was generously rewarded by the productions of the vegetable kingdom we found, including several new species of plants which for neatness and elegance succeeded anything I had ever seen [*Massonia hureas*]. By night we got clear but entered a rugged country which the inhabitants named Canaan's Land though it might better be called Land of Sorrow, for no land could exhibit a more wasteful prospect, the plains being nothing but rotten rock intermixed with a little red loam in the interstices supporting shrubby bushes,

---

[1] Presumably leopards are meant.

evergreens but by the scorching heat of the sun, stripped almost of all their leaves. But we found new succulents never seen before which appeared like a new creation.'

On 21st November they reached the Doorn River and camped under a mimosa tree during a welcome rainstorm but a frightening thunderstorm, with lightning licking the nearby peaks of the Kamnasie range. Next day they entered Lange Kloof, a narrow valley extending 100 miles above the 2,000-foot contour, at its broadest not above two miles but with panoramic views over ranges of mountains and their dividing valleys like a giant relief map before their eyes. From the heights they made a slow descent to sea level again at Algoa Bay, and on the way saw several villages where Masson noted that the Hottentots who tended large herds of sheep and cattle lived in rough shelters made of poles with thatch over the top.

Lions were a danger now, and as the party crossed Kromme River, and on 30th November arrived at Essenbosch, they slept in open fields well clear of the woods for fear of lions taking them unawares during the night. Hyenas had already attacked and severely wounded one of their oxen. On the first day of December they reached the Zeekoe River, where they rested eight days, ranging the fields and adding to their plant collection. 'We lived with an old German', wrote Masson, 'in a handsome house with vineyards and gardens and 100 Hottentots as servants. The woods were almost impenetrable and on the river banks hippo pits were a danger. We found in the woods *Euphorbia antiquorum* 40 foot high. Still determined to continue our journey about 150 miles further directing our course towards the middle of the country I furnished myself with a set of fresh oxen and a fortnight's provisions and Mr Rock gave us one of his sons for a guide and to serve as an interpreter, he being a perfect master of the Hottentot language'.

On the 9th, after staying a night with a rich Dutch grazier, the last Dutchman in these parts, they left for 'rugged, hilly country covered with thick copses of evergreen trees. But the way was so rough that our waggon was almost shaken to pieces. Towards noon we crossed the Camtous [Gamtoos River] where we rested during the heat of the day and amused ourselves in woods frequented by lions, elephants and with deep pits of the river hippo. We found many plants here notwithstanding our stay was so short'.

As for the danger from the wild beasts, Thunberg must have quieted any fears that Masson had about them, for, as Thunberg wrote later, everybody knew a lion would not attack if a man but stood his ground and looked it sternly in the face, faced the snarling beast and did not take to his heels and, in any case, said Thunberg comfortingly, 'they had much rather eat a Hottentot than a Christian, perhaps because the Hottentot, being smeared with grease, always stinks, and because he never uses salt or spices the juices of his body are not so acrid'. There was also a sure sign of impending danger for, if a lion lay still without wagging its tail there was no danger, but if it made any motion with its tail then it was hungry and you were in great danger. Masson does not tell whether he ever stayed to observe this infallible sign. It was almost as easy with buffaloes, said the learned doctor. With charging buffaloes one had only to remember to step aside quickly as with lowered head he made for you, then he would miss you

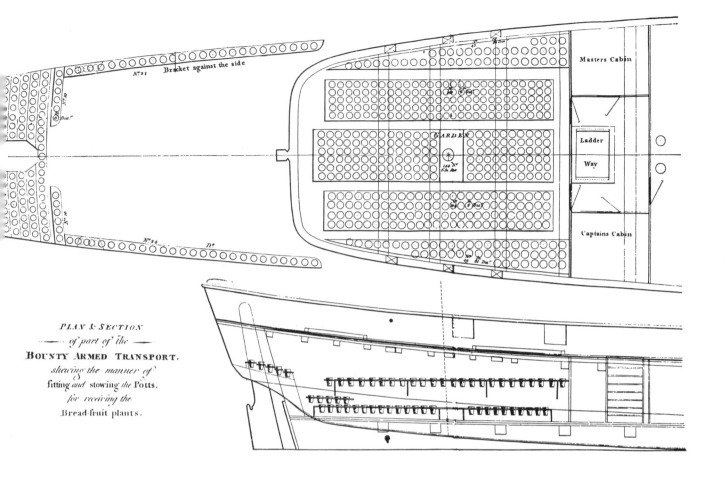

PLAN & SECTION
—— of part of the ——
BOUNTY ARMED TRANSPORT.
shewing the manner of
fitting and stowing the Pots.
for receiving the
Bread-fruit plants.

Masters Cabin

Ladder
Way

Captains Cabin

Bracket against the side

GARDEN

BOUNTY

Above: Plan and section of *Bounty* showing for the first time ever on a British naval ship the Great Cabin labelled 'Garden' and transformed into a plant pot store for breadfruits. *Below:* David Nelson, the *Bounty*'s gardener, Banks's nominee, among the party set adrift with Bligh.

March 22 went five or six miles to the south of Freetown to the top of one of the highest mountains to see the African nutmeg but the tree was so very high that I could hardly distinguish the form of the leaves on the way I met in with three sort of Passiflora but none of them in flower one resembling P. quadrangularis I met in with a Melastoma which I had not seen before which made it the 6th species which I had seen there also saw for the first time the Glycine subterranea and a tree with a Platanus shaped leaf which the people called the Corra grana which they said was an excellent fruit and a very curious Epidendrum.

23 This day I went to their town a distance of 3 miles from Freetown but a distance of 5 miles for me as living at the Governors ... when I had got about half way I met in with a very curious plant a Bletia or Cyrtopodium which I took up a few plants of. I believe it is a new species of one of the above mentioned Genera ...

Two pages from George Don's Journal to be seen at the Lindley Library of the Royal Horticultural Society. Don was sent by the Royal Horticultural Society to collect in Brazil, the West Indies and Sierra Leone.

altogether. Another danger in this wooded country were artfully disguised lion and buffalo traps which, did you happen to fall in, would find you impaled on a cruelly sharp stick set plumb in the middle.

On again they trekked to Loeries River, passing through clouds of brightly hued butterflies and being visited by several savage and aggressive-looking Hottentots 'who came out of the woods armed with lances but behaved very obligingly and slept by our fire and we gave them tobacco'. A day later Masson wrote of 'smooth green hills, woods and groves which could not but charm us who for upwards of three months had been climbing rugged mountains and crossing sultry deserts. In the evening we came to Van Staads [Van Staadens] River and were visited by Hottentots again and next day, having crossed the river, we came to a Hottentot kraal of two hundred Hottentots who were dressed in mantles of ox hides with the hair outside and with their breasts, bellies and thighs naked. Some had skins of steinbock hung over their breast with the skin of its forelegs and hooves. As a cover for their private parts a muzzle of leather exactly covered the extremity of the penis suspended by a leather thong from a girdle ornamented with brass rings. Behind, as an ornament, others had a buffalo tail fastened to a girdle which was fastened round the thigh, others a porcupine quill stuck through each ear, others had plates of brass six inches square fastened to their hair hanging on each side of their head, others wore large ivory rings round their arms or several other fancies too tedious to mention. The women's dress was almost the same except that a great number of small thongs of leather suspended from their girdles reaching down to their knees to some measure concealing their nakedness. All were armed with hassaguays, eight or ten in the left hand. We found here the true Cape Jasmine [*Gardenia stellata*] and the coral tree [*Erythrina corallodendron*]'.

For two days, the 13th and 14th, they stayed in this area, 'collecting new plants and keeping out of the way of fierce buffaloes which in the day time retire to the woods which renders it very dangerous to botanize there. We here saw two lions for the first time at about four to five hundred yards distance, but they took no notice of us'.

Then it was on to Swartkops River and to the salt pans near by, a lake which had dried up and left the salt. They were now at Algoa Bay, near Port Elizabeth, 489 miles from the Cape by the shortest road route, and camped at night, with fires burning fiercely, their cattle tied to the wagon wheels, for the night was loud with the 'howling of wolves and the dreadful roaring of lions'. Flies were so troublesome here, they almost covered the top of the milk in a thick layer, and made it almost impossible to eat for fear of swallowing hundreds. Many of the Hottentots, friends and volunteer guides— as many as two hundred—who had been coming round their wagon in a day, seeking gifts of tobacco, or mirrors, or beads, had now left them, as on the 17th December they turned inland in the direction of Sundays River, travelling 'through miserable parched country covered with shrubs and succulent plants of various kinds but the grass was entirely burned up by the heat of the sun. We saw spoor of elephant and lion'.

By noon they reached Sundays River, where a halt was called and a pow-wow held with the guides and servants about the feasibility of continuing their journey into the middle of the country to the Snow Mountains and the Camdeboo range. 'But', wrote Masson, 'they refused to accompany us, finding we were now on the borders of a vast nation of Hottentots called "Caffers" which they said would kill us were it only to get the iron belonging to our waggon. In consequence of this and the bad state of our waggon, being ready to drop to pieces and many of our oxen sick, we with much reluctance decided to return the same way we had come.'

Masson did not really mean this, for they kept parallel with the Indian Ocean sea-board on their return and took the still higher ridge over the Lange Kloof bordering the Great Karoo plateau for a considerable part of the way.

'On returning', said Masson, 'we passed through the driest country ever seen—plains covered with loose stones, not a blade of grass to be seen but found many rare species of crassula, mesembryanthemum and other succulent plants.' This was the Karoo where the red soil showered back the heat in shimmering clouds which affected their eyes already open in wonder at the stabbing masses of primary colour—'flowers of the sun', which, Thunberg said, were solar chronometers in themselves and did service as barometers too to the discerning. 'By the opening and closing of flowers', he wrote, 'one may know with certainty, as from a watch, what hour of the day it is as well as if the weather will be fine or rainy. . . . The *Moraea undulata* [butterfly flower] never opens before nine o'clock in the morning and before sunset at four in the afternoon it closes again. The *Ixia cinnamomea* opens every evening at four and exhales its agreeable odours through the whole night. The approach of rain is announced by the flowers of various bulbous plants such as the ixias, moraea, irises and galaxias, the tender flowers of which do not open in the morning if rain is to be expected soon and if a shower is to fall in the afternoon they close some time before.'

Botanically this was exciting; the finds were all richly rewarding, many were most beautiful and the odours, sun-drawn over the Karoo, were some little recompense for the treacherous travel conditions about which Masson wrote: 'There was no water for 30 miles distance, no animals and even the beds of large rivers dried up.' A welcome respite was taken on 30th December when they visited Olifants River hot bath and climbing the mountain 'found a heath quite remarkable for having its branches and leaves covered with a fine hoary down or nap which we thought singular'.

From here they sent the wagon forward with orders to meet them in Riet Valley, while Masson and Thunberg on horseback decided to ride across the 'dry carrow' (Karoo) to their right. But there was no track, they missed their direction and the farther they travelled the farther they went astray so that at last they could not even find their way back. They rode on into the deep mauve dusk as far as their lean horses could take them and, as the sun went down, found a tiny brook and, making a fire of canna bushes with their gun-flints, they lay down to sleep with saddles as pillows. So cold was the night, however, they could not sleep and spent their time replenishing the fire and walking round it to keep warm. As they sat and then circled the fire over this bare, scorched, rocky land, as if to compensate for the searing day there came the balm of scented air as though the sun's going down had drawn with it the very hearts of the flowers, and a sweet pervading scent, as of pinks, poured from the gladioli, irises and the *Ixia pilosa, fucata* and *cinnamomea* around them.

In Lange Kloof they met their wagon to find many of the oxen were sicker than ever, having caught a disease affecting the hooves, which dropped off before the cattle succumbed. This was the first day of 1774 and the heat they experienced was almost too much to bear. 'The birds could hardly fly and the air almost too hot to be breathed,' said Thunberg, who reckoned that the temperature was several degrees above 100° Fahrenheit.

Again on the 3rd they left the wagon and its sick oxen to make its way through Attaquas Kloof as best it could, while the two travellers set out on horseback to examine a large tract of Karoo 'where the oxen could not manage because of the scarcity of water. Late in the afternoon we came to a peasant's house where we asked our way and were told that in four hours' journey we could come to another house who would put us up, but at sunset there was no sign and returning four miles we found another track on which we continued until one, when we found ourselves in a dismal valley enclosed on one side with a dismal precipice and then found ourselves in the middle of a thicket of thorn [*Mimosa nilotica*] where we unsaddled the horses and kindled a fire. There was nothing to eat for man or horses but we found water in a stream and spent the night in gathering wood and keeping a fire going until day break when I climbed a high precipice and surveyed the country and collected several interesting plants, geraniums and *Stapelia euphorboides*. I came down and directed our horses towards high mountains in front where we expected to find some relief but were disappointed for after being parched up with insupportable heat we met with not a drop of water to quench our throats during the whole day's journey. Fortunately we found a house and were welcome'.

Next morning they overtook the wagon at the kloof with the oxen little better, one having to be left behind in a dying condition. By the 12th they had reached Buffel Jakts, the Company's rest station, and stayed for a few days, spending their time in the woods around, where they found many curious trees in bloom.

From here, somewhat refreshed, they made their way to Swellendam, crossed the Breede River ferry and saw more zebra near another Company post at 'Tigerhoek' and saw baboons in the Hottentot Holland Mountains before reaching Cape Town on 29th January after a journey of four months and fourteen days and well over a thousand miles of mountain and valley trek.

Masson spent a busy winter, as did his friend, sorting and mounting his herbarium species and packing and dispatching his hundreds of bulbs, seeds, hardy ericas and other woody plants to Banks and Aiton at Kew. They both spent a little time showing Lady Ann Manson, on her way out to her India-based husband, the botanical wonders of the near Cape. The lady was about sixty, but her aristocratic femininity and her knowledge of botany and botanical draughtsmanship must have been a startling and refreshing change after a diet of Hottentot society.

Soon enough it was spring, and on 25th September Masson collected his gear about him and followed Thunberg, who had gone on a few days ahead, to make at first for the west coast, with this time only two Hottentots as servants, to drive his wagon and look after the horses.

It was over the coast flats again, with rain and floods causing trouble at the start towards the Hottentot Holland Mountains. Because of the floods the small convoy made short-stage journeys along the foot of the Stellenbosch range in the direction of Paarl, with the fairy-tale peaks of the Drakenstein on their right. At Paarl he met Thunberg and on 4th October they climbed the 2,000 feet or so to the top of the Paarl Mountain, that well-known feature crowned with its three enormous granite boulders, the Paarl, the Britannica and Gordon's rock, 'where', says Masson, 'we greatly added to our collection'. Now their direction lay northwards to Horse Mountains and Van Riebeek's Casteel, where on the 6th 'we mounted to the top of the Paardeberg (some 3,000 feet) where we found a treasure of new plants we had not seen before. We then went through a level country covered with low shrubs, but it now being spring it was everywhere decorated with flowers of the greatest beauty; every hour's march brought new charms of delight to feast upon and on the very narrow top we collected here many remarkable new plants, in particular a hyacinth with flowers of a pale gold colour'.

By the time they came to the Berg River it was unfordable owing to the recent heavy rains coming down from the mountains. Luckily they managed to get the wagon and its load of food and collectors' equipment across in a large boat and made the oxen swim over.

'From thence we proceeded through a barren, uninhabited country and consequently we were obliged to content ourselves with the shelter of a large Leucodendron tree that protected us from the south east winds which at this season sometimes blow very cold.'

They reached the foot of the Piquetberg on the 13th, noting the sandy plains and keeping a sharp lookout for 'tigers'[1] which frequented the district and which, they were told, could not forbear to attack if anyone said 'fa fa'. Here they found *Stapelia incarnata* and a great variety of beautiful plants, especially aspalathus, with its brilliant yellow flowers to add to the glorious kaleidoscope of ixias and hundreds of wild geraniums in startling reds and mauves. Travelling to the east of the Piquetberg, the plant hunters came to the Verloren valley to find it 'barren and the sand hills so loose that sometimes our horses were up to their bellies which made our journey most fatiguing'.

They reached the Atlantic seaboard about the mouth of the Verloren River, crossed it and leaving the sea on their left hand made in a northerly direction towards the mouth of the Olifants River. 'The heat now became great which the whiteness of the sand still increased and obliged us to travel in the evening and early in the morning and resting in the middle of the day.

'It was also not a little fatiguing to travel on horseback, the mole casts being so deep that the horses fell up to their shoulders each six or seven minutes. The country is furnished with a great variety of elegant shrubs.' The country they were traversing was

---

[1] Presumably leopards.

dry 'carrow field' as they made up Lange valley where snakes abounded, ran between their horses' hooves, slithered over Masson's and Thunberg's legs as they lay down to rest or ate in the shade of the wagon and, on one occasion, one actually coiled itself around Thunberg's leg. The imperturbable doctor, however, was again a great source of comfort to Masson, for he had a theory for snakes too—if they were not attacked or trampled on they would not attack you, he said.

On the 24th they set out for Heerenlogen early in the morning, expecting to find a river or a *fontein* where they could rest during the heat of the day, but travelled till noon and found nothing. 'The oxen's tongues were hanging out with the heat,' wrote Masson, while Thunberg comments: 'It was one of the hottest days of the summer and the heat was so intolerable that we were afraid our beasts would grow faint and drop down exhausted. By this insufferable and tormenting heat our bodies swelled up as it were and the pores opened up in the highest degree.' This was the day they saw the rare and much sought after *Codon royeni* and in attempting to take its flowers the white, brittle and transparent prickles with which the bush was covered punished them severely with painful punctures and deep scratches. 'About 1 o'clock we saw a lake in the distance,' wrote Masson, 'but on our arrival our horses refused to drink, it was salt and not until evening did we find water.'

The next morning another complication besides lack of water arose when a peasant going to the Cape told them he had been attacked by a lion which was dangerous at night and lay beside the trek waiting for the unwary traveller. He advised them to seek cover that night for their own safety. Luckily they reached a Dutch farm by nightfall after passing over the roughest of tracks, and such was the farmer's hospitality that they stayed a few days to recuperate both men and beasts.

The countryside around was sterile—no grass, nothing but naked hills and the soil a red loam—yet Masson noted the farmer's sheep eating succulents, and on these same bare hills he 'was surprised to find all the plants entirely new to us. They are the greatest part of the succulent kind, mesembryanthemum, euphorbias and stapelias of which we found many new species'.

On 30th October all the party gave a hand to empty the wagon and transported all the baggage across the Olifants River in a small boat, afterwards urging the oxen across with an empty wagon which almost upset in mid river, which was fifty yards wide at this point and in parts very deep. About a day's journey from the ford elephants were seen. They had crossed the river near Vredendal and trekked west of Windhoek to reach the Troe Troe River and, going north over the plain west of the Bokkeveld Mountains, came to what is now known as the Van Rhynsdorp Karoo, but to Masson 'The Great Carro'. For this the botanical appetite of both plantsmen had been whetted by a peasant 'who told us', said Masson, 'that in winter the hills were painted with all kinds of colours and said it grieved him often that no person of knowledge of botany had ever had the opportunity of seeing this country in the flowering season.

'We had now the Great Carro to pass, a desert of three days' journey where no fresh water was available and only pits of brackish water, enough to preserve the lives of our cattle, were to be found. The pits were at some distance from the road which makes it difficult for strangers to find them. While we were considering these approaching difficulties, thinking that if we should miss the pits we should probably perish in this inhospitable desert, to our great joy we were overtaken by a Boer with his wife and children who were going the same road but, he having a fresh team of oxen, we could not keep up with him. However, he directed us in the way and said he would tie a piece of cloth on a branch of a tree where he knew there was water but desired us not to go near these places without firearms as there was commonly a lion lurking near them.'

All around them was bare plain, red-russet in colour, strewn with rock and boulders, relieved by the gnarled, twisted clumps of mesembryanthemum bushes in their full range of reds and mauves; to be sought with diligence under their feet were the pebble-emulating *lithops*, betrayed here and there by an intense stab of colour, a flowering stone; by the track of the roughly eroded side of the kopjes, glaring, eye-piercing patches of red and gold betokened huge clumps of aloes; crassula, rhenoster bush and euphorbias added their glories of form and colour, while the acacia karoo put back the sunshine gold into the shrieking primaries of the red hyobanches, crassulas and the ruschias; contrasting in all innocence were the snow-white blooms of *Ruschia nana*. It was an amazing sight and their wonder and excitement at such botanical treasure added still further to their difficulty in finding a track. Fortunately for the two newcomers to this floral treasure house, but travel-difficult Karoo field, they caught up with the Dutchman and his family at night, finding him camping on a bare eminence. 'We were more in favour of a small wood of mimosa trees along the bank of a dry river but he told us it was much too dangerous on account of wild beasts and that there were often such sudden showers in the night that people who lodged by the river had, with their waggon and their oxen, been carried away during the night while they lay asleep.'

They were obliged to stay until noon next day at this spot to let the oxen feed on the sparse vegetation growing in the shade of the trees by the watercourse. Then, mounting their horses and hitching the oxen, they moved on but found no water that day or the next.

'We travelled over the thirsty land where we suffered from the heat of the sun and want of water,' said Masson, 'but our feelings were aggravated when we thought of our poor animals who often lay down in the yoke during the heat of the day. I would have liked to collect cacti and succulents but had to press on and could only collect 100 by the wayside never before described, but if we could only have come in the rainy season.'

Succour for their poor animals' distress reached them on 2nd November when the peasant, who had now got home, sent two teams of fresh oxen to help them up the 2,000 feet of the Bokkeveldberg. 'We ascended by a winding road which was so very rugged and steep that it took five Hottentots with ropes made fast to the waggon to keep it from overturning. The face of the mountain consists entirely of scattered soil covered with woody plants most of which were new and some were aloes 12 foot high [*Aloe dichotoma*]. We were now at the top of the mountain and enjoyed the cool breeze 220 miles north from the Cape. We carried on on top of the mountains [the top was a barren plateau] until the 6th when we directed our course northwards again.'

The now refreshed travellers descended to the plain near Nieuwoudtville, still in dry, barren country, and made east-north-east for Hantamsberg by dry riverbeds and over a soil which was nothing but 'rotten rock'.

They were 350 miles north from the Cape and now were traversing the Lower and Middle Roggeveld before changing course to strike south-east and descend to the Tanqua Karoo. 'It was uninhabited country much like the former,' wrote Masson, 'surrounded by high mountains, but we never saw the smallest rivulet or fountain issuing from them. All the water we found being that which was left stagnant in the deepest parts of the rivers that were formed by the rains in the wet season, which rivers, towards midsummer, became entirely dry.' Their journey pleased, however, for the two found *Hydnora africana* (Hydnum?), 'without doubt', commented Thunberg, 'one of the most extraordinary plants that have been discovered of late years. It always grows under the branches of the shrub *Euphorbia tirucalli* and upon the roots'.

A peasant told them next day that a lion had been following their track, and a dead zebra left by the wayside, obviously killed by a lion, possibly by the very one that was following them, convinced them of the truth of the warning, but nothing untoward happened and they rode along the Rhenoster River to the Drooge River valley to come to the foot of the Roggeveld Mountains which, on the 16th, they climbed by an extremely rugged road to find that the veld extended for several hundreds of miles along the ridge of the mountains.

'Arid, rocky and treeless,' Masson described the country here, where, he said, the Dutch kept large flocks of sheep which the natives frequently raided, carrying hundreds off at a time, killing the shepherds with bows and arrows if attacked (the tips of the latter being poisoned with the venom of serpents) as they made off to the cavities of the rocks 'where they lived like baboons'.

In complete contrast and causing considerable discomfort to the travellers, who were now nearly 4,000 feet above sea level and who had for so long been seared and burned by the sun, on 22nd November 'the ground was white with frost and the wind sharp. We were going to go to the end of the veld to the north-east but the ruggedness of the road made both horses and oxen so tenderfooted that they became unserviceable and we were obliged to drive them ourselves a greater part of the way home'. So severe was the frost and the cold—'it blew a violent storm, the ground was white with frost and there was ice upon the pools'—that they had to stay on the mountain top for two days until the storm had abated. With ice still on the pools 'as thick as a rix-dollar' and snow by the wayside, they decided to descend the mountain by means of the track, a series of great broad high steps. Fortunately they had fresh oxen, but to stop the wagon overturning or running down its own oxen 'several Hottentots with long thongs of leather attached to the top of the waggon stopped it from overturning while we made both hind wheels fast with chain. After two and a half hours of hard labour, sometimes pulling on one side, sometimes on the other and sometimes all obliged to hang on with our whole strength behind the waggon to keep it from running over the oxen, we arrived at the foot of the mountain where we found the heat more trouble than the cold had been at the top'.

They were back in Karoo country once more—the Tanqua Karoo—with a four-days' journey before them, in which no more than three brackish water pits were to be found and no other live creature on the desert; 'not even a sparrow could exist on it', said Thunberg.

On 4th December they travelled through Gousbloem Kloof in the Koedoes Mountains to arrive at Ongeluks River next day, where they had to remain a day to rest the oxen and let them get what sustenance they could out of brackish water and the reeds growing by the side. They were also waiting for a Dutchman who had promised to take them across the next part of the Karoo, even drier and more inhospitable than the last stretch, but he failed to put in an appearance, and as a man could just as easily die of hunger or thirst, or both, waiting, they set off alone in the evening at eleven o'clock and travelled in the comparative cool of the night to daybreak, when they camped by a little rivulet. About eleven next night they cleared the desert and had arrived at the foot of the Bokkeveld Mountains where, rejoices Masson, 'we found a rivulet of pure water where we spent the night and part of the next day in great luxury'. They had returned to Christendom, remarked Thunberg, after having for the space of several weeks for the most part wandered in deserts, often encamped in the open air and in the most dangerous places and several times been in want of the necessities of life.

The track now lay over the Doorn River through the mountains between the Karoo and the Cold Bokkeveld range to the Verkeerde valley, uninhabited but 'where we rested three days,' said Masson, 'having found good pasture for our oxen and a large lake of fresh water well stocked with water fowl. We lived on wild duck and snipe'; and how they must have lived!

It was the home stretch now and on the 15th the convoy trekked to Hex River and through the Hex River kloof to Roodezand, climbing down to the river by the mountain buttress of the Great Karoo tableland they were glad to have left behind them. Cape Town lay ahead, and what happened at Christmas Masson has no time to say. This was the second time in two years he had journeyed through the festive season without even a mention; perhaps his Scottish upbringing made him look forward to the New Year! By the Paardeberg, by Koopman's River, Great Breede River, they arrived at the Cape on 29th December. A three-months' journey had ended in which Masson and Thunberg had journeyed over some five hundred miles of valley and mountain terrain.

The next few months were busy ones for Masson, arranging, cataloguing and mounting his herbarium species for Banks, whose vast herbarium, which later was to form the basis of the British Museum collection, was indebted almost solely to Masson for his Cape plants. His rough field notes had to be transcribed, and the following example shows what a painstaking, careful observer of plant life he was, meticulous in detail and unsparing in his thoroughness. Of the silver tree, the beautiful half-hardy evergreen *Leucadendron conocarpum*, he writes: 'This tree grows on the skirts of the mountains in hard, stony soil and stands in sandy and gravelly earth; grows to a height of 8 or 10 feet with many irregular branches which spread on all sides and never aspires with an upright stem. The leaves are dentated and all over hairy and of a white silvery colour but shine more as in *Protea argentea* (*L. argenteum*). They flower in October/November. The flowers are of a beautiful gold colour collected into a head but without squamae. The style is long, a little behind. The flower is burst by the style, is hairy and curls back. The style afterwards becomes a down or pappus which adheres to the seed. The seed is ripe in March. It contains a hard coat (but comes up plentifully from the seeds which spread themselves sometimes over adjacent vineyards). It is very plentiful at Constantia when the fields are set afire and the under shrub and grass are burnt off. The young plants come up plentifully next year. In the time of flowering the trees are plentifully stocked with birds, viz: *formosia, violacea* and a brown one with a remarkable long tail, where they feed on the nectar of the flowers which they extract with their long, curled bills. The people of Cape Town use it for burn-wood which is carried by their slaves for 5 or 6 miles on sticks about 5 feet long with a large bundle on each end which they carry over their shoulders. It would make a fine ornament among the green-leaved plants in Europe and is to be raised only by seeds, to be managed in the same way as *P. argentea*.'

Seeds and plants were dispatched by all available shipping, for at Kew there was growing what was to be known throughout the botanical world as the Cape collection. Masson's bulbs from the Cape were grown together in glazed frames called bulb borders which were attached to the front of Botany Bay House, a most appropriate juxtaposition of the beautiful and unusual floral finds of both master and man. The frames, which were warmed by the flues of the big house through openings left in the brickwork, were 234 feet long and five feet wide. Cold weather saw specially made shutters being hurriedly put into place over them. The frames carried Masson's collections for many years and the Cape House was a constant source of wonder and pleasure to both the professional botanist and the general public.

As Curtis said in an early volume of the *Botanical Magazine*, talking of the cultivation of old flowers: 'Now there is not the necessity especially since the vast accession of plants from the Cape and New Holland made within these few years.'

The proteas never failed to attract and surprise and for years *Protea mellifera*, one of Masson's introductions, was the flower to wonder at.

The records of Masson's career during the next year or so are a little vague, but it is obvious from what few letters there are relating to the period that because of the unusually arid, dry heat of their native haunts and the temperate heat and wet cold of the British climate, as well as the unfamiliarity of gardeners with this new material, much was lost, but he kept up a regular supply of plants and seeds from the Cape until he went home. It is probable he did not again make the long arduous journeys of his early years, but just sporadic visits to areas where he knew he would find a readily accessible harvest when the season was ripe.

He came back home late in 1775 and spent some little time at Kew with Aiton helping to arrange and grow his Cape material. On 4th May 1776 there is a note from the Rev.

Michael Tyson which says: 'Mr Masson showed me the New World in his amazing Cape hothouse, erica 140 species, many protea, geraniums and cliffortias more than 50.' We have also in that year a letter from Masson to Linnaeus, dated 26th December, written only two years before the great botanist died, in which Masson, in his quaint, garden-hand style, writes to the old and greatly revered botanist of world fame and stature: 'I hope your Goodness will excuse the liberty I have taken in addressing myself to your superior merit and your exalted character in natural history. I have been employed for some years past by the King of Great Britain in collecting plants for the Royal gardens at Kew. My researches have been chiefly at the Cape of Good Hope where I had the fortune to meet with the ingenious Dr Thunberg with whom I made two successful journeys into the interior parts of the country. My labours have been crowned with success having added upwards of 400 new species to His Majesty's collections, all living plants and I believe many new genera.

'I expect to go out soon on another expedition to another part of the globe to collect plants for His Majesty.'

Enclosed with the letter were seeds of a new genus which, said Masson, his fellow traveller Thunberg desired to call *Massonia* but he (Masson) asked that 'Dr Linnaeus only would give me that title'.

On 9th May 1778 Masson, indefatigable and impatient as ever, was off on his botanical travels again, this time bound for Madeira, the Canaries, the Azores, Teneriffe and the West Indies. Unfortunately there is no journal of his wanderings in these tropical isles, but there are letters which help to piece together his adventures.

To the Western Isles, as he called them, he went, making his first port of call Madeira. By July Banks had received a first consignment of sixty plants from him. He was well received by the authorities in Madeira, he told Banks, when on 27th May of the following year he sent 123 species of plants. He found time to write again to Linnaeus, thanking him for having hearkened to his appeal and conferring 'the Massonia honour on me'. He continued to give the great man a description of Madeira.

'I have observed', he wrote, 'that all the rare plants grow either on high cliffs near the sea or on horrible deep chasms that run towards the middle of the island, but towards the top which is a mountain 5,000 geometrical feet perpendicular I have found nothing but a few European plants especially *Spartium scoparium*.'

He went on to explain that Forster (the botanist with Cook on his second voyage) had done him (Masson) an injustice in naming *Aitonia rupestris* for Linnaeus as it could never be introduced into Europe. He thought that *Campanula aurea* should be the name as it turned out to be that flower.

Again from Madeira on 12th December 1778, to the young Linnaeus, Masson told of his experiences in the Caribbean and said he had now ended his 'perigrinations among the Fortune Isles where I have found great pleasure as well as novelty'. He described Madeira again as being of 'tremendous broken precipices covered with the most luxurious evergreens. The Azores are remembered for hot springs but their natural produce comes nearer to those of Europe. The Canaries are remarkable for the enormous height of the land abounding with rare plants which nearly approach the products of Africa. . . . I now await', he told the young man, 'a passage to the West Indies but the present war in which my country is involved will, I fear, render my voyage less extensive than I at first expected'.

But his energies and experience stood him in good stead. Two cases of cassia were sent to Kew, *Erythraea massonia* came from the Azores. Come threat of war, come weather, the young Linnaeus's Canary Islands collections was all due to Masson, who sent *Muschia aurea, Convolvulus floridus, C. scoparius, Echium candicans, E. giganteum, E. strictum, Senecio echinatus, Cytisus proliferus* and *Carlina xeranteroides*.

Unfortunately for Masson, Great Britain's trouble with France militated against his work. He was unable, as he had wished, to visit and collect on the Spanish Main. 'The Islands themselves', wrote a contemporary, 'he found in such an unsettled state that it was with the utmost difficulty he found means to send home his collections, parts of which were frequently lost by capture or by waiting convoy.' Neither Masson nor Banks, nor, for that matter, any botanist or plant hunter, had yet found the means of preserving plant life for such a lengthy period as that involved in waiting in port for convoy. Even seed lost its viability, rotted, mildewed and sweated, while even the toughest roots packed in sand in tightly bound boxes shot into the holds of ships either sweated or were frozen to death. The difficulties certainly mounted up against him, and apart from those affecting his beloved plants he experienced physical danger to life and limb.

He was collecting in Grenada and finding the work going well after his note of introduction from Banks to the Governor, Lord Macartney, had eased his way, when he found himself involved dramatically on 2nd July 1779 when Count D'Estaing, with the French main fleet, arrived off the island, captured thirty merchantmen in the harbour and immediately landed 2,000 troops and attacked the fort and the town. There were just 125 regular soldiers to throw into the fight and in great haste the Governor raised a scratch militia in which all able-bodied men on Grenada were impressed. Masson found himself one of these, and when the island submitted to superior forces and surrendered on the 6th he was taken prisoner fighting in the trenches.

Luckily for him, either Banks intervened at high government level when he heard of his gardener's plight or the French recognized Masson for what he was, just a plant-loving garden-hand. He was released, but when next heard of was again 'in the wars'. He happened to be plant hunting in St Lucia in October 1780, during the terrible hurricane there when many lives were lost, ships were wrecked at anchor and there was a great loss of property. In the general havoc and destruction, when almost everything above ground was flattened like a wheatfield after a storm, Masson lost all his specimens, seeds and plants, all his drying papers, his packing-boxes and the greater part of his clothing (but for those he was lucky enough to be standing up in), as well as all his books and rough notes of his plant-hunting finds. This was the last straw and, as a friend wrote soon afterwards, 'finding by fatal experience that in time of war the purposes of his mission could not be effectively fulfilled he returned home in November of that year'.

When he got back in 1781 after a most trying and, to him—the ever-conscientious seeker-out of rarities—disappointing two years searching the Caribbean Islands for botanical treasures he had, more than he would ever know, endowed future gardening generations with a priceless pearl. This was *Senecio cruenta*, illustrated in Curtis's *Botanical Magazine* as *Cineraria cruenta* and sent by Masson from the Canaries as seed in 1777, and was the greenhouse parent of the garden cinerarias, the plant from which all those startlingly hued and favourite pot plants of today had their being.

It is interesting to reflect what ground Masson covered on this Caribbean expedition and just how much these journeys cost Banks and the king in the late eighteenth century. Fortunately there are some rough accounts extant in the Banks correspondence for Masson's journeyings from May 1776 to April 1782.

From 5th June 1776 to 31st May 1777 in the Azores his bill was £242 15s. 3d., from 31st May to 1st January 1778 in the Canaries it was £114 11s. 6d. and from 1st January to 4th October 1778, on his return to Madeira, it was £110. From October to May 1779, including passage to Madeira at £30, it was £118 15s. 6d. He took off £55 18s. od. expended on his own account, leaving Banks and Kew to foot a total outlay of £530 4s. 3d., a not inconsiderable sum of money to pay for flower-hunting in those days.

In the West Indies proper Masson's bills show how he covered the ground. There is a bill for August 1779, at Antigua, for £30. Next year, plant hunting at St Eustachia, St Christopher and Nevis cost £130. October 1780, at St Lucia, cost £40, and in March 1781 a Jamaican visit ran up a bill of £106, which, with his passage home at £40, totalled £346, less £50 spent on himself, which left a grand total for travel of £296 for the West Indies alone. His salary at £100 a year from April 1776 to April 1782 came to £600.

A fascinating account of his bills for passage itemized for Kew ran as follows:

England to Madeira	£15 15s. od.
Madeira to Azores	£10
Among the Azores	£30
Madeira to Teneriffe	£4
Teneriffe back to Madeira	£30
Madeira to Barbados	£31 10s. od.
Barbados to Grenada	£3
Grenada to St Eustachia	£4
St Eustachia to Antigua	£3
St Eustachia to St Christopher	£3
St Christopher to St Lucia	£6
St Lucia to Nevis	£3
Nevis to Jamaica	£10
Jamaica to England	£40

A total of £193 5s. od.

When Masson got back to London in 1781 he returned to Kew, attending to the propagation of his many new plants and to the cataloguing and arranging of Banks's great herbarium being assembled up at Soho Square. He had friends too in the nursery trade to visit and yarn to of his travels, including old Mr Lee, of Lee and Kennedy, of the Vineyard, Hammersmith, but keep as busy as he might the old Adam of botanical travel would not be quieted. He was a slave to plant hunting and with an ever-present urge to seek pastures new and collect green treasure for his royal patron and noble master, he sailed for Lisbon and Portugal in 1783. In Lisbon he was engaged in laying out a garden, and he collected plants in the countryside around before moving on to Spain, where he went to Cadiz, San Roque and Algartia before going for a short time to Gibraltar. From here he crossed the Mediterranean to Africa and sent Banks plants from Salle (the home of the notorious sea rovers) and Tangier, before returning to Kew in 1785.

At the end of that year and after only a very short stay in London, and with more experience of plant hunting behind him than any man had ever had, he sailed for the Cape a second time, in the East Indiaman *Earl of Talbot*, and reached it after a twelve-weeks' passage.

'He now combined experience and foresight', wrote a near-contemporary and botanist, Sir James Edward Smith, 'with zeal and activity; he was prepared to take advantage of different seasons; in some to collect specimens, in others roots or seeds; so as best make up for former deficiencies or losses; and had already made himself acquainted with the various situations or tracts of country most promising for every purpose. In consequence of this knowledge it was settled in conjunction with Sir Joseph Banks that his travels should now be restrained to within forty miles of Cape Town. That space of country was found to be as yet inexhaustible almost, perhaps inexhaustible as to what it might afford for our gardens, and the expense as well as the labour of the undertaking were by this plan considerably lessened.'

Masson arrived at the Cape on 10th January 1786 but found the political climate there not at all a happy one. His country was now at war with the Dutch. Another plant hunter and adventurer, a Lieutenant Patterson, who gave it out that he was collecting for Lord Strathmore, was thought by the Dutch to be engaged on espionage work and using his botanical travels as cover for his warlike activities. He had made the Dutch authorities apprehensive, watchful and suspicious of Englishmen who wanted to wander off at will into the hinterland or even to browse around the Cape peninsula. It was promulgated that no foreigner could go anywhere not within three hours' journey of the coast and could not cross the mountains except on pain of instant arrest. All inhabitants of Cape Province were empowered to arrest and take into custody any foreigner found beyond the government limit and haul him back to the Cape to appear before the Governor.

An early letter from Masson to Banks showed he was well briefed, however. He had with him credentials from the Dutch Ambassador in London and papers to the Governor of Cape Province, who told him he could travel within limits. By March 1786 he told Banks, 'Since I last wrote I have had permission to visit the Hottentot Holland Mountains for only five days and was so fortunate as to find some of the rarest ericas and proteas in seed. I also found some new protea which is not yet fully described and some other genera which now convinces me that these mountains, although so near the Cape, have never been properly explored.'

He sent home a parcel of 117 species, among which were seed of an erica he had called banksia. 'As all the seed are in their capsules,' he warned, 'some are so minute that great attention must be had to rubbing them out when they are sown otherwise many will be lost. *E. retorta, coronaria, pinastra* and *massonii* grow on the mountain in white sand produced from the sandstone rock which composes the mountain and in England will require a turf soil with a little sharp sand.'

It was obvious that Masson was by no means hamstrung by the Dutch ordinances. They might have restrained lesser men, but not Masson. After all, his master had allowed him a rope of forty miles inland, but he would have liked to go farther, and at first was a little disconcerted, for he wrote home asking for a botanical posting to India. Receiving a negative reply, he there and then determined to stretch Banks's forty miles and turn a blind eye on the Cape ordinance. Although no journal exists of his trek, his accounts at Kew show his unwillingness to be a prisoner at the Cape, his determination, regardless of the consequences, to travel inland again, to visit the Veld, the Karoo and once more to climb doggedly the Cape mountains, to stand 'upon a peak in Darien' and view the distant blue of rolling, jagged mountain landscape, to see the countryside below him as a bird on the wing. No ordinances, no masters could curb Masson once he had scented floral prey, as his bills here show in no uncertain manner. The accounts are of absorbing interest too in showing the sort of impedimenta and services necessary to a pioneer plant hunter in unbroken territory.

One account of his expenses, in rix-dollars, then worth about four shillings, covered the period from 1st March 1788 to 1st January 1789, 'precluding a journey to the Elephant River being about 200 miles from the Cape':

	Rix-dollars
To two journeys to False Bay	20.6
To boat hire on various occasions	14.7
To coolie hire on various occasions	22.1
To garden pots and boxes	75.3
To stationery ware	22.0
To a large chest	12
To basket	7
To a large carriage	220
To 10 oxen at 12 rix-dollars each	120
To a Dutch waggoner and Hottentot for five months at 15 rix-dollars per month	75
To powder and shot	12.6
To cooking utensils	20.7
To various necessities for a journey	45.6
To 10 months board and lodging	400
	1,068.4 schell [1]

[1] 8 schell = 1 rix-dollar

It was obvious from this first set of accounts that Masson was ignoring both the instructions of his master Banks and those of the Dutch authorities, and Banks assumed, quite correctly, from the plants he was receiving that this was so, for on 3rd June 1787 he wrote a stern note to his travelling botanist. The letter commenced encouragingly enough: 'The plants you have sent home', read Masson, 'succeeded so much better than any you sent home when you were last at the Cape that I have every reason to praise your industry and to see the propriety of a search near the place of your residence in preference to expensive journeys up the country which seldom produce an adequate return in really ripe seeds.'

The writer went on to hope that Masson would take up his hunt at False Bay as he had been instructed and added that he (Banks) had been going to see the king to order Masson to Botany Bay, but he had been shown a letter from Masson to Aiton at Kew, which showed that Masson had an objection to Australian plant hunting so he had looked out for another man.

Then came the wigging. Banks referred to a letter accompanying Masson's seeds and scathingly remarked: 'These letters mention your having undertaken two long journeys which surprises me as your instructions are absolute on that subject. What I recommended is a fixed residence during the ripening season at any place where plants are abundant, but more especially that any direction relative to False Bay be complied with until you have exhausted that place and Hout Bay which, I expect, will be proved rich. I trust you will remain quiet. Afterwards you may explore.'

Poor Masson; the farther he trekked from base the farther he wanted to go. It was as if an El Dorado of floral gold drew him on, and in a further account covering the period 1st January 1789 to January 1790 he included expenses for a journey to Kamiesberg, up the north-west coast about 400 miles.

These disbursements included 18 rix-dollars 'to a person in the course of three years for watering my plants in my absence', 30 for a 'musquet', 5 for a spade and a watering pot, 12.6 for leather, canvas and coarse linen for seed bags and 75 'to keeping my horse for seven months'.

During 1790 he was still, despite the Dutch and Mr Banks, trekking far inland again, this time to the Kleyn Roggeveld, into mountain country and Karoo land, a long haul up to the 4,000-foot level, and for this extended trip there was new equipment needed. The Cape ox treks literally shook the old Cape springless wagons to pieces, so that his next bill for South Africa struck off with 300 dollars for a new wagon, 42 for a saddle and 1 dollar for three new spare wagon wheels. For tobacco for the natives he paid 4, and 20 for 'liquours for the journey'. An ordinary packing-box cost him 4 dollars but 'boxes for seeds' cost him 23. For 'slave hire' on different occasions, 23 dollars was his charge and to keeping his horse, 60.

Masson's last expense sheet from the Cape was dated 1791 and included equipment for mounting herbarium species with elephant paper costing 25 rix-dollars and cartridge paper, 20.

There was 8 dollars 'to coolie hire for carrying boxes to False Bay' and 40 for boxes and flower pots. Out of season his trek wagon had to be stored under cover and there was a bill for eight months for 'store house room for my waggon', of 16. Board and lodgings cost 480. For the plants he was to bring home Masson came to learn, as did many other plant hunters to follow, that it was a good plan to acclimatize them to the artificiality of either pots or garden ground. He gave a man 12 dollars 'who took care of my plants in my absence'.

The war with the Dutch brought more restrictions and more suspicions of foreigners. In March 1795 Masson sailed for home, 'having satisfied the wants of Kew' and his master, and tried to settle in England. For a time he was happy enough among his botanical friends in the greenhouses full of Cape blooms and in working on his book *Stapelia Novae*, which was published in 1796, with forty-one coloured plates of as many species.

But how did a plant hunter, with a background of thousands of miles of venturing in fascinating foreign climes, settle down? How curb his burning desire to be off again over the mountains, how relate a roof over one's head, regular meals, a soft warm bed and the round of writing, social calls, gardening at Kew, with a vast open sky for cover, an unknown destination at journey's end, new plants to find, adventures and new scenes round every turn and one's own mastery of self, situation and the day's exciting work and discoveries? It was nigh impossible.

He could stand the strain of ordinary common or garden living no longer and sat down to ask Sir Joseph (for his master was now a Knight of the Bath) for yet another commission to travel and to botanize.

He was anxious to return to work again and reminded Sir Joseph that 'still enjoying, in the afternoon of my life [he was fifty-seven] a reasonable share of health and vigour I am now ready to proceed to any part of the globe to which His Majesty shall direct me. Many are the portions of it which have not yet been fully explored. All of them are equal to my choice'.

Aiton and Banks discussed the botanical traveller's *cri de cœur* and decided to ask George III if they could send Masson to North America.

It was a magnificent tribute to a most loyal and conscientious servant which Banks penned to the king. After reminding His Majesty that in 1773 he had graciously allowed Masson, then an under-gardener at Kew, to proceed to the Cape of Good Hope to collect seeds and living plants for His Majesty's Royal Botanical Gardens at Kew, he further reminded the king that his first three years at the Cape had cost £583 8s. 6d. and that soon after his return His Majesty had allowed him £300 [this was salary at £100 a year].

'In the course of his voyage', continued Sir Joseph, 'Mr Masson collected and sent home a profusion of plants unknown until that time to the Botanical Gardens of Europe, a full account of which will appear in Mr Aiton's catalogue of plants in the Royal Botanical Gardens at Kew which is nearly ready for publication; by means of these Kew Gardens has, in great measure, attained to that acknowledged superiority it now holds over every other establishment in Europe, some of which, the Trianon, Paris, Upsala, till lately vied with each other for pre-eminence without admitting even comparison from any English garden. . . . In the year 1776 you were graciously pleased to consent to Masson again undertaking an extensive plan of operations; in it he was sent to visit Madeira, the Canaries, the Azores and by way of the West Indies was to penetrate, if possible, to the Spanish Main (south and/or west shores of the Caribbean Sea).

'This he undertook and succeeded at least as fully as before in sending home from Madeira, Teneriffe, the Western Isles, in a manner, the whole of their produce, the greatest part of which proved new to European botanists. . . .' Banks told the king how difficult it had been for Masson because of the war and went on to say:

'In having thus brought Mr Masson home from ten years' employment in collection of plants for the Royal Botanical Gardens at Kew, I can wholeheartedly say that during this time he has proved himself sufficiently instructed in the science of botany for the purposes of his mission and indefatigable in the execution of his duty. I am confident that the famous journey to the Levant made by M. Tournefort by the order of Louis XIV at an immense expense did not produce so great an addition of plants to the Paris gardens as Mr Masson's voyage to the Cape only has done to that at Kew. As far as I am able to judge His Majesty's appointment of Masson should be acknowledged among the first Royal bounties which have not been in any degree mis-applied.

'At present the war in Europe making it necessary for ships from all parts of His Majesty's domains to come home in convoy almost precludes the idea of Masson being employed with success in any part of the world. Should His Majesty be graciously pleased to consider his past services and those he is likely to perform when peace is arrived at and to appoint such part of his salary as your royal wisdom shall seem meet for his personal sustenance; and that he having been by ten years absent from the employment of his profession, and by being during all this time admitted to the society of men of education as well as circumstances much superior to his own, in great measure incapacitated from following it. Should, I say, His Majesty be graciously pleased to appoint him a part of his salary for his sustenance consigning him in this manner to the Royal Gardens and to order him out again as soon as those concerned in the management of it can find a proper opportunity, I am confident that such royal bounty would conciliate the gratitude of all who make the science of nature their study throughout Europe and more especially, those in this Kingdom, I may say, under His Majesty's particular auspices and protection, who follow that most engaging occupation of glorifying the Creator by observing the wonder of his works.'

Surely no king could resist that plea, and in September of 1797 Masson left home on his last voyage for North America, new ground indeed. The fates were not exactly with him on this voyage—he seemed destined to fall in with dangers and difficulties 'as the sparks fly upward', and from New York in December he wrote a long tale of woe to the younger Aiton at Kew.

'We arrived here', he said, 'in great distress after a passage of four months from Gravesend during which period we experienced many difficulties. Regarding the Western Isles, we were stopped by two French privateers, one of which boarded us, examined our papers and let us pass. Nothing happened until the 8th of November towards night when we saw three sail bearing down upon us, one of which was a French privateer belonging to St Domingo, who fired several shots and a volley of small arms into our ship and soon after boarded and took possession of us. The passengers were then put on board a Bremen vessel bound for Baltimore and after having suffered many hardships from weather, want of water and provisions were ultimately taken on board another ship and so to New York.

'After staying in New York I went to Niagara and the shores of Lake Ontario, then west to Queenstown, then to Fort Erie returning to Niagara and then to Montreal.'

He sent home seeds and herbarium species to Banks, and in the British Museum in the Banksian collection can be found a collection of flowers collected among the Great Lakes, including *Trillium grandiflorum*.

Round about Christmas 1805, despite his toughened frame which had borne the heat and burden of years of hard unbroken country, the extreme cold of a Montreal winter—compared with the burning veld and the tropic shores of the Canary Islands—was too much for him, and the first working plant collector died, aged sixty-five.

What a colourful, incredible difference his life's work had made to the British gardening scene!

Sir J. E. Smith wrote of the pleasure given him by the 'novel sight of African gera-niums in York or Norfolk soon after Masson's death. Now every garret and cottage window is filled with numerous species of the beautiful tribe and every greenhouse glows with the innumerable bulbous plants and splendid heaths of the Cape. For all these we are principally indebted to Mr Masson, besides a multitude of rarities.'

Aiton's *Hortus Kewensis* not only showed two plates of Masson's but of the 102 species of pelargoniums enumerated no fewer than forty-seven were credited to Masson. His queen had honoured him by allowing her name to be used in the naming of the weirdly beautiful bird of paradise flower, *Strelitzia regina*,[1] which Curtis singled out, giving a plate twice as big as any other, as being 'one of the most scarce and magnificent plants introduced into this country', while his finding of *Nerine sarniensis* in South Africa solved the riddle of a flower which had been found growing wild in Jersey and was thought to be a native of that island.

The great Loudon, in his *Encyclopaedia of Gardening*, 1825, said of Masson's amazing collection of ericas that in Philip Miller's time—he died in 1771—there was scarcely any exotic heath known and none of the Cape species. 'Almost the whole of these have been introduced to Europe during the reign of George III and the greater part by Masson.'

In the first twenty volumes of Curtis's *Botanical Magazine*, of the 786 plates of floral introductions almost one-third are Masson's. And what a magnificent collection they were, including, in Curtis's nomenclature, lachenalias, sempervivums, oxalis, *Cheiranthus mutabilis*, ixias, cystanthus, *Diosma uniflora* (only recently introduced again to British gardens as the Wand flower), proteas, polygala, aspalathus, *Silene ornata* (one of the fly-catching plants so loved by our grandfathers), gladioli, calendulas, xeranthemums (one of the everlasting flowers), cytisus, hibiscus, gnaphalium, *Erica cerinthoides*,

---

[1] She had been a Princess of Mecklenburg-Strelitz.

ansteas, indigofera, crotalarias, *Nymphaea caerulea* (the blue water lily), tritonias (the red-hot poker), babianas, lobelias, maricas and amaryllis, gardenias (particularly *rothmannia*, which scented the evening hour), melanthiums, moraeas, tulipas and ornithogalums, as well as the scores of pelargoniums, the numerous heathers of exquisite beauty, the stapelias and the fragrant massonias.

Yet he is unhonoured and unsung; massonias, the genus of plants named after him, are not the sort of plants to be universally popular, curious and unusual as they are.

No one is quite sure whether he died in December 1805 or January 1806. He has no known grave. His few but trusted friends bemoaned his fate as a poorly paid victim of his professional zeal.

James Lee, who was a lifelong friend, wrote from the Vineyard Nurseries, Hammersmith, where among his collection were raised many Cape plants which it seems obvious Masson must have sent to him, probably in tacit agreement with Banks, who knew Lee well and knew his skill as both a gardener and a propagator of rarities. In March 1806 James Lee's son, another James, writing to Sir J. E. Smith, said: 'We are sorry to have to communicate to you of our dear friend Masson who died in Montreal in January last. We lament his fate most sincerely. He was very hardly dealt by in being long exposed to the bitter cold of Canada in the decline of his life, after twenty-five years' service in a hot climate and all for a pittance. He has done much for botany and science and deserves to have some lasting memorial given of his extreme modesty, good temper, generosity and usefulness. We hope when the opportunity comes you will be his champion.' Alas, the opportunity did not occur, although later in the year, in July, the younger Lee, writing again to Smith, returned to the subject:

'He [Masson] had been ill paid considering what he had done for the service of botany. He explored the Cape of Good Hope twice, Madeira, the Canaries, the Azores, Spain, Gibraltar, Tangier, Minorca, Majorca, the West Indies and Canada. Masson was of a mild temper, persevering in his pursuits even to a great enthusiasm, of great industry which his specimens and drawings of fish, animals, insects, plants and views of the countries he passed through evince, and though he passed a solitary life in distant countries away from society, his love of natural history never forsook him. Characters like him seem for the present dwindling in the world, but I trust they will revive.'

Some of these drawings, about a hundred in all, most of them of Cape plants, were presented by a grandson of old James Lee to the Botanical Library of the British Museum in 1885.

It could truly be said of this Scottish gardening hand that he gathered the flowers of the sun in all their radiant glory and in their arid uncouthness. To him fell the spoils of the extremes of flora's kingdom, from the vividly hued flamboyance of pelargoniums, ixias, gladioli, proteas and ericas, to the bizarre, misshapen strangeness of the succulent and cacti kingdom; from the sun-drawn aromas of the scented pelargonium and the belladonna lily (*Amaryllis belladonna*) to the evil stench of carrion plants, the stapelias. Greenhouse and border throughout the world owe more to Masson than gardeners ever realize.

4. The First Floating Garden

ALTHOUGH Masson's harvest had been a rich one and our gardens and greenhouses were brighter, more colourful and more diversified because of his untiring work, at Kew, as at other nurseries such as Lee and Kennedys, Loddiges and earlier London and Wise, plants from foreign lands were not being introduced without many dismal failures.

Sir James Edward Smith, writing of Masson's splendid work, had to say that although the country's gardens were indebted to him for innumerable plants and a multitude of rarities, yet the difficulty of preserving and propagating them confined them to the more curious collections only, and 'many of these have only survived to bloom once or twice within the walls to which they were first consigned, to be defined and named by the skill of a Solander, a Dryander or by the younger Linnaeus in his transient visits among us, and have then disappeared'.

There is a sad vignette of Banks arriving at Kew one summer day in 1790 to see new Indian plants—probably shipped by William Roxburgh, the botanist of the East India Company's botanic garden at Calcutta. Aiton having sent word that the package had just arrived, Banks came post-haste by carriage only to be grievously disappointed. Of the scores of plants sent 'there were only four stumps left and they were apparently dead'.

Seeds were raised with infinite care, patience and skill after they had withstood the dangers of mildew and rot on the long sea voyages, while the succulents and sun-dried pelargoniums had managed to travel and keep alive sufficiently to be tenderly nursed back into condition in British greenhouses—all this by men who could have had no possible conception of the vastly different conditions and environment under which

74

their rare charges flourished in their natural habitats. Plant transportation methods were as yet still unscientific, rough and ready, very much a matter of rule of thumb.

One brave attempt to cut through the fug of ships' holds and the fog of gardeners' understanding was made by Dr John Fothergill, of Upton in Essex, a Quaker who, after retiring from a lucrative London practice, set out to collect medicinal and exotic plants from whatever part of the world he could get them. It was said of his greenhouses at the time that they were unmatched in either Britain or Europe for their variety and wealth of plant life. One of his associates was Dr John Coakley Lettsom, a fellow Quaker and botanist. Between them, after many disastrous experiences in an attempt to transport plants and seed, they drew up and published in 1781, 'some directions for bringing over seeds and plants from different countries'.

Lettsom wrote in his introduction of the disappointments and failures of a plant hunter's and plant collector's life, saying:

'The gardens of the curious have already been enriched by many valuable acquisitions from different countries, but many attempts to introduce several other plants equally rare have been unsuccessfully made owing to the bad state of the seeds or plants when first procured, or the method of disposing of them during long voyages and such accidents as the utmost caution cannot prevent.

'For the purposes of transportation ripe seeds should be chosen which have been collected in dry weather and kept dry without exposing them to sunshine. Internally they should be plump, white and moist.

(*a*) They may be preserved by rolling each in a coat of yellow beeswax about half an inch thick, and afterwards a number of these thus prepared may be put into a chip box which is to be filled with melted beeswax not made too hot, the outside of the box may be coated with a solution of sublimate of mercury and kept during the passage in a cool, airy place. In this manner tea seeds, the stones of mangoes and all hard nuts and leguminous seeds in general may be preserved.

(*b*) Instead of putting small seeds in beeswax, they may be enclosed in paper or cotton which has been first steeped in melted beeswax and then placed in layers in a chip box, some of which may be filled as before with melted beeswax. Pulpy seeds such as those of strawberries, mulberries, arbutuses may be squeezed together and dried and then put into the cerate paper or cotton above mentioned. I lately received seeds of *Mimosa japonica* and *Aeschynomen movens* from the East Indies enclosed in linen that had been steeped in beeswax and these seeds appeared as fresh as when first collected.

(*c*) The small seeds, when dried, may be mixed with a little dry sand, put into cerate paper or cotton and then packed in glass bottles which are to be well corked and covered with a bladder or leather. These bottles may be put into a keg, box or any other vessel filled with four parts of common salt, two of saltpetre and one part of sal ammoniac in order to keep the seeds cool and preserve their vegetable power.

'The following methods which are attended with less trouble have also been found successful:

(d) Seeds and nuts in their pods may be enclosed in linen or writing paper and put into canisters, earthen jars, snuff boxes or glass bottles, the interstices between the parcels of seeds should be filled with whole rice, mullet, panic, wheat bran or ground Indian corn well dried.

'To prevent any injury from insects a little camphor, sulphur or tobacco should be put into the top of each canister or vessel and their covers well secured to exclude the admission of external air.

(e) Seeds well dried may be put into a box not made too close, upon alternate layers of moss in such a manner as to admit the seeds to vegetate or shoot their small tendrils into the moss. In the voyage the box may be hung up at the roof of the cabin and when the ship is at the place of her destination the seeds should be put into pots of mould or boxes with a little of the moss also about them on which they have lain.'

Then Dr Lettsom mentioned the usefulness of an airing for all seeds on the Indian run at St Helena, a point well noted by Banks on his first voyage. He advised that all seeds from the East Indies should be examined in any case at St Helena and some of those which appeared in a vegetative state could be planted there to grow apace on the remainder of the journey home.

'More of the same seed (that in a vegetative state) may also be sown after the ship has passed the Tropic of Cancer near the latitude of 30 degrees north. And if very small bits of glass are mixed with the earth or thrown plentifully over its surface in the boxes it may prevent mice or rats from burrowing in it and destroying the tender roots of the plants and growing seeds.

'In whatever method our seeds have been preserved it should be a constant precaution to sow them as soon as they are exposed to the external air, otherwise they probably will never vegetate.'

Plants were obviously a vastly different proposition altogether. Much care, diligence, skill and lots and lots of luck were necessary to bring any living foreign plants to England, however vigorous and healthy they were when consigned from some tropic shore to run the gauntlet of ocean storms and tempest, almost the whole gamut of climatic variation, and some of the worst keeping accommodation on board ship it was possible to imagine in situations where fresh dry air, cleanliness and freedom from vermin were as rare as orchids at the Poles.

Yet Dr Fothergill and Dr Lettsom had had experience of plants having been sent to them, in all optimism, from Jamaica, India, Egypt, America, Mexico, Canada and Africa—many, it is true, sent as seeds; but valiant attempts were made to send the growing plants on long sea and overland journeys for which the Upton gardens worked out a series of plant collectors' 'briefing notes'.

The instructions for collecting and packing the plants started basically indeed:

'In order to take up plants and shrubs that are to be transported a mattock and a spade should be provided; with the mattock a small trench should be opened round the plant to be taken up. The spade should then be put underneath the root, which may be lifted up with a very large ball of earth surrounding it; the bulk may afterwards be pared carefully with a knife and reduced as small as can be done without wounding any of the larger roots.

'Of each kind the youngest plants of shrubs and trees that can be found should be taken; none of them should be above a foot high; as young plants are found by experience to bear removing much better than old ones.

'When the naturalist is in search of vegetable production different soils and situations should be examined; as the sea and its shores, deep running water, dikes, marshes, moors, mountains, cultivated and barren fields, woods, rock, etc. afford each their peculiar plants; and wherever any are collected the particulars of soil and situations should be remarked. Sometimes it may prove inconvenient to convey the plant which may be discovered when it would not be so to send them dried. . . .'

Masson, as will have been seen, used boxes and casks to convey his plants; and Dr Lettsom and Dr Fothergill, who had acquaintance with Banks, the three being probably the keenest and the foremost natural philosophers and amateur botanists in England at the time, must have seen at Kew some of the results of this form of transportation. So often it resulted in failure and disappointment, due, Banks thought, to the exclusion, by tight boarding, of fresh, free-circulating air and to conditions conducive to overheating, sweating and subsequent mildew and rot.

Lettsom and Fothergill, profiting from this experience and their own at Upton, to which friends and emissaries from abroad forwarded a constant stream of rarities from all parts, laid down the sort of container and shipboard conditions they had found served the would-be plant collector's purpose with some possibility of success.

They had discovered that the most convenient kind of boxes for the conveyance of plants on long voyages were 'to be made about four feet long, two feet broad and two deep; these when half filled with earth can be conveniently carried by two men holding the rope handles fixed to their ends.

'These should be filled about half full of mould with a few rotten sticks or leaves at the bottom and the plants intended to be sent planted in it as soon after the ship's arrival as possible.

'When the ship is about to sail and they are sent on board hoops are to be nailed to the sides in such a manner that, arching over it, they may cover the highest of the plants; small ropes are than to be twisted between these in the form of a net to prevent the dogs or cats from getting at them and scratching them up on account of the fresh mould.

'For each box so hooped and netted provide a canvas cover which may, when put on, entirely protect it and to protect this cover from being lost or mislaid nail it to one side and fix hoops or hooks to the other by which it may be occasionally fastened down.'

This was, for the time, reasonably sound practice, but, as all plant hunters and the receivers of their green treasure found, there loomed large in all this careful preparation the human element.

How would the swashbuckling Jack Tar and his captain deal with a mouldy old box or so of plants, probably placed inconveniently on their poop deck or in some cabin window, when the raging seas did roar and the tempest blow? Then, plants in their boxes were the very last item of cargo anyone on shipboard would worry his head about.

But even these human failings were taken into account in the botanical doctor's instructions, taken care of in so far as one could persuade a sea captain by good money, fair words or for dear friendship's sake to work to the rules, which were set out as follows:

'The captain who takes charge of them must be particularly informed that the chief danger plants are liable to in sea voyages is occasioned by the minute particles of salt water with which the air is charged; whenever the waves have frothy curls upon them these particles fall upon the plants and, quickly evaporating, leave the salt behind which, choking up the pores, prevents perspiration and effectually kills the plants; he therefore should never let the covers be off except on days when the wind is not sufficiently high to beat the water into what the sailors call white caps.'

It is a matter for nautical conjecture whether with 'white caps' abeam hands were piped on deck to cover boxes; it might well be thought that reefing of the topgallant and topsails would be a whit more important. But these early botanists and their collectors were nothing if not fanatically keen and supremely optimistic.

The rules continued with even more stringent instructions to suffering captains:

'He must not keep them [the plants]', they directed, 'always shut up during the voyage, for if he does they will mould and perish by the stagnation of air under the covers; and if at any time by accident or necessity they should be exposed to the sea when the waves have white caps, he must be desired to water them well with fresh water, sprinkling all the leaves with it to wash off the salt drops which cover them. In this manner plants may be brought from almost any distance; many come from China every year in a flourishing state.'

Then followed the absolute in these counsels of perfection:

'If it is convenient to the captain to give up a small part of the Great Cabin to the plants this is certainly by far the best station for them, nor are they much in the way, and, as the place which suits them best is close to the stern windows in this case they need not be furnished with their canvas covers and they may frequently have air by opening the windows when the weather is quite moderate.'

Here then were instructions good as far as they went, an ideal to work to, but, alas, not consonant with bringing over the tropic wonders the plant hunters saw and the botanist knew were on many a foreign strand ready for the taking if means could be found to ensure their travelling to this country in a healthy, growing state.

This was not to be for some years hence, but in the interim Joseph Banks, probably musing over the exotic flora he knew existed but could not capture in the islands and the countries of the sun-drenched Australasian seas, and the unusual and curious he had

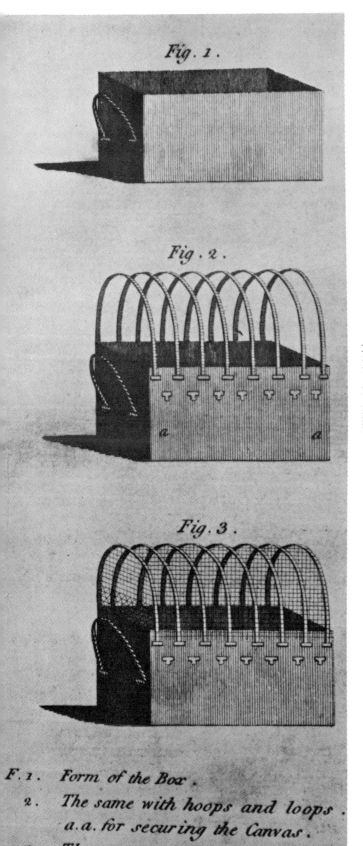

Fig. 1.

Fig. 2.

Fig. 3.

F. 1. *Form of the Box.*
2. *The same with hoops and loops.*
   a.a. for securing the Canvas.
3. *The same netted.*

Left: The kind of crude plant transportation boxes which were used during the eighteenth century. They were lashed on the poop deck or, if the captain would allow it, kept in the Great Cabin.

Above: A Wardian case, invented by Nathaniel Ward, a London doctor, early in the nineteenth century, which made possible for the first time reasonably safe and sure plant transportation on long sea voyages.

Francis Masson (1741–1806), a Scot, the first plant hunter sent by Banks from Kew in 1772. He collected in South Africa, the Canaries, the Azores, Spain and Portugal.

William Bligh, chosen to command the *Bounty* which in 17? sailed to the Society Islands for a cargo of breadfruit plants to take to the West Indies.

1822

Sept 22 Set out with Lockart after
breakfast whilst cool about 5 OClock
to a hill about 6 miles distant
the hedges round the Plantations were
Jamadax ytton (Hamespechecoum which
had very much the appearance of
thorn the only plant here were Aloeonia
If near the Aloeonia Bidea here is very
different to the plant at Maranhoa which
is as large as Barahalie Madagascarensis
which I suppose to be a new species
growing by the side of rivulets
containing. I also met with many old
faces to keep ours company &c among
the ... I met was a curious
Alarantu flores cristatus Coreulenus
and several curious ferns returned in
the evening very much fatigued

13 this morning Lockart & I set out to a
valley to the North ... of the town a distance
of 4 miles this valley is surrounded
by 2 ranges of high mountains on the
sides of these mountains are many very fine
palms intermixed with the other trees but
Cocus pisiformis Chris occidentalis
... on the lower ports of the mountains
are Areca Catechue oliracea and a new ...
a plant I saw also at the Island of Maran
Buchis Minor with ... climbing other
met in with many of of Melastomo
Bidhia quinquenervia many ferns also met
in with Guaee a Sp of Mihanie ... common
Imberica ... Sapans ...

An illustration of the kind of South American coastal scenery among which Don hunted for plants.

noticed at the other end of the climatic scale on his Icelandic quest, was quick to furnish a gardener plant hunter for Captain Cook's third and last voyage to the tropical South Seas and to the ice-bound Alaskan shores to seek out the practicality of a northern passage to the Atlantic.

Banks did not come across a man ready-made at Kew and, casting about for the gardener he wanted, asked his botanical acquaintance, old James Lee, of the Vineyard Nurseries, Hammersmith, if he knew of anyone who would not only be willing to make the long and hazardous voyage but would seek out and know plants and seeds, secure them and handle them tenderly and skilfully for transmission to Kew.

On 25th April 1776, some ten weeks before Cook sailed, James Lee replied to Banks at Soho Square and sent the letter personally with a young gardener whom he recommended as a fit and proper person to take care of seeds and plants on Captain Cook's voyage.

When Banks opened the envelope handed to him by this young gardener he read:

'HONOURED SIR,

I have sent you the bearer, David Nelson, as a proper person for the purpose you told me of; he knows the general runn of our collections and plants about London, understands something of botany, but does not pretend to have much knowledge in it. I have inquired personally into his character and find him exactly suited for the purpose of a collector.

'I have injoined him to secrecy whither you make a bargain with him or not. One thing he desires me to mention, which is he will want a little advance money to rigg him out. I am dear Sir with the greatest regard your obedient, humble servant,

JAMES LEE.'

It is apparent Nelson was taken on at sight, given an advance and put on the Kew pay-roll to spend the remaining weeks, before sailing with Aiton and Banks, learning the proper care of plants and seeds on long voyages and being exhaustively briefed by Banks on what to look for in the many differing climes and countries the expedition was expected to sail to.

He was mustered supernumerary crew on board *Discovery*, of 300 tons, sister ship to Cook's *Resolution*, under Captain Clerke, and made ready to sail from Plymouth in July. In his new 'rigg' David Nelson, very much of a greenhorn, a quiet, unassuming garden-hand, must have found both his shipboard accommodation and his new companions a strange, frightening contrast to the peaceful, unremarkable daily routine of Kew Gardens.

There he was at Plymouth on board a converted Whitby collier packed and better packed to the gunnels with stores, which beggared description, for a long and extended voyage to unknown oceans and unknown lands. He must have been supplied by the resourceful and knowledgeable Banks with his professional equipment, spades, mattocks, trowels, a few books on botany, his plant presses and drying papers, his wooden boxes and casks and a curious, unique assortment of native trading 'cash'—coloured beads,

tawdry mirrors, nails, pins, coloured ribbons and pieces of cloth; he could never have
conceived how vitally important this trash could and would be. How he ever settled
down to a sailor's rough daily round he never had the opportunity to tell; he must in
such a small incommodious ship have been bunked with the deck-hands in cramped
unsalubrious quarters with, as a special privilege, an occasional opportunity to use part
of the Great Cabin to prepare his specimens.

How he changed his gardener's easy-going gait for sea-legs we shall never know, but
the occasion came soon enough, for no sooner had they weighed and entered into the
Channel from Deal on 18th June than *Discovery* sailed into the teeth of a gale that blew
until the 26th, and blew her into Portland Roads already so damaged that she hauled for
Plymouth and called for carpenters and shipwrights and was still in dockyard hands
when Captain Cook, in *Resolution*, sailed for the Cape on 11th July. It was August
before *Discovery* was away, and almost immediately she ran into another hazard of those
dangerous days, for on 10th August all hands were ordered to battle stations when what
looked like an American privateer—it was the period of war with America—bore down
on them. Fortunately it turned out to be a Lisbon trader.

By mid August, although *Discovery* was the better sailer of the two ships, gales had
so retarded her progress that Nelson had his first taste of the many hardships, privations
and dangers which hardened sailors took in their stride—the ship was put on rationed
water allowance and on 1st September 'a dreadful tempest arose', says the keeper of
Discovery's journal, 'in which we every moment expected to be swallowed up. The
thunder and lightning were more alarming than the sheets of rain which fell so heavy as
to endanger the sailing of the ship, and, at the time though in the open day, involved us
in a cloud of darkness than which nothing could be more horrible.'

Worse was to come, for the quiet, unassuming gardener heard for the first time, but
not the last, the spine-chilling crashing and rending of splintered wood and saw the
calamitous havoc of tempest-torn sail and rigging as *Discovery*'s 'main topgallant mast
was carried away in the slings and the sails frittered in a thousand pieces; the jib and
middle staysails tore clear off and the ship so strained as to make all hands to the pumps
necessary'. Nelson's hands too in all probability; a disastrous exchange (he must have
thought) for a trusty spade and firm, solid earth.

On 5th September, so early too in this epic voyage, Nelson had his first taste of the
unusual when he, with the rest of the crew, dined on shark steaks when one was caught
and portioned out as a delicacy.

A few days later the first tragedy of many hit the ship when a corporal of the marines
sitting idly on the bowsprit fell overboard and was never seen again.

Yet another storm hit them hard on the 15th of the month, which they rode out
under reefed sails and were thankful this time for the heavy rains accompanying it,
for with baskets, blankets and leather buckets the sailors caught the rain for drinking
water.

Nelson was one of those mentioned by the journal, which, on 1st October, reported:
'After two months at sea without ever a man putting a foot on dry land, those who were

unaccustomed to such long voyages began to put on a very different aspect to that they wore at first setting out.'

But on 11th November land hove in sight, as in Table Bay, Cape Town, they caught up with the *Resolution*. Until the 30th Nelson was one of those fortunate 'gentlemen' allowed ashore, where he had the most fortunate experience of travelling upcountry with Francis Masson and William Anderson, Cook's surgeon and naturalist, to carry out his first ever plant collection on foreign soil. It was after this more opportune acquaintance with the mysteries of his chosen profession that both Anderson and Clerke wrote to Banks with a Nelson progress report, a favourable one at that.

On 24th November Anderson wrote to tell Banks that *Discovery* had arrived, 'and in her is a person who understands botany, who will be able to procure for you every new article in that branch, a task which I have not vanity enough to expose myself again to, but shall nevertheless continue to collect whatever presents itself lest any accident should happen to him on his ship.

'We carried him with us to the country but unluckily few plants were in flower at the time, yet when such things offer I think his diligence will let few of them escape.'

Captain Clerke also took the opportunity of a shore rest to write home to tell Banks how his botanical protégé behaved on his first voyage and through his first experience of sea and seamen.

'Your man Nelson is one of the quietest fellows in nature; he seems very attentive and I hope will answer your purpose very well. He had made a trip up the country here with Gore.' (This was Lieutenant Gore of the *Discovery*.)

On 30th October both ships sailed for the Pacific, and a day or so later Nelson underwent his first baptism of climatic extravagance when, after spending weeks stewing in Cape heat, he encountered snow and hail so severe as to cause the sailors to canvas-line the hatchways to keep the frost from their own quarters. Shortly afterwards extra hammock blankets and the heavier trousers and jackets provided by the Admiralty Board for such an occasion were handed out to the crew. From the 17th to the 22nd of December the crash and roar of *Discovery*'s guns punctuated Nelson's days and nights as black fog closed in around them and *Resolution* was lost to sight if not to hearing. Gales accompanied the fog, carrying away the jib sheet and splitting the jib. Flagging spirits revived when the fog cleared and *Resolution* was seen ahead.

Christmas time was spent repairing rigging, masts and sails at Kerguelen Island, where David Nelson saw and collected *Stilbocarpa polaris*, a curious sight with its great bristly rhubarb-like leaves and upright bunches of waxy yellow flowers, about the only inhabitant of the vegetable kingdom which would withstand the rigours of a sub-Antarctic climate.

Repairs finished, wooding and watering completed, Nelson and his crew mates were able to celebrate Christmas Day on the day proclaimed—22nd December—with a double grog for everyone and meat of seals, penguins and sea-fowl for the festive board.

The next day Nelson was on shore with a foraging party scouring the island for fresh greens, if any, it being noted that 'Mr Nelson, a gentleman who Mr Banks sent to collect such varieties as he could find indigenous to the islands and climates through which we should pass, found growing among those cliffs a kind of yellow moss of a silky softness which he had not yet discovered in any of his researches'.

On 1st January 1777 both ships were at sea again and steering for Tasmania. Fog and gales continued to harass them, so that from the 14th to the 19th fog bells and guns were continually making the men's heads ring with their clangour and crash. Although a driving gale cleared the fog on the 19th it left destruction in its track, having carried away *Discovery*'s topgallant sail, split her middle staysail and left scarcely half a yard remaining on her jib.

Welcome land—Adventure Bay, Tasmania—was reached on 29th January, when Nelson saw his first savages—'the Indians', as Banks always called them, irrespective of race—the naked, tattooed inhabitants of Van Diemen's Land. Ashore he gazed in wonder at the soaring timber full of the striking colours and cries of beautifully plumaged parrots and parakeets as he searched for plants for his master, finding *Oxylobum ellipticum*, a shrub with leaves in clusters along the stem and bright yellow pea-flowers in dense racemes as well as specimens of eucalyptus and acacia; one of these mimosas, *Acacia verticillata*, being later known as 'Nelson's mimosa', became, and still is, a conservatory and greenhouse favourite, with its dark, prickly foliage and fluffy balls of lemon flowers.

Sail was set for New Zealand on the last day of the month and twelve days later the two ships rendezvoused in Queen Charlotte Sound in Cook Strait between the North and South Islands after *Discovery*, striking a rock, had to be warped off by the *Resolution*, fortunately without much damage.

Here on a trek inland Nelson found *Cordyline australis*, a plant to be used much later in subtropical gardening, and noted the giant flax, *Phormium tenax*, a species of *Philadelphus*, deadly nightshade and nettles growing to the size of small trees as well as many tree-ferns.

As they left New Zealand for the Friendly Isles (Tonga) on 25th February, a roll-call on *Discovery* indicated a deserter. A search boat was manned and the man, who had decamped and taken to himself a native wife, was hauled on board for Nelson to get his first sight of the iron discipline of shipboard life as the man was stripped, roped over a gun and given twelve lashes with the cat-o'-nine-tails until the skin of his back split and blood flowed on the deck.

The Pacific gave *Discovery* and her crew a gruelling time before the next landfall on 31st March, when they discovered Mangaia. She lost her fore topmast and another main topgallant yard, as well as her deck being cleared of everything not battened down, by mountainous seas which raked her prow to stern. In a six-hour tropical rainstorm the rain was so heavy that men working on the yards were in danger of being washed off the ship. Rain and stormy weather dogged both ships for days as they sailed for Anamocka (Nomuka) in the Friendly Isles, an island whose floral fragrance reached them before they even moored, and where Nelson saw a picture of vivid greens emblazoned with the brilliant hues of blossom trees. For the next three months the ship's gardener was busy enough, as the ships sailed from island to island in the group, and was the appropriate leader for the many foraging parties which scoured them for green vegetables for the table, as well as for plants for Banks.

The natives of the islands were troublesome for thieving, so Captain Clerke sought to make an example of those caught by shaving their heads, since flogging did not prove the slightest deterrent. It was a life of coconuts, hogs, fruit and fowl for Nelson and his fellows, a distinct change from the hard tack doled out on the high seas. At Tongatabu, on the last day of June, Nelson himself fell foul of the natives, undergoing a most frightening experience. He was alone on the hills of the island collecting plants, a fair distance from the shore, when he 'was attacked by the Indians who first began throwing stones at which they are very dexterous and then finding he had no firearms, closed in on him, stripped him of his clothes and his bag which were all that he had about him'.

His naked plight as he came back in the cutter to the ship was a subject for much ribald laughter and lewd comment, but this was no laughing matter for Captain Cook, who decided to seek redress. Two boats were manned and, taking Nelson with him, the captain sought out the chief. When it was found that the savages were youths and that the worth of both Nelson's clothes and his bag of plants was pretty low, the captain agreed with Banks's gardener not to press the case and the parties left on good terms and next day, on 17th July, weighed for Tahiti.

In mid Pacific the ill-fated *Discovery*, and, by now, Nelson must have thought, an ill-fated Nelson, ran into the vortex of another tropical storm which carried away the maintop, the topgallant mast, split the mainsail and carried away the jib. The courage and tenacity of the sailors were admirable, for they, noted the journal, 'mounted aloft with incredible rapidity and cleared away the wreck by which they preserved the ship'.

On 1st August Nelson and his fellow sailors—for surely they must have accepted him as such after all the mishaps he had shared with them—celebrated their first year at sea with a double allowance of grog all round. Celebrations and sore heads were forgotten two days later when the carpenters, who were replacing the top mast, found the mainmast head shattered with a storm beating hard about them. They needed help from *Resolution* urgently, but no ship's boat could live in those high seas, so they thrashed through the havoc-ridden seas and skies with makeshift rigging and sails, the ship leaking so badly that every hand not working the sails was working the pumps.

But, even more to sailors than to other men, there was always tomorrow, and on 14th August the sailor's earthly paradise—Tahiti—was in sight at last, where they could rest, eat, love and, for Nelson, collect plants among the luxuriant, brightly hued vegetation of a tropical island.

Some three months were spent in the Society Islands Group, Nelson visiting in turn the islands of Eimeo (now Moorea), Huahine and Bolabola (Borabora). Here he sampled again good living with menus daily of barbecued pig, stewed fowl, roasted breadfruit, bananas, yams, coconuts and the many other delicacies he could purchase for a red feather or a few nails. Here too he could collect and note the curious and novel in the tropical forests, on sandy shores or on verdantly clad mountainsides amid the cooling roar of high waterfalls, where mosses, ferns and lianas formed a green and coloured backcloth of oriental splendour, one which but four months ago the Kew gardener could never have pictured in his wildest horticultural dreams.

Opportunity was taken while *Discovery* was at her moorings to clear completely the cramped and verminous quarters, which Nelson shared with the crew, and to clear the rats, cockroaches and weevils and open all hatches and ports to let in good air and sunshine. The holds of both vessels were washed down in vinegar as much for the sake of the plants as for the men.

At Huahine more thieving by the natives, always so gay yet so troublesome, led to the spectacle, which Nelson saw and shuddered at, of a native having his head shaved and both ears cut off before being put into irons and next morning, with head still bleeding, cast ashore as an example to other would-be thieves. It was not exactly the sort of thing a Kew gardener could normally expect to come across.

When Omai, the Tahitian who had been taken to England on Captain Cook's last voyage and was now being returned to his homeland, was put ashore at Huahine, David Nelson was able to show his skill as a gardener proper, with spade in hand—a sower, not a reaper—as he cut out the undergrowth and made a garden for Omai round the home that the crew had built him, planting many seeds of vegetables, corn, flowers, shrubs and trees brought from England.

When, in 1777, Christmas day came round, *Discovery* and *Resolution* were anchored off an island Cook called Christmas Island. To celebrate the occasion all got plenty of brandy, and in the evening there was a turtling party, which Nelson joined and which succeeded in catching two hundred turtles, which were taken aboard for meat and soup.

An incident which happened to one of his shipmates on one of these expeditions must have proved a most salutary and terrible object lesson for the gardener, who was used to walking for miles inland on these verdant isles, being drawn ever farther from the shore by the lure and sheer beauty of the flowers.

Thomas Trecher of the *Discovery* had strayed farther than the others and was lost for forty-eight hours in the dense forests. When found after search parties had combed the island for a night and a day, he crawled out of a thicket on all fours unable to stand, blistered from head to foot with insect bites, his skin seared with ugly thorn scratches, nearly blinded by snake bites and the scorching heat and the sun, and almost speechless from extreme thirst and frantic with worry. It was a week before he was fit again for duties on deck.

Weighing anchor on 2nd January they sailed for twenty days without sight of land and with water scarce, a great hardship in the blistering heat, and on the twentieth day came in sight of a group of islands Cook called the Sandwich Isles in honour of his patron at the Admiralty. Here more hogs were taken on board and Nelson's services were enlisted to bring on board green stuff, of which he found enough to last for two months. As they sailed for Bolabola Nelson had to guard his precious plants drying on the deck against another most unusual gardening hazard—four hundred hogs which *Discovery* carried on her decks.

At Atooi (Kanai) in the Sandwich Group (Hawaiian Islands) Anderson and Nelson found not only giant, flashily coloured gourds growing in abundance and in all shapes and sizes, a giant thistle bearing flowers like a white poppy, Cape Jasmine and mallow, but also found and heard irrefutable evidence that the native population were only too happy to eat their enemies or anyone else who happened to leave their body on the island. From Atooi they sailed for Oneeheow and on 8th February sailed northwards, making for the Californian shore of America. It was almost a month before they came in sight of land again and as Nelson walked the decks he strode over bent figures of sailors patching piles of canvas and spare sails which, being taken out of store, were found to be more than half eaten into holes by rats.

By early March the *Discovery*'s crew had reason to know they had left the South Seas, for the cold was piercing, and the Magellan jackets handed out were welcome indeed. As the coast came in sight rations were running out and the gentlemen in the gunroom and the crew welcomed as a delicacy 'a fricassee of rats which they accounted a venison feast'.

On 8th March the coast of New Albion was reached and they 'were so far advanced to the northward and eastward as to be far beyond the limits of European geography and to have reached the void space in our maps which is marked as a country unknown', the *Discovery* journal noted.

Beating up an inhospitable shoreline both ships sought a safe anchorage for very obviously needed repairs and found one on 29th March in Nootka Sound, now known as the west coast of Vancouver Island. Here, instead of the natives offering parakeets, yams and hogs, it was the furs of beaver, racoon, bear and squirrels that Nelson and his comrades bought for making into coats as protection against the cold. The Indians here were a frightening sight to sailors, never mind a landlubber, with feathers in their hair, red ochre linings on face and breast and some wearing the fiercest of animal masks. Even more ghoulish than their fierce, forbidding looks were their offerings of human hands and heads with the flesh still attached, which they explained by signs were trophies from fights with their enemies.

There was snow on the ground, with a temperature below freezing, as Nelson helped the carpenters to choose some of the giant conifers, up to 150 feet high, for new masts. By mid April they were still in the south and spring had come, with a temperature that had soared into the sixties. Just before *Discovery* left on her northward exploratory probe, the gardener's services were called for once more. The crew had cut grass for the live animals they were carrying. 'We also', wrote *Discovery*'s chronicler, 'by the assistance of Mr Nelson, whose business as has already been observed was to collect the vegetables and other curious productions of the countries through which we passed, were enabled to stock ourselves with a large proportion of culinary plants which was of infinite service to us in our more northerly progress.'

Apart from the currant bushes, wild raspberries and juniper they saw ashore, the sailors relied on Nelson for guidance on any other fruits they saw for the first time, for these bushes bearing fruit 'were known to none but Mr Nelson'.

All May and June the two ships sailed the coastline to the barrier chain of the Aleutians, their landward view being white with snow, while seaward around the ships were herds of seals, sea-lions and occasionally whales.

Sailing in fog much of the time and with *Resolution* having sprung a leak, it was a dismal time of constant vigilance until on 12th May the two ships anchored in a reasonably sheltered bay for repairs. It was during this stay that Nelson and his colleagues, taking it easy below, were suddenly alarmed and awakened by the cry of 'Action stations!'; in a great hullabaloo everyone tumbled on deck, with cutlasses flashing, to find that a group of Indians in full war-paint, brandishing knives, were trying to take over the ship from the solitary sailor on deck watch and had already thrown a ship's rudder overboard. Fortunately the sight 'of lusty tars with larger knives than theirs scared them off and they plunged over the sides and made off in their canoes'.

By mid May, when *Resolution*'s leak was repaired, they steered northwards again, and on 12th June, thinking they had found the secret of their great design, a seaway round the Alaskan peninsula into Hudson Bay and the Atlantic, they sailed up a wide creek, but finding the salt water turn to fresh, they realized it was not and turned back to the rough, bleak and blustering conditions of the coastline, sailing in and out of bays, hugging the cheerless coast as much as they dare in a latitude probably as high as any European had ever been before.

At Unalaska Island at the beginning of the Aleutian Chain, on 2nd June, Nelson was able to stretch his legs again to look for plants nearer the Arctic Circle than anyone had ever attempted before. On this botanizing trip he 'was accompanied by several other gentlemen', says *Discovery*'s journal. 'They found a great variety of plants and flowers peculiar to the country, besides others with which they were all well acquainted, such as primroses, violets, raspberries, junipers and many other northern fruits now in blossom,' a pleasant sight indeed to remind him of his Surrey lanes.

Fog and contrary winds detained the ship for some days, so while the sailors saw to urgent matters of maintenance, 'our botanist and his attendants were busily employed and sent plenty of celery and other wholesome herbs on board as well as for the use of the Great Cabin as for those of the subordinate tables down even to the lowest of the ship's company'.

Yet by early July everyone of the ship's crew was put on two-thirds ration, salt and maggots having eaten into their beef and pork, and rats and weevils eaten the heart out of their bread, so that on handling it the bread crumbled to dust and the meat was putrid. Nelson and the rest of them were put on fishing for their suppers, and were glad to.

This was as they beat up the bleak, uninhabited shores of the Alaskan peninsula in fog and in shallow waters hiding dangerous rocks and reefs.

Yet on one day in mid July when he went ashore on an uninhabited promontory to see what he could find in the way of plant life on these stark, barren shores, he found more inhabitants than were welcome. As he searched assiduously among the sparse green with little other ground cover and hardly a tree or shrub in sight, his botanizing was punctuated by the 'howling and yelling of wolves and other wild beasts'. Bears, foxes and some deer made a brief appearance, but scurried away quickly on his approach.

Now as they strove northwards the two ships were in a trying and hazardous position, with a rock-strewn, shallow coastline which called for constant heaving of the lead as storm and tempest blew and changed direction erratically while daggers of hail beat on anyone on deck. To add to the difficulties *Resolution* lost her bow anchor, the grappling for which was made an order for every member of both crews. Cook and Nelson took their part, 'for every officer on board both ships', states the journal, 'was obliged to do the work of common men', so desperate was their plight.

Not until the 20th could a safe sounding of from eight to twenty fathoms be found as the ships bore through the narrow strait. Spirits soared and there was new heart in the men, with more water under the ship's keel, less damage, until two days later, when for four solid days Nelson's handiness with a spade was needed as all available hands were called on deck to deal with a 'prodigious fall of snow'; so thick did it lie that 'it was with difficulty the deck could be kept clear though the watch was constantly employed in shovelling it off day and night'.

The cold, bleak conditions weakened the men, but for poor tubercular Anderson they extracted the last ounce of strength, and on 3rd August Cook's surgeon and naturalist, the officer counterpart of Nelson and the only other botanist on the expedition, died, leaving David Nelson, the young, unassuming under-gardener from Kew, in sole charge of all natural history collecting, responsible to Cook as well as to his own Captain Clerke for all botanical discoveries, and all written notes that were necessary to accompany the seeds and dried specimens they were to take back to London. On the day Nelson heard of the death, some days after it had taken place, he had been ashore on Sledge Island to help to provide his ship with some fresh greens—wild celery and a kind of vetch.

The extreme climate now began to take its toll of many more members of the expedition and, by the 9th, rain, snow, fog and the damp miasma it brought to the crew's quarters, where overcrowding, smells, moulds and bad air were prevalent, hit fifty of *Discovery*'s company of seventy with colds and slow fevers, leaving just twenty able-bodied men to man the capstans. The greatest difficulty was experienced in weighing the anchor, the job wounding and laying low two of the strongest hands in the doing of it.

The Arctic Circle was crossed on the 12th when the ships reached the westernmost point of America, named by Cook Cape Prince of Wales, and by crossing the Bering Strait he could anchor off the coast of Asia. Still they drove northwards so that by the 17th Nelson experienced weather conditions he could never have imagined. Ice was sighted, there was a bright, eerie glow on the horizon, the winds grew even more piercingly cold and a frost set in so hard that the running rigging was soon frozen fast in the blocks, taking six men to do the work of one.

By the evening of the 17th ice was hanging from the men's unkempt hair and from their noses and fingers if they exposed these extremities to the air for five minutes. Pack-ice now surrounded the ship and became thicker as they ploughed on. Nelson, whose experience of frost was to have seen that a few degrees of it did not damage a tender plant or two in the conservatory or greenhouse, now saw hot food freeze on the mess table and islands of ice 'some of which hung over our heads as we passed them'. Some of the ice reared menacingly twelve feet above the deck. No land, no chance of plant hunting now as *Discovery* and *Resolution* crunched on, ships and crews driven by the determination of Cook to find a northward passage. But as the fog cleared they found themselves in even thicker fields of ice with 'sea horses' (walrus) and other amphibious animals to the number of thousands. The 'sea horses' were shot by the crews, Cook ordering that no other provisions should be touched but this fishy, tangy flesh, and flour. There was trouble on board Nelson's ship when the crew rebelled against their dishes of fat, black, stringy meat, and Clerke gave way.

The ice became thicker, closer; icebergs bore down on them fast; *Discovery*'s men were tumbled out of their hammocks as they hit the ice with a terrible crunch and a shaking of the ship's frame from stem to stern. The carpenters scurried below forward, for the captain was sure irreparable damage had been done. Fortunately the shaking of ship and crew was the only injury.

Progress any farther northwards was now seen to be impossible, for, as the old charts say, 'here the ice', and on 29th August both ships turned southward, to find food and water before sailing for winter quarters in Hawaii, preparatory to essaying the northern passage again the next summer. It was a hard struggle back in shallow waters, in an ice storm in which pieces of ice between two and three inches square fell and wounded men on deck, in heavy seas which almost swamped the ship as they swilled over her bowsprit in the troughs of huge waves which rose above the yard-arm. Did David Nelson, landlubber that he was, ever breathe a word of complaint or wish he had never seen the *Discovery* or Joseph Banks? No mention is made of his reactions to his unique and terrifying experiences sailing unknown seas, largely a helpless spectator, or at the most a ham-handed helper when sailors had vital and ship-saving work to do.

Early October saw the ships anchored in 'Samganooda', or Unalaska, harbour for urgent repairs when Nelson collected fruit berries ashore rather unhappily among Indian warriors.

On 20th October they left northern water behind them and made for the Sandwich Isles. They reached Hawaii by the end of November, but gales, contrary winds and lack of harbourage found the ships standing off and on shore for over a month without ever a landfall. Consequently Christmas Day, instead of being a day of earth-based jollity and feasting for the crew, was marked only by a pint of brandy for each of them as they tossed about on an offshore swell. Not until 17th January 1779 did they find a harbour, where Nelson and his shipmates saw the sight of their lives, a colourful carnival of natives, three thousand strong, in the sea, on the sea and on the shore—a welcoming, yelling mob. This welcome did not seem too sincere when on two occasions later *Discovery* was surrounded by thousands of war-painted and armed natives in canoes hurling stones through cabin windows and at the caulkers at work on the sides. Nelson was almost as shaken as they were when Captain Clerke ordered two of the great cannon to be fired to warn off the natives.

Now in the green and tropical island, where Cook was received as a king, an opportunity soon came for the gardener to carry on with his work. In any case, the ship was hardly anything but a floating brothel, with native women swarming all over it, being kept on board by the crew, so that he was relieved when several of the officers decided to explore the interior of Hawaii and ascend to the top of the snow-covered peak which had intrigued everyone since first seeing the island—a tropical island with a snow-covered mountain seemed slightly ridiculous, so the party set out to probe its secrets. On 26th January Nelson and four officers set out to scale the peak, but after two nights and two days of dangerous and fatiguing travel in 'a savage country' they were obliged at last to return without being able to satisfy their curiosity. . . . On the way they were insulted by the rabble who, without offering any violence to their persons, would make faces, twist their mouths and use the same contemptuous gestures with which it was their custom in war to provoke their enemies.

When they returned to the ship on the 29th Nelson at least had not had an unprofitable journey, for he had collected 'a curious assortment of indigenous plants and some natural curiosities'.

On 5th February the ships sailed for another harbour on the island, but meeting with a severe storm *Resolution* sprung a mast and was generally so very badly knocked about that both ships had to return to their old anchorage. Daily, as the carpenters worked on, the ship's relations with the natives worsened. A war canoe full of armed warriors came alongside looking determined for trouble, but paddled off. Great activity was noticed ashore, the massing of people, crowds here and there, a great to-ing and fro-ing. Things blew up on the 11th when Nelson, on hearing a great commotion above decks, went up top to find that *Discovery*'s cutter had gone. Cook was told and went ashore to remonstrate and see to its return. The next news those left on board *Discovery* heard—and Nelson was one who was left out of this serious ship's business—was the most tragically dispiriting yet on this fate-dogged voyage; in the commotion they had seen on the shoreline Captain Cook had been attacked: Captain Cook was dead.

Captain Clerke, Nelson's captain, left the ship to command the *Resolution* and the expedition.

The days that followed were the most noisome, nerve-shattering days Nelson would ever spend. Whatever sorrow he might have felt for the loss of a gallant and great man, who had brought them safely so far, mourning for him was out of the question, for everywhere was horrible turmoil and bloodshed. Every step ashore might be the last, everywhere on shore any member of the crew went he went with musket at the ready and bayonet fixed. Blood and fire were carried to the natives, between which attacks gruesome ceremonies and bargaining went on for pieces of Captain Cook's flesh and bone. Feeling ran too high among the men for any captain to sublimate it into any other channel but revenge, as the crews fought a musket battle with hundreds of ill-armed natives, killing many; and then, as a final act of jungle justice, they ran through the island villages with lighted torches and unrelenting fury laying them waste by fire. One boat crew came back from a shore raid with the heads of two of the native ringleaders stuck on the prow of their boat. The cabin space of Nelson and his fellows was filled with war clubs, bows and arrows and other arms and gaudy feathered accessories of all kinds his crew companions had ripped off the bodies of the natives they had killed.

It was 22nd February when the two ships set sail from the tragic island for another of the Sandwich Group—Hihua (Oahu), where they had another short, sharp engagement with firearms (during which several of the islanders were killed) before they could land in safety and trade for food and water. By 16th March the expedition left for the frozen north once again on direct course for Kamchatka, on the Asian shore, and by 1st April the heat and the balmy air of the tropic seas were exchanged for cold and fog, when thick, figure-hugging flannel jackets were issued. But even with this protection forty hands were frost-nipped as they struggled at *Discovery*'s pumps; she had sprung a leak, making seventeen inches of water in three hours. Snowstorms and gales blew up again, making a miserable voyage to Kamchatka, which *Discovery* reached towards the end of April, without *Resolution*, which they had not seen for days and had given up for lost. At Kamchatka, although the harbour was ice-covered, they managed to nudge their way in and, to their great joy and relief, found *Resolution* already there.

Here, with friendly Russians to deal with, Nelson's mess-table was a picture. For the first time since leaving England three years earlier fresh beef and fresh flour were eaten, and the Russians gave them tobacco too—the first on board for three months—tea and sugar as well, and new sails and cordage for both ships.

There was quite a celebration on His Majesty's birthday, 4th June, when everyone got a double allowance of meat and liquor and a walk ashore amidst snow-covered forest and scrub. They weighed on the 15th, only to be met with thunder and such a great fall of ash that everyone was driven below, where the shockingly sulphurous fumes which accompanied the ash necessitated battening down the hatches, so that a state of near-suffocation was the men's lot. When they dared to show their faces again Nelson was able to add to his store of natural curiosities 'pieces of pumice stone as large as walnuts' and found the deck from stem to stern covered with thick volcanic dust and ashes from the volcanic eruption which had chosen to signal their departure.

By early July the ship was in the midst of ice, polar bears and sea-cows. By the 23rd *Discovery* was icebound. During the next few days she was pounded and pressed by ice fore, aft and amidships, and started to leak three inches an hour.

Nelson's spirits and those of the crew sank as they ran over their situation—icebound, anchors out, provisions short, winter coming on apace, still no sign or hint of a northward passage. Some of *Discovery*'s crew had to be goaded into action to work at all. They had begun to think that whatever they did would bring them nothing but disaster and an icy, watery grave.

On the 27th *Discovery*'s position was so desperate, completely surrounded as far as the eye could see with death-dealing, loose-drifting ice that Gore, now *Discovery*'s captain, went on board *Resolution*. But there he found Captain Clerke so ill, dying of consumption and so past all hope of recovery that Gore was unable to ask for instructions.

A council of officers took the decision that they could sail no farther, having reached 69° 12′ longitude and 187° 16′ latitude, and they turned for Kamchatka, beating down the Asian shore. Within sight of land on 22nd August Nelson heard the dreadful news that the third of his superior officers, Captain Clerke, under whom Banks had put him to serve, had died. Gore took on the *Resolution* and Nelson found himself under his third captain, Lieutenant King. Nelson, in his best gardener's rig, was among those who followed Captain Clerke's body to the grave, along with officers, marines in full dress uniform and the seamen, dressed as much alike as they could be, slow marching to muffled drums while minute-guns from both ships boomed out over the slow procession. It was another sad and momentous occasion for the poor landlubber of a gardener, but now the sun shone, the snow had gone, and berries, fruit and flowers coloured the scene. He was able to sleep ashore in a tent and roam the woods of fir and spruce. It was high summer now, with grass as high as his knee and corn turning to golden brown. 'Mr Nelson', reported the journal, 'reaped a rich harvest of plants and had the additional pleasure of gathering them in their most exalted state.'

He was also able to see something of the natives, for whereas in the winter they had cowered in holes in the ground covered with timber and branches, now they were living in thatched huts raised well above the ground and entered by ladders. He saw the Mongolian features of these Eskimo-like people, with pieces of bone inset into their faces, and noted how their winter dress of furs had given away to lighter clothes of skins of birds and birch bark.

Critical repairs to the sheeting and keels of both ships had taken time, and it was 9th October 1779 before they weighed and were at last on the homeward leg. Twenty-one days at sea went by before they anchored again at Macao, the Chinese port where Nelson was able to get from the English factory there London newspapers and magazines for 1776, 1777 and 1778—the first time in over three years that he had had any contact with his native land. For the first time he was able to talk to the people on shore without sign language and for the first time he was able to talk to another gardener about gardening matters.

Christmas in Macao Harbour was a time he enjoyed and relished, spending some of it ashore browsing round the many nurseries in Macao, the surrounding district and at Canton, for here plants had been domesticated for hundreds of years and foreign plant hunters were permitted, if not welcomed. There was no need to plunge through virgin forest or savage unbroken country to get at his beloved plants and flowers, for in China the nurserymen had brought in the country's floral beauties and encased them in pots where they could be bought and, with luck and skill, safely transported home. Here it was a question of deciding what was worth while to buy and which would do well in an English climate and a Kew greenhouse.

Despite the evident joy of a gardener being among people who cared for plants and valued beautiful ones, there was to be a shadow cast over Nelson's enjoyment, for at Macao the ships learned of the French war, which prompted the captain to raise the *Discovery*'s parapet against musket shot and strengthen stanchions and rails and cabins against cannon ball and shot. Nelson also saw extra cannon bought ashore being mounted on deck, the better to meet any enemy attack.

All this done, they weighed anchor on 13th January and with high spirits set sail for home through the Banca Strait, sailing past Sumatra and Java on a direct course to the Cape of Good Hope, which they made on 12th April, anchoring in False Bay.

On 3rd May, with 120 sheep on board, they were off again. Storms hit *Discovery*, damaging her topmast again, and in a gun accident the arm of the carpenter's mate was shattered and a deck-hand wounded.

Reaching the Channel and within sight of home, fate played her last trick on the expedition, contrary winds driving them along the west coast of Ireland and up the coast of Scotland, where they were forced to anchor at Stromness in the Orkneys. A long, wearisome, fretful month was spent here, waiting for the right winds until they weighed and with fair weather reached Woolwich on 6th October 1780, having been absent from home, family and friends for four years, three months and two days.

For Joseph Banks, anxiously waiting the outcome of these far-ranging voyages, David Nelson had both plants and seeds. Of seeds there were two hundred packets of different plants, representatives of almost all the anchorages *Discovery* had stayed in. Specimens of all these were sent to Göttingen Botanical Gardens in Germany, probably because of the intimate interest George III and the Hanoverian family had in this famous university.

By seed also he introduced to England *Rhus semialata* and from Macao and Canton he brought for his master—the dried specimens can still be seen in the British Museum herbarium—*Evolvulus chinensis, Melastoma sanguineum, Striga hirsuta, Hypericum chinensis, Spermacoce hispida, Indigofera hirsuta, Gynura divaricata, Sideroxylon wightianum, Utricularia bifida, Asparagus lucidus* and *Lindsaya flabellulata*.

The far-flung Aleutians are still linked with his name in *Ranunculus nelsonii*, one of the common buttercups there, and from the tropics his name is perpetuated in *Nelsonia campestris*, a pretty little violet flower with felted leaves.

For seven years nothing more was heard of Nelson as he sank back into the obscurity of a Kew gardener, although he must have been the obvious man to take care of the South Sea and Australasian plants in the houses there and the one to assist Banks and Aiton in the compiling and cataloguing of herbarium specimens from all parts of the world.

One would have thought too that the Kew station was just the posting for Nelson, and that all he could wish for the rest of his days was to potter about the potting sheds and glasshouses there; to find, after he had retrieved his land-legs, a quietude of days marked by substantial, regular meals, a temperate, predictable climate, a bed that stood foursquare on a rock-like floor, and a return to a gardener's apple-cheeked health which must have been far from him when he stepped ashore from *Discovery*.

Whether the work at Kew palled on him as the years passed by and the regularity and routine of his days lacked the excitement and unpredictable dangers of exploration, or whether it was after memory and time had erased some of the deeper scars of his first argosy, so that he could not settle down to a serenity of days ashore, we shall never know, nor is it possible to gauge in any way his reaction when Sir Joseph, early in 1787, put before him the proposal that he should accompany an old shipmate of *Discovery* days, Lieutenant Bligh, to the South Seas as botanist and gardener-in-chief.

Did he volunteer cheerfully and with an eagerness to go down to the sea again? Was it a call that could not be denied, or was Sir Joseph's proposal more in the nature of an instruction, an order? History is silent on the point, but Nelson was the man chosen for this ill-fated voyage.

Yet on the face of it the opportunity of the undertaking was unique. For the first time in history a ship—and one of the Royal Navy's at that—was being commissioned for no other purpose than to act as a floating conservatory; to transport plants of the breadfruit from Tahiti to the West Indies where British traders and planters had suggested to the king that this fruit would prove a cheap and most acceptable home-grown diet for the thousands of slaves in Jamaica and the other islands. Furthermore the gardener had complete responsibility and charge of the botanical side of the voyage, with permission—nay, instructions—to command captain and crew to carry out his gardening orders.

Sir Joseph Banks's was the hidden hand behind most of the negotiations for this trip; Bligh was more than likely his nominee, since he knew him from Cook's second voyage when he was sailing-master in the *Resolution*. He drew up too all the instructions for the handling of the breadfruit and the plans for the complete transformation of the *Bounty* into a floating garden.

A memorandum to Lord Sandwich at the Admiralty decided Nelson's fate, albeit also gave him a well-deserved character and a most generous recommendation. It ran:

'MY LORD,

It is fully my opinion that the plan of sending out a vessel from England for the sole purpose of bringing the bread fruit to the West Indies is much more likely to be successful than that of despatching transports from Botany Bay and I am inclined to believe it will be at least as economical. . . .

'The name of the person intended to take charge of the plants is David Nelson, and the terms I propose for him are £25 as an outfit to purchase clothes and necessaries, a salary of £50 a year with his mess on board and as he stands engaged to the present undertaking on those terms and has left his place to accept them, I hope I shall not be thought unreasonable in proposing that his pay shall be continued from the time he is engaged and that he be allowed Board wages till he is ship'd at the rate of ten shillings a week.

'He sailed with Captain Cook on his third voyage round the world in my service for the purpose of collecting plants and seeds and was eminently successful in the object of his mission. He had been regularly educated as a gardener and learned there the art of taking care of plants at sea and guarding against the many accidents to which they are liable which few people but himself have had the opportunity to know practically. He

learned also how to conduct himself on board ship and made acquaintance with the inhabitants of the South Sea Islands and their language which will in all probability facilitate
his obtaining the number of plants wanted, a matter in which the Indians have never been
accustomed to sell them and as a large number will be wanted, difficulties may arise.'

To Lord Sydney, Chancellor of the Exchequer at Whitehall, Sir Joseph sent a copy of
his memorandum for the instruction of the gardener. It was Nelson's briefing, thorough
and complete in every detail.

'As the sole object of the Government in chartering this vessel in our service at a very
considerable expense is to furnish the West Indian islands with the bread fruit and other
valuable productions of the East, the master and crew must not think it a grievance to
give up the best part of her accommodation for that purpose. The difficulty of carrying
plants by sea is very great; a small sprinkling of salt water, or of the dew which fills the
air even in a moderate gale, will inevitably destroy them if not immediately washed off
with fresh water. It is necessary therefore that the cabin [Great Cabin] be appropriated
to the sole purpose of making a kind of greenhouse, and the key of it given to the
custody of the gardener; and that in case of cold weather in going round the Cape a
stove be provided, by which means it may be kept in a temperature equal to that of the
intertropical countries.

'The fittest vessels for containing the plants that can easily be obtained I conceive to
be casks, sawed down to a proper height, and properly pierced in their bottoms to let
the water have a passage; in both which articles the gardener's directions must be
followed. Of such half-tubs, properly secured to the floor as near to each other as they
can stand, a considerable number may find room in the cabin, each of which will hold
several plants; and those I consider as a stock which cannot be damaged or destroyed
but by some extraordinary misfortune. As these tubs, which will be very heavy, must
be frequently brought upon deck for the benefit of the sun, the crew must assist in
moving them; as indeed they must assist the gardener on all occasions in which he
stands in need of their help. Besides these must be provided tubs so deep that the tops
of the plants will not reach to their edges. These must be lashed all round the quarter-
deck along the boom and in every place where room can be found for them, and for
each a cover of canvas must be made to fit it; which covers it will be the duty of the
gardener to put on and take off as he judges fitting and no one else must interfere with
him in so doing on any account whatsoever.'

Strong words these to Navy men, but it showed Nelson his own importance in the
scheme of things.

The memorandum went on: 'As the plants will frequently want to be washed from
the salt dampness which the sea air will deposit upon them, beside allowance of water a
considerable provision must be made for that purpose; but, as the vessel will have no
cargo whatever but the plants on board, there will be abundant room for water casks of
which she must be supplied with as large a quantity as possible, that the gardener may
never be refused the quantity of water he may have occasion to demand.

'No dogs, cats, monkeys, parrots, goats or indeed any animal whatever must be allowed on board, except hogs and fowls for the company's use, and they must be carefully contained in their coops. Every precaution must be taken to prevent or destroy rats, as often as convenient. A boat with green boughs should be laid alongside with a gangway of green boughs laid down from the hold to her, and a drum kept going below in the vessel for one or more nights; and as a poison will constantly be used to destroy them and cockroaches the crew must not complain if some of them who may die in the ceiling make an unpleasant smell. . . .'

Nelson and his instructions arrived at Deptford early in September, where he was surprised to see the transformation of a ship for the benefit of nature and to the detriment, and certainly to the discomfort, of His Majesty's naval officers. For he found that the whole of the Great Cabin, traditionally sacrosanct to the captain, had been taken over and enlarged, a false deck had been laid throughout the cabin and in it hundreds of round holes had been cut to receive plant pots. Three extra air scuttles had been cut in each side of the cabin and two extra large skylights in the roof added to the daylight through the great stern windows stretching across the ship. A false floor under the false deck was covered with lead with a small outlet drain let into it at the foremost corners to carry off the surplus water into tubs placed underneath so the water could be caught and used time and time again. On the plans, as Nelson saw them, so much was the ship in the hand of Sir Joseph and his botanical fanaticism that across where the Great Cabin was had been written 'Garden'. Could naval traditions, rules, regulations, Navy Yard shipwrights and draughtsmen go further? It was a Banks-Nelson take-over in every sense.

Subsequent letters and memoranda from Sir Joseph to busybodies in the government and the Navy Board, who tried in vain to keep an Admiralty hold on Admiralty property and personnel, proved that even more. Sir George Yonge, Minister of War, after a visit to Deptford, complained that Bligh had no instructions and that 'he supposed Nelson had his own instructions but the Captain of a ship cannot be expected to take his orders from a gardener'. The reply was definite indeed: 'As to Bligh learning the gardener's trade,' wrote Banks, 'I earnestly hope he will not attempt it as I have seen so much mischief done by dabblers.'

By December Mr Nelson had taken over his duties and was busily engaged in equipping the ship for a gardener's purposes. He wrote to Sir Joseph: 'The number of pots for plants I have taken aboard are of three sizes, 800 in all. They are deeper than the usual kind. They are sold by the 100 and the total cost was £5 8s. I had them made deeper so that I could put shells in the bottoms of them for better drainage.' He also asked for descriptions of flower, fruit and leaves of several plants he thought he would come across on the voyage.

Nelson by now knew he was a man to be reckoned with on the voyage, for his master had made that perfectly clear to all. He also had an assistant in William Brown, another young gardener from Kew.

But Bligh was happy in his command and happy to have Nelson, and said so writing to Sir Joseph from Spithead on 5th November in a general letter of progress: 'The conduct of Nelson and the garden is satisfactory and we all seemed embarked heartily in our cause, which I shall cherish as much as possible.'

The ship he was in, *Bounty*, to be his home for over a year, was a very cramped one, of 215 tons, with an overall length of 90 foot 10 inches and a beam of 24 foot 3 inches, not a lot of room for an active garden hand to stretch his legs. She had a scratch crew of forty-four and the two gardeners, with one commissioned officer, the captain, William Bligh.

On Sunday morning, 23rd December 1787, the garden ship sailed from Spithead and almost immediately Nelson was where he came in on his last voyage. It must have been a grim reminder too when, just after they had managed to celebrate Christmas Day without incident, a fierce storm broke furiously over the ship, stove in a boat, washed away casked beer on the deck and crashed through the stern planking, filling the Great Cabin with water and ruining completely a large quantity of stored bread.

At Teneriffe he was quickly employed in his mission, Bligh writing that he 'had got leave of the Governor for Mr Nelson to range the hills and examine the country in search of plants and natural curiosities'.

Just out of Santa Cruz on 10th January 1788 Nelson was again sharply reminded of his former hardships when the crew was put on two-thirds allowance and water was being filtered because of its bad condition.

Bounty, by Admiralty instructions, although the season and weather were all against it, was to proceed to Tahiti by Cape Horn. Beating their way there in wet, close weather, with a temperature of eighty-two in the shade, below-decks became damp, musty and mildewy. As an antidote fires were lit, timber and equipment washed down with vinegar. With their precious cargo in mind it was essential to destroy moulds, and opportunity was taken also to wash and dry in the sun the personal clothing and bedding of the ship's company.

By March Nelson was brought face to face again with the harsh discipline of the Navy when he saw blood spilling from the back of a flogged sailor tied to a grating and given two dozen lashes. Then, leaving the humid warmth of mid Atlantic, *Bounty* spent almost a month in the midst of most dispiriting and filthy weather attempting to round Cape Horn. So wet was the ship from the angry seas breaking over her that the pumps were manned every hour, four being kept constantly busy; water poured through the decking into the cramped crew quarter so that even the 'garden' in the Great Cabin was pressed into use as a drier, more airy crew space for hammocks until their own hammock space was dried out.

Sleet, hail, high winds and formidable waves dogged their progress, or lack of it, so that the boat slithered up and down the giant troughs like a switchback car. Live-stock on board could not stand the strain and died off, leaving no fresh meat but for the extra-ordinary experiment tried by the crew of catching albatross and cramming them with ground corn before killing them for the mess table.

On 22nd April, to the heartfelt approval of all, Bligh gave up the unequal struggle, turned tail and beat before the wind for the long way round to the Society Islands by the Cape of Good Hope.

Here during a thirty-eight day stay Nelson collected seeds and plants which he thought might go well at Tahiti, *Bounty* not weighing anchor until 1st July for Adventure Bay, Tasmania. At this old anchorage of Cook's he went ashore and came back with a story of giant trees he had measured, one of which he told Bligh was 33½ feet round with a height in proportion, somewhere in the region of 130 feet. He also brought back to the ship a dead opossum.

On the east side of Adventure Bay Nelson, who spent his time thoroughly exploring it, recommended to Bligh that he should plant some of the fruit trees he had chosen and brought along in a living state, most probably planted in some of the breadfruit pots as a practical exercise in plant preservation. So Nelson found himself busy enough along with Brown, planting three healthy young apple trees, nine vines, six plantains, the pips of oranges and lemons, the stones of cherries, plums, peaches and apricots and the seeds of apples and pears, pumpkins and two varieties of Indian corn. The stones and seeds were spread around the circle of the bay by Nelson, who saw to it that the undergrowth was cleared and chose the sites for suitable soil and aspect. Near to the boat's landing stage he planted onions, cabbages and potatoes, a good start for future populations. Both Nelson and Brown walked long distances ashore, Nelson taking stock of the native vegetation for his detailed report to Banks, but not without incident. For whereas no natives had been seen about for some days after their arrival the gardener on one of his excursions came face to face with a frightening group of stark naked aborigines, faces scarified in deep-cut designs and their whole bodies rubbed over with a soot-like substance. But nothing happened.

Not until 3rd September did *Bounty* leave Adventure Bay to sail, without incident, to an anchorage in Matavai Bay, Tahiti, on 26th October after a voyage, by the ship's log, of 27,086 miles.

Within a matter of days Nelson had reported back to Bligh that breadfruit were plentiful, although the careful gardener pointed out they were in flower so he could not guarantee they would safely travel in that state. It would be a question of waiting until the trees fruited, which, in the event, meant a stay at Tahiti of some six months. On his breadfruit tours Nelson saw in a flourishing state and reported to his captain 'that two fine shaddock trees which he had planted in 1777 were full of fruit'.

In the meantime Bligh was rather craftily taking stock of the situation and sizing up any opportunity which would enable him to get breadfruit trees for nothing and without any trouble from the natives. He took Nelson to the district of Oparre, for the gardener to spy out the land while ostentatiously Bligh made great play with the fact that he and his companion had come to pay their respects to Earow Rahie, a youth who was a venerated figure of the highest rank. The two walked the mile or so from the shore through beautiful glades of breadfruits to a clearing where the young king was brought to them on a male courtier's shoulders, but only after both Bligh and Nelson had agreed to take off their headgear and wrap a piece of cloth around their shoulders.

So great was the press of the excited, gibbering natives, who danced in front of them, that they were unable to leave the beaten paths through the glades at all, but Nelson saw enough to report to Bligh that breadfruit was as plentiful here as at Matavai Bay.

On Sunday, 2nd November, the work of getting together the breadfruit started in earnest by the establishment on shore of a tented camp, which was tabooed by the chief to keep his native marauders away.

Nelson, Brown and seven seamen made up the plant-collecting party. Pots were brought ashore in their hundreds and the work of digging up the trees with as much earth round the roots as possible began. By Sunday, 9th November, the tented camp soon began to resemble a corner of the big tent at Chelsea Flower Show given over to a display of tropical trees. The natives assisted 'and perfectly understood the method of taking them up and pruning them', reported Bligh.

As some return for the generosity of the Tahitian chief for putting no obstacle in the way of securing the trees, Nelson cleared some ground near the camp, digging a garden plot, where Cape of Good Hope seeds were sown along with the stones of fruit trees and some rose seed. Two orange plants, some vines, a fig tree and two pineapple plants were also given to Poeeno, one of the other chiefs.

Very soon a hundred trees had been lifted and potted and looked none the worse for their move. By the middle of the month Nelson sent twelve full pots on board to be placed in the garden cabin to see how they thrived in the cooler air of the ship, for the shimmering heat of the shore had not proved at all propitious for the seed they had sown in the chief's garden. Insects had seen off the melons and cucumbers, and hot sand had proved of no use at all for seed germination.

Not to be defeated, Nelson set to and dug another garden farther inland in more loamy soil, in which a similar assortment of seed and plants was sown.

The weather, always a vital factor to be guarded against by gardeners and sailors (and Nelson had had more than his share as a man with a foot in both camps), came near to ruining his efforts one stormy Sunday night in early December.

Luckily Nelson did not have to experience a most unhappy night on deck in which no one dare go below in the pitching, tossing *Bounty* in the bay, but after a terrible night of rain and lashing winds when he thought the tents were going to smash in on his trees, either from the violence and weight of the rain or from the winds, he found next morning at dawn that his garden camp was an island. The river which ran into the sea on one side had burst its banks and there was every danger of tents, pots, plants and men being washed out into the foaming surf. Men were hurriedly called from the ship and, with his own men all armed with spades, a second passage for the river, higher up than the camp, was dug to lead the speeding flood-waters by another channel into the sea.

A careful survey when the danger was passed showed Nelson that all was well. His covering of the trees with canvas had preserved them from the spume and salt spray. He noticed too that while many of the plants were dormant others were sending out young shoots.

With weather like this to threaten the ship any day or night without warning, Bligh was ready to be off, but he had Nelson and the breadfruit to consider, and the young gardener knew his position and his job. It would be better to wait for a week or so, he told his captain. In the meantime Nelson, who had been studying the trees, had decided that they would propagate from the roots, so he had many pots filled with roots that could be stored as an additional guarantee of his mission's success.

A spell of finer weather in the bay put Bligh in a better mood, and far from hastening away he and Nelson and one of the chiefs decided they would take a long exploratory walk into the interior on 19th December.

They walked through the lush green groves for three miles before they came to the foothills of the mountains, passing a fertile valley of yams, taro and ava. A serpentining river in their path was crossed many times, both Nelson and Bligh being carried across on the shoulders of hefty natives. On they walked, to be brought up with the sound of thunder in their ears and a precipitous rock before them. It was a most beautiful sight as they raised their eyes to see a 200-foot cascade of water dropping sheer through rocks, greenery, trailing plants and a myriad sparkling hues into a deep pellucid pool below; a ceremonial pool, they were told, where the natives made pilgrimage to bathe in its cool delights. The precipitous sides of the mountain were too much for the travellers, so they turned heel and on the way back stopped for roast hog and yams with an old friend of Nelson, for whom he had planted the shaddock back in 1777, and both saw what a fine upstanding tree it now was.

On Christmas Eve Nelson had a busy day superintending the transporting through the surf of 774 pots of healthy trees, 302 of the plants in the camp having been rejected by Nelson as having died at the roots, or at least showing no signs of growth. Seven hundred other plants for Kew had also been collected and potted by Nelson, most of them representing the lush tropical vegetative cover of the island—hibiscus, musa and tree-ferns.

Christmas Day came with no time for celebration as *Bounty* moved anchorage and ran aground in doing so. She sailed for a better anchorage in Toahroa harbour and reached it next day. Nelson now did his work in reverse, for all his plants were landed again, the tents set up and his party of eight landed with them as a guardian and gardening party.

Trouble started here again, for three men and the ship's cutter were found to be missing and a great hue and cry was raised. While many were out of the ship on search parties those who remained washed down the garden cabin and all between-decks with boiling water and vinegar as a last onslaught on the cockroaches and other vermin that could easily dest oy the breadfruit once it was brought on board again for the long haul home. Boiling water was also in demand for swabbing the decks after the deserters were caught, brought aboard, all the ship's company lined up and the lash descended, one man being given twenty-four, twelve there and then and twelve more in a fortnight before his poor flesh had healed. The two others were ordered forty-eight.

When March came along the number of breadfruit collected by Nelson to add to his previous stock was sufficient for his purpose. The first collected were now rooting through their pots and in fine fettle, so that on the 31st, in 774 pots, 39 tubs and 24 boxes, Nelson had placed in the garden cabin 1,005 breadfruit trees. He had also collected in a growing state plants of the native fruits, the avec, the ayujah, the rattah (rather like a chestnut), the orai-ah (a superior sort of plantain) and matte, from which the Tahitians made a beautiful red dye, and a root called peeah, of which they made a pudding.

On 4th April, after a stay of twenty-three weeks, *Bounty* weighed anchor and set sail for the West Indies with her precious cargo. At Anamocka (Nomuka), which they reached on 24th April, Nelson had to report some losses in his stock and some rather seedy-looking plants that did not look as if they would stand the long voyage. Bligh and Nelson, as soon as they had anchored, went ashore to collect more plants to replace them. While carrying on with this work on Sunday, the 26th, Nelson had a vivid reminder of an incident on his last voyage, for while digging he was assaulted by natives, jostled and insulted, and had—of all insults to gardeners—his spade wrested violently from his hands. He had to put the best face he could on it and, with the Annamockans' raucous laughter following him, make his way back to the shore and the ship. At noon that day they unmoored and on Tuesday, the 28th, just before sunset, Nelson found himself involved in the most drastic and tragic calamity his fateful two voyages had ever brought him. In his cabin he awakened to shouts, cries, the crash of doors, people running in all directions on deck and clambering up and down the hatchways.

Almost as soon as he had rubbed the sleep from his eyes sailors armed with cutlasses and firearms had roughly hauled him out of his hammock, forced him up the companion way, screaming threats at him to hold his tongue and do as he was told. Once on deck all was confusion. Fletcher Christian, the mate, was standing guard with raised cutlass over a trussed Bligh clad only in his shirt. Men were racing here and there brandishing cutlasses and muskets; oaths and hoarse cries made the scene even more incomprehensible until Nelson saw a boat being put over the side. It was mutiny; and willy-nilly Nelson had been sorted out as one to be tossed overboard with Bligh and seventeen others into the ship's boat that was already showing but a few inches of freeboard, so great was her load. Brown, Nelson's assistant, had either chosen to be with Christian and stay on *Bounty* or had been shanghaied into his role because of his subsequent usefulness to the mutineers.

A few provisions, clothes and pieces of equipment were thrown into the boat with them; Bligh had managed, because of his clerk's astuteness, to bring some ship's papers with him, but for the others there was nothing—just the clothes they stood up in and some carpenter's tools; there was not even a spade for Nelson, and certainly none of his valuable papers, seeds or specimens, which is so obviously the reason we have no personal record of his work.

As the boat dropped astern in *Bounty*'s wake, Nelson saw his life's work disappearing into the sea as mutineers, with cries of delight and encouragement to each other, threw overboard the breadfruits in their pots. It was a final, irrevocable step by the mutineers, signifying dramatically their complete and utter break with Bligh, Nelson and their garden mission. Hadn't the pots and plants made hammock space and cabin room even less on what was already an overcrowded ship before the Great Cabin was altered? 'Good riddance!' screamed the mutineers as they jeered at their former captives falling quickly away to stern into a wilderness of Pacific Ocean—in a boat 23 feet long, with a beam of 6 feet 9 inches and 2 feet 9 inches deep.

To secure more supplies—for Bligh was determined to sail to the East Indies, and the provisions for nineteen men were small indeed: 150 lb. of bread, about 32 lb. of pork, 6 quarts of rum, 6 bottles of wine and 28 gallons of water—the boat made for the nearby island of Tofoa, which they reached next day. Boat-breaking surf pounded on the beaches there, and only those who could swim, of whom Nelson was one, thrashed their way through the crashing rollers to see what supplementary food they could find.

The cliffs, however, rose almost precipitous, but Nelson, Bligh and a few others scaled them by means of the long, sinewy vines which clothed their rocky sides. Although unarmed, they made off into the interior, to find only a few bananas, a few coconuts and but a drop of fresh water. They walked to the foot of a volcano over barren, dry lava formations and returned downcast and weary to the shore; Bligh turned dizzy on reaching the cliffs and had to be manhandled down the sheer sides by Nelson and his clerk Samwell.

For two further soul-searing days Nelson and a small shore party, who spent the nights in a cave on the rock face, made journeys through the island looking desperately for food and water or for natives who would sell them some. They came across some natives but could obtain only a few coconuts and bananas, enough for a day's ration for the boat's company and no more. Another day Nelson and his party were down to bedrock as they searched for water with half-shells of coconut for its keeping.

Now more and more natives, canoes and chiefs came about the solitary boat, inquisitive, prying, testing the strength of the small party of foreigners, for the first time without a big ship and loud, explosive cannon behind them. As they sought food on shore they knew the natives were spoiling for something; they were already rubbing stones together, a sure sign of trouble. Nelson and Bligh were repeatedly asked to sit down and parley, but the gardener, who had seen all this before, warned Bligh that the instant they did they would be seized or stoned to death on the spot. They ate their meal of coconut standing up and uneasiness grew among the small party as a belligerent atmosphere grew about them.

There were only five or six of them ashore; the rest had stayed to guard the boat. As the small party edged their way to the surf and nearer to the tossing boat the islanders approached with warlike, menacing gestures, clubs, stones and spears gripped firmly and pointing in only one direction. Now there were two hundred threatening faces about them as they threw themselves into the pounding surf to the nearby boat at the other side of the great breakers.

They were up to their shoulders in the water and as they were roughly and quickly hauled aboard the natives struck, stones flew with deadly aim, strong hands from the sea gripped the boat's stern, others on shore hauled on the painter. It was a tug of war to the death. First the islanders were winning as the boat was pulled slowly to the beach, then the boat crew as they desperately rowed to find the open sea. One man ashore was frenziedly trying to free the rope from the grapnel. With one shriek the islanders bore down on him and beat him to death in sight of his comrades, bursting his head in with great ugly-sided stones. Then Bligh slashed the rope with his cutlass and the boat painfully, slowly rose through the surf into quieter waters. But canoes were seen to be manned. It was war—eighteen men were rowing for their lives, with stones raining round them, hitting many of them and filling the boat bottom with unwanted ballast. Nelson and Bligh could see nothing for it against this unequal struggle but subterfuge— subterfuge at a terrible cost as they threw clothing and some of the provisions they had so dearly won into the sea. As the native canoes stopped to pick up this treasure the boat pulled away and a nightmare death was left behind them.

The struggle to keep alive now really began as the castaways took stock—they had 30 lb. of pork, 150 lb. of bread, a few coconuts and some sadly mangled breadfruit, trodden on in the excitement of escape, rolling about the boat bottom. It was short commons from then on, starvation rations which left almost everything to the imagination and a mere nudge to the digestion as they agreed to one ounce of bread a day and one gill of water, with a token taste of pork.

As if their situation was not desperate enough, frighteningly high seas sprang up in a shrieking gale. Weighed down as they were, the little boat took in the sea broadside as well as the licking, curling wave crests on the prow and following seas by the stern. Baling, baling, baling was a twenty-four-hour torture, a treadmill which only fear of death kept them at, as the whirling, swishing waters in the boat bottom rose ominously higher while coconut shells and tin mugs were plied by desperate hands. The situation could not have deteriorated more as Bligh and Nelson went through the company's equipment strewn in the boat bottom for a vital choice to lighten the boat—more spare clothing went overboard with rope and spare sails. The bread swimming in the boat bottom was rescued, the carpenter's chest emptied and the bread stored as dry as might be in that.

The boat rode higher in the seas as a result, and a teaspoonful of rum heightened the spirits of the men too. They were on a compass course for Timor in the Dutch East Indies as, wet, cold, cramped and aching, they took turn and turn about to work the boat, those not working miserably failing to find sleep or even comfort on the still-swilling bottom boards. Cold and wet, baling, baling, hurricanes, high crashing seas, less and less in their insides was their dismal, doleful lot.

Whereas with the *Bounty*'s guns and firearms behind them, the sight of natives pulling out in their canoes from some green island had always been a sign of fresh provisions from the shore for the price of an odd nail or bead, now the sight of a canoe brought fear to their breasts. They steered away as fast as seas and wind would allow, for they could not risk their lives on a chance that the pursuing canoe was full of

friendly natives or those bent on destroying strange white people for a change in diet—
from hog meat to human flesh!

They had this galling experience off Fiji when they were down to an ounce and a half
of pork, an ounce of bread, half a pint of coconut milk and a teaspoonful of rum each
day. They could not even catch a single fish on their trailing lines, but managed to catch
a booby or two, no bigger than a pigeon, and tearing it to pieces apportioned every
single item of its anatomy even down to the beak and entrails by the traditional method
of one man turning away as he was asked 'Who shall have this?' and selecting any of
the crew names that came to him. The blood was given to the sickest among them. A
trifling but most welcome amelioration of their lot came when Bligh managed to raise
the freeboard by about nine inches by tacking a canvas weather-cloth round the boat,
for high winds, high seas and lashing rain still pursued them across the Pacific.

No sleep now, only baling was the order of the nights. At daybreak each day a teaspoonful of rum was given all round to enable the eighteen desperately sick men to feel
the slightest warmth and bestir their cramped, fixed joints and alleviate a little the cruel
pain in their insides.

Bligh decided that since they could not hope for sunny days to dry their dripping
clothes wrapped about them like winding sheets they should take them off, wring them
in the salt water and put them on again. This surprisingly brought some easement of
their miserable condition.

A deluge, always baling, high seas, lightning and thunder, hurricane winds, severe
illness among the crew—so the log ran, and Bligh added, 'At dawn of day some of my
people seemed half dead; our appearances were horrible, extreme languor was now too
evident. Rain almost filled the boat, no sleep, seas constantly breaking over us.'

After fifteen days the sun deigned to shine; it was a miracle, and the naked men sat
lapping up the warmth while their tattered rags hung drying near by. But two days' sun
was too much for this emaciated boatful of pitiful humanity; faintness, languor and
indifference to life itself affected them all. On the thirty-second day of this disastrous
argosy the sick men heard and delightedly saw breakers on the long, curving line of
reef—they had hit the Great Barrier Reef off the Queensland coast of Australia.

Providence saw them through a mill-race of a channel into smooth water near an
island, and hope rose. They landed, found oysters and fresh water, made a fire and slept
on the good solid warm sand while Nelson on a foraging sortie found kangaroo spoor
—but not kangaroo, for what would have been twice-welcome steaks. He also found
palm trees and knew that the heart of leaves in the top made a luscious cabbage meal for
sailors in need of fresh tack; for starving men it made a gargantuan, ambrosial feast. He
cut down the trees and knifed out their hearts; he also found a large stand of ferns, the
root of which he thought might well serve as bread if roasted; he was mistaken in this
but found it to be a great thirst quencher when sucked.

Some of the men found berries too, some like elderberries, some like large gooseberries and some like brambles. On 30th May when it was found that only two pounds
of pork were left, and an oyster and bread stew was being prepared, it was decided to go

the whole hog so the remaining pork was thrown in to make the most satisfying and savoury meal the eighteen men had had in over thirty days. They left the island on this day, and just in time, for twenty to thirty black, naked, bushy-haired aborigines armed with spears and throwing-sticks made their appearance with throaty cries. The poor sailors dared not risk meeting them and bore off in smooth water to the north for Endeavour Straits and Timor.

The next day they landed on another island within the reef where, when the men were asked to go ashore in search of supplies, a miniature mutiny broke out, some of the painfully fatigued men saying they would rather go without a meal than have to search for it. One of the company, more mutinous than the rest, challenged Bligh's command. At this Bligh seized a cutlass, thrust one into the sailor's hand and told him to defend himself. Fortunately the affair ended reasonably peacefully after Fryer, the sailing-master, had intervened, although Bligh wrote later that in this trouble he was 'assisted only by Mr Nelson'.

The search for food was resumed and clams, oysters and some small dogfish were found, as well as 'some small beans called by Nelson dolichos'. These, with the clams, oysters and the fish, were made into a stew. But the island yielded nothing else and after but a few hours ashore they set sail.

A day later, on 1st June, they landed once again, this time on a lagoon island, Nelson heading a party seeking supplies. At noon Nelson was seen returning to the boat 'in so weak a condition that he was obliged to be supported by two other men. His complaint was a violent heat in his bowels, a loss of sight, much drought and an inability to walk. This, I found,' wrote Bligh, 'was occasioned by his being unable to support the heat of the sun and that, when he was fatigued and faint, instead of retiring into the shade to rest, he had continued to attempt more than his strength was equal to. I was glad to find that he had no fever; and it was now that the little wine which I had so carefully saved became of real use; I gave it in very small quantities with some pieces of bread soaked in it and he soon began to recover.'

The boatswain and the carpenter also complained of severe pain, Bligh putting this down to the dolichos which Nelson had found on long vines climbing to the very top of the trees, which the men had eaten raw, Nelson telling Bligh that the men so 'constantly teazed him whenever a berry was found, to know if it was good to eat, so that it would not have been surprising if many of them had been really poisoned'.

Poor Nelson, even in the midst of his own violent sickness, still found himself responsible for finding wild vegetables and fruits and for deciding whether they could be eaten by ravenous shipmates. He himself found he could not eat the dolichos, so that Bligh had to feed him more small pieces of bread soaked in wine.

The afternoon of that day was spent in blessed sleep on the warm, comforting beach under the shade of the palms, everything about them pointing to a night of sound healing sleep, but it was not to be. Someone carelessly lighting a fire set light to tinder-dry grass and undergrowth, and at sun-down Bligh, frightened it would bring hostile natives to the scene, would stay only a short time longer while the men collected twelve

noddies, while others on the look-out for turtles found none. After they had rowed off
and the birds were divided among the crew Nelson had half a glass of wine and came
off his invalid diet, feeling much better.

They were still within the Great Barrier Reef and sailing between many small, sandy
islands. *Bounty*'s boat pressed on round Cape York at the extreme tip of the north-east
coast of Australia and on 3rd June, after six days within the reef, they were once more
in the open sea when baling had to start afresh, for running seas were coming over their
stern. Rationing was instituted again with a few oysters, dried clams and now and then
a twenty-fifth of a pound of bread to each man, with a drop of water. The men spent
their days and nights cold, shivering, wet to the skin, aching in every bone. A small
dolphin they caught and divided down to the last crumb raised their spirits and their
strength a little, but by the 10th all of them were suffering from extreme weakness,
swollen legs, hollow and ghastly countenances and without the will to keep awake, and
made a sorry picture. On Friday the 12th the miserable creatures, hardly understanding
anything that was said or done, heard from Bligh that Timor was but two leagues away,
but he was not sure of the direction of the Dutch settlement at Campang, so that it was
two more days and nights before they landed, a ghostly, ghastly skeletal array, as they
were helped ashore to a paradisial breakfast of tea and bread and butter after a journey
of 3,518 miles of open sea in a cockleboat.

Ever conscious of his duty to Banks, the first thing Bligh reported he did on getting
ashore was to see the Governor to request that 'Nelson might have permission to walk
about the country in search of plants which was readily granted with an offer of whatever assistance I should think necessary; and the Governor assured me that the country
was worth examination as it abounded with many curious and medicinal plants'.

But, Bligh added testily: 'From this indulgence I derived no benefit; for Nelson who
since we had left New Holland had been but in a weak condition about this time was
taken ill in consequence of a cold caused by imprudently leaving off warm clothing'—
quite against his captain's orders, and almost as if he had done it on purpose.

It was evident that Nelson was ill indeed, and on the 20th July 1789 he died of a fever
brought on by the extreme privation and hardship he had suffered. Captain Bligh, now
he had lost his botanist and naturalist and a well-favoured protégé of his own patron,
Sir Joseph Banks, relented in his diary, in which a few days before he had blamed poor
Nelson for falling ill, and said: 'On 20th July I had the misfortune to lose Mr David
Nelson, he died of inflammatory fever. The loss of this honest man I very much
lamented; he had, with great care and diligence, attended to the object for which he was
sent, and had always been ready to forward every plan that was proposed for the good
of the service in which we were engaged. He was not less useful in our voyage hither,
in the course of which he gave me great satisfaction by the patience and fortitude with
which he conducted himself.'

The next day David Nelson was buried. 'The corpse was carried by 12 soldiers
dressed in black, preceded by the minister, next followed by myself and the second
governor, then ten gentlemen of the town and the officers of the ships in the harbour

and after them my own officers and people. After reading our burial service the body was interred behind the chapel in the burying ground appropriated to the Europeans of the town. I was sorry I could get no tombstone to put over his remains.

'This was the second voyage Mr Nelson had undertaken to the South Seas having been sent by Sir J. Banks to collect plants, seeds, etc. in Captain Cook's last voyage and now after surmounting so many difficulties in the midst of thankfulness for his deliverance he was called upon to pay the debt of nature at a time least expected.'

William Brown, Nelson's assistant, too died an untimely death. He was obviously kept aboard *Bounty* by the mutineers because of his usefulness as a gardener, and did actually help to found the colony at Pitcairn and to cultivate the land there for food. But one day while digging in his allotment he was shot in a dispute about the ownership of some land.

So Nelson's mission was ended. According to a note of Sir Joseph Banks's, he heard the sad news in March 1790 from the newspapers. His sufferings, privations and sacrifices for botany's sake have probably never been surpassed, yet his introductions, despite the tremendous range of countries and climates he visited, are not easy to track down, for they were all consigned to Banks at Kew and are among the hundreds of plants introduced there by Banks, grown by Aiton and listed in the *Hortus Kewensis* under Banks's name.

Botanists are absolutely certain of Nelson's introductions of *Oxylobium ellipticum*, a shrub from Tasmania, with leaves in clusters along the stem and bright yellow pea-flowers in dense racemes; of *Melaleuca squarrosa*, with stiff little leaves and oblong bottle-brush flowers of pale yellow, as well as the South African *Podalyria sericea*, with pleasing, compact, box-like foliage and delicate pink pea-flowers. On a specimen brought from Tasmania by Nelson L'Héritier founded the famous genus of eucalyptus *E. obliqua*. The botany of Cook's third voyage is almost all founded on David Nelson's specimens now in the British Museum National Herbarium. His Sandwich Island collections are cited in the *Flora Vitiensis*, and many others are found in the Solander MSS. prepared for the Banks Herbarium but never published.

Dr Brown dedicated to him the genus *Nelsonia* in the acanthus family, citing: *Hortulanus meritissimus qui in ultimo itinere Cookii pluremas novas species plantarium idetexit.*

5. The Treasures of Cathay

IT WAS not a particularly happy record of plant hunters which Banks found himself compiling—no one but himself as yet had been fated to die peacefully at home in the full roundness of years. So, apart from his voluminous correspondence with British residents abroad and his ever active and consuming interest and influence with both naval and merchant ships to see that residents collected and sea captains brought new-found plants, principally in seed form, back to Kew, there was a lapse of some ten years before another collector was sent overseas.

In the interim the science and technique of plant transportation had progressed but little. There was, however, one major step forward when the next botanical traveller and his ship sailed. The plant boxes which both Masson and Nelson had carried were now provided with glass tops as well as laths and tarpaulin. There was a definite move to plant seeds too in the plant boxes, rather than rely on their being sent home in bags, bottled, or wrapped in all manner of chemical and natural wax concoctions. And once again Sir Joseph had his greenhouse or plant cabin built on the quarter-deck. The collectors, largely as a result of Nelson's experience and the success of the European residents in Macao and Canton with establishing plants ashore potted in their native loam before they were taken on shipboard, were now briefed to carry out this practice whenever the circumstances or the length of their stay permitted.

For his choice of collectors, Scottish gardeners and gardeners of the north country generally were always favoured by Banks over all the men dispatched hither and thither throughout the world to enrich his, Kew's and the country's store of horticultural and botanical treasure and knowledge.

107

It is interesting to note in the choice of the next man the catholicity of Banks's method of personnel selection and to note through the following years how right in every way were the botanical travellers chosen for what has always been, and certainly was in any part of the eighteenth and for the first half of the nineteenth century, one of the most exacting, dangerous, physically and mentally exhausting of strictly individual tasks any man could embark on.

Ever since Banks had explored the narrow coastal strip of Australia from Sydney to Cape York, New South Wales had never been far from his thoughts. Although he had never gone much farther inland than a mile or two from the sea the possible horticultural richness of the vast unexplored continent, so new, so botanically virgin to the explorer and plant hunter, had fascinated him since those eventful days with Cook in 1768–71.

So it was with the keenest interest and a readily triggered enthusiasm that he read a letter dated from Manchester, which arrived on his study table in Soho Square in March 1795.

It was from a raw-boned, husky young Yorkshireman called George Caley, with very little to offer except youth, brute strength, an overwhelming urge to go a-hunting for plants in foreign parts, a knowledge of horses and a smattering of self-taught botany acquired with infinite labour and dogged persistence. For young Caley, then about twenty, the son of a Craven horse-dealer, had been brought up in the trade and had gathered what he knew about plants and botany on the long journeys across country to trade at horse-fairs and by way of extensive rambles in his native limestone dales of the Pennines.

But there was also a nostalgic link for Banks with this would-be young traveller in botany, for Banks came from Bank Newton in Craven, where the family arms still adorn the hall there and Gargrave Church near by. Banks too knew the hard, unrelenting country of limestone fells, over which the stone walls now march to Ingleborough and Penyghent, and their unique alpine flora. This was the man Banks chose to take over at Botany Bay where he had left off.

He sailed with fifty convict women in the whaler *Speedy* in the suite of Captain King, who was sailing out to the colony to take over from Governor Hunter. They left in November 1799, reaching Botany Bay by the following April. Although Caley's name became a byword in the colony for tough, rough independence and his long exploratory treks through virgin bush towards the Blue Mountains, his plant hunting was different only in quantity from that of his master some years before.

There were other lands and other botanical worlds to conquer—there was all the magic of China with her fabled stories of beautiful blooms and picturesque garden landscapes, which had been grown and made by clever Chinese nurserymen and temple priests over the centuries.

Lord Macartney's embassy, which went out to China in 1792 with two attendant gardeners, one called John Haxton and another whose name has been lost to the record, tried valiantly to botanize but found it almost impossible, so closely was the embassy confined and restricted in its movements. Sir George Staunton, secretary to the embassy, was a keen collector but, although the party got as far as Jehol and travelled through the country by boat from Peking to Canton, plant hunting was difficult. We know that herbarium species were collected, though records are poor as to their importance or rarity. The only plants we are sure of having been introduced by the embassy are a weeping cypress (*Cupressus funebris*), *Rosa bracteata* (the Macartney Rose), *Macleaya* (*Bocconia*) *cordata* and *Polygonum chinense*.

But from the account which was written of the country by Lord Macartney, from the stories of sea captains and the few English merchants and officials out there with the East India Company, there were descriptions of plant beauty which whetted the appetites and stimulated the desires of the wealthy enthusiasts of greenhouse and stove, for whose wants there were abundant money and even more abundant ambitions. They had heard of, and almost certainly seen, the dramatically limned Chinese prints and drawings of the fabulous chrysanthemums, the glorious and rosy beauties of the peonies, the graceful dignity of the lilies and the riotous colours and heavy fragrance of the azaleas, the ethereal dignity of the camellias and gardenias.

These were floral prizes well worth the winning, and so it was that the comparative failure of Lord Macartney's mission on the botanical side only made the new stove and greenhouse owners the keener.

Banks himself had already introduced *Hydrangea macrophylla*, almost certainly from seed, as well as *Magnolia conspicua*. He knew how his countrymen's gardens could be enriched by the flora of China, so in 1803 a young gardener at Kew, William Kerr, son of a nurseryman from Hawick (another Scot!), was selected from the staff, minutely briefed by both Banks and Aiton, and sent out to China to become the first botanical traveller to hunt plants in China for more than a few days or weeks.

There is little to record about Kerr's background apart from obvious upbringing by his father on the family nursery, so that the first mention we have of him is in Banks's voluminous correspondence.

We first hear of this 'well behaved and considerate young man', as Banks called him, on 13th April 1803, when he was sent by Banks to East India House, cap in hand, to meet David Lance, who, as superintendent of the East India Company's Canton factory, was to travel out there in a matter of days. From Lance, Kerr got the details of his sailing orders and his reception on the other side of the world.

He was to be given £100 a year by Kew, to be accommodated and victualled by the East India Company, but, most of all, he was to understand quite clearly that while in China he was under the direction of Lance personally and other East India Company officials.

Although he had been told by Banks that the Canton post was his, the royal assent for the appointment was still awaited. It was not long in coming, for on 18th April Banks wrote to Kerr to tell him he had been appointed by Kew 'as a collector of plants from foreign lands'. He was to have opportunity for advancement if his conduct was meritorious, he was reminded.

He was charged on arrival to inquire about the native methods of cultivation and botanical information of every kind, and to communicate regularly with Aiton. 'You are to pay special attention', wrote his master, 'to plants producing fibres and other economic plants that can be acclimatized. If a botanical garden is provided great care must be taken in its cultivation.' For Kerr's further guidance to the oriental mind and climate Banks enclosed extracts from Grosier's *Description of China*.

So that everyone was *au fait* with just what Banks, Kew and the country wanted from China, he wrote a long letter of advice to Lance. From the dispatching of Kerr, he told Lance, he hoped 'both England and her colonies will derive solid and substantial benefit'.

They were most eager to obtain not only oranges and peaches 'but we are certainly very desirous of obtaining the best and most palatable kinds of all fruits the produce of the countries you are to visit. The Chinese possess, I believe, all the fruits known in Europe, vines are said to be abundant in some provinces where raisins are made, though the policy of the country forbids the manufacture of wine; strawberries are grown in the cooler parts of the Empire; and apples and pears of several kinds will not succeed at Canton or in its neighbourhood. The Chinese are said to possess fruits generated by ingrafting oranges on quinces and walnuts on chestnuts, but as such a mixture cannot succeed, this opinion of their origin must be false; no doubt, however, they have fruits which seem in shape or in flavour to partake of different sorts, such fruits of course are an object for our gardener as indeed are every good kind of walnut or chestnut that differs from ours here'. He spoke of the dates of the Chinese which were dried in the same way as figs and could become an article of commerce in the Levant where, if we lost Malta, we should have to fix a permanent establishment.

Sir Joseph then went on to oranges: 'You have several kinds that have not yet been brought to Europe. These are an object of commerce also; for our personal gratification I shall be grateful for good varieties of apricots, peaches and plums or cherries, and have no doubt we shall be enabled by observation the gardener will make to cultivate them to advantage.'

As a warning note Sir Joseph spoke of an additional difficulty for plant hunters— prejudice of the Chinese gardeners, who would not plant any more than one kind of fruit in one garden, since they believed that only one sort of soil could produce one kind of fruit at the same time. 'They also think that a peach or other fruit engrafted on the stem of a different kind receives a mixture of pieces which endangers the wholesomeness of the produce; a peach, they say, ought to be grafted on a peach and a plum on a plum; if you cover an ass with a horse the foal would be a mule.'

But Lance and particularly Kerr were to need much more than literary extracts and home-based advice if Kerr was to find his way around and do his job as collector in early nineteenth-century China. Macartney's 1792 embassy, weighed down with all manner of presents, costly, curious and engagingly scientific for the emperor and his courtiers, with at least one Chinese-speaking member in the *entourage*—a boy of thirteen—had been almost an out-and-out failure, certainly politically and botanically, with its plant-hunting members so harried and restricted that their labours amounted to almost nothing.

This then was the sort of country to which Kerr was going, loaded down with instructions of what to look for, how to find it, how to handle it and how to export it.

Sir George Thomas Staunton, the son of the deputy on Lord Macartney's mission and then the boy of thirteen who spoke Chinese, now in Canton, was written to and asked to help Kerr in his task and to keep a watchful eye on him generally.

The prospect looked well enough seen from Kew, but all Kerr found after the usual long, tortuous and uncomfortable storm-tossed voyage was antagonism, unco-operativeness, an almost complete lack of facilities for travel and a people who almost spat at his shadow. That he was a gardener representative of King George of England made not a rice-grain of difference here.

To a young gardener straight out from Kew, the teeming, incredible multitudes of people and shipping on the Canton River must have seemed like a bizarre scene from an Arabian Nights adventure. Even before his ship reached Canton the atmosphere had been tense, for the fierce pirates from the islands in the delta were always a real and ever-present danger. Once in the Canton River the bright green of the rice-fields on the banks of this great tidal waterway, the water-retaining embankments full of luxuriant bamboos, sugar-cane, bananas, the tropical fruits of mango, guava, or the ethereal-looking but edible water-lilies, all against a scenic backcloth of graceful pagodas and mountains, indubitably heralded a strange and completely unfamiliar land to the young, apprehensive plant hunter.

Off Canton Kerr saw the fabulous floating city, hundreds of thousands of boats of all shapes and sizes, all housing families of like nature. Yet looking down on this almost indescribable scene of what seemed utter confusion, there was a semblance of order, for this floating town was arranged in rows for streets among which the boat-borne tradesman plied his wares.

On land, but still pierced in all directions by canals and waterways, was a great welter of crooked, irregular streets of wooden houses built on stakes driven into the river mud. Where there was any sizeable stretch of dry land, the more substantial but distinctly oriental buildings of government offices and officials arose. In the distance could be seen the factory compound of the East India Company where Kerr was to live. Here, as he soon found, business was still carried on under the 'Hong' system for traders, under which all the foreigners were confined to a specially reserved factory area and compelled to deal with a small group of Chinese merchants allocated by the court.

To travel outside the compound any distance at all meant difficulty, danger and possibly death.

William Kerr, in his rough gardener's clothes, soon found this out as he asked, and got permission, to visit the celebrated Canton Fa-tee gardens near the town. It was impossible, as he quickly discovered and wrote to tell Aiton and Sir Joseph, to plant-hunt in the accepted sense of the phrase. He could neither travel nor hunt in China. If he in sheer boredom were to take a stroll a mile or so beyond the East India compound he was likely to be met with haughty, condescending looks and behaviour from the many servants travelling with the mandarin and upper classes generally, and rude approaches and rough handling by the peasants, not necessarily cruel or brutal in its nature but frightening in the extreme, as they gathered round this strange-looking white-faced man. They would feel at his clothing and look at and take away any movable part of his equipment, such as his carrying-bag or hand trowel, or his cap. Dangerously enough, any reaction of even a purely defensive nature might well set off an ugly mood and scene among the crowd which could end in an attack on him if he didn't take to his heels, as Robert Fortune found to his cost some thirty years later.

But to Kerr's credit he was quick to get on with his work in the restricted field open to him. The Fa-tee gardens, or 'the flowery land' as the name implied, were two or three miles from Canton on the opposite side of the river and were in fact, he found, nursery gardens where plants were grown and exposed for sale to the plant- and flower-loving Chinese.

As one approached the gardens on the deep mud-stained deltaic waters, the scent of the flowers was wafted to the senses long before the gardens were in sight. It was a delicious preamble to a wealth of floral beauty, exciting colour and unique forms.

As the small boat drew up to the ramshackle wooden landing-stage Kerr saw about a dozen gardens side by side on the bank, each self-contained by wall or hedge and each watched over by the gardener's house at the entrance gate. They were not very large, an acre or so at the most, and most of them were divided into two strictly separate compartments—a stock ground, where plants brought from other parts of the country were planted out in the native earth to become acclimatized, and the show-piece opposite the entrance. This was one to astound and excite any gardener, but particularly one of Banks's men, armed with the most comprehensive instructions on what to look for and what to get for Kew, for here it almost looked as if all China's flowers had been hunted for, collected and potted up for show. In front of Kerr was a blaze of colour such as he had never seen before—the exotic, glorious shimmering of reds, purples, yellows and oranges of the azaleas, the graceful green, gold and white of the orange trees, the pink and red of roses, the grace and velvety charm of tree-peonies and the bright dark shiny green of their leaves, the innocent white of the gardenias. But this kaleidoscopic scene of natural beauty seen for the first time, even for an experienced gardener like Kerr, was too much to take in all at once. With his Chinese assistant—for Kerr had none of the language, only his own Scottish tongue—he wandered round the paved paths in a dream; at each side of him were all the plants in earthenware pots forming rainbow borders to the many narrow paths by which the garden was traversed.

He noticed with unveiled astonishment the *bonsai* (as the Japanese call them), the dwarf trees of conifer and others, grotesquely formed, many over a hundred years, by the patient hands of Chinese gardeners, to whom the art was a religion. Among the dark greens of the conifers, mostly used for dwarfing and shaping, he came across the colourful mandarin orange, grown in dwarf state, with its large, flat, dark-red-skinned fruit shining amidst its yellow leaves like so many jewels.

But the catalogue grew; there were the showy clusters of yellow, orange, rose, scarlet and all the shades between of the ixias, and an evergreen, odoriferous flowering shrub he came to know later as the cumquat *Citrus aurantium japonica*, and others— *Murraya exotica*, *Aglaia odorata* and *Lagerstroemia indica*. Of the azaleas much coveted in England, Kerr found growing in colourful abandon *albiflora*, *phoenicea*, *variegata* and the yellow, most fragrant *sinensis*.

To add to the cold but ethereal beauty of the gardenias was the richly fragrant *Olea fragrans* (*Osmanthus fragrans*), whose scent rose above all other. A delightful plant to see in bloom also was *Daphne odorata*. To excite a comparatively flower-starved gardener were the fascinating form and colour of the genus *Chrysanthemum*, only one of which was known and grown in England—Blanchard's variety, Old Purple—first sent to Kew from France in 1790.

But here in massive diversity were the results of generations of growing and culture, for although the Japanese had made the chrysanthemum a sacred and secular emblem above all others, it was from China that the flower had been taken. As Fortune was able to report some years later, it was such a favourite with gardeners that a man would rather leave and look for other work than be forbidden to grow the flower.

Here then, in this Aladdin's cave of floral rarities, Kerr was able to browse, not hunt, but pick his flowers from the pot or bargain for seed, although there were stories of one wily old nurseryman who always boiled his seeds before he sold them. That way he was sure they would never germinate in another country. It is true that the East India Company also had a garden in the compound, but it was a mere walled enclosure sixty paces each way, and held but few ornamental plants, though these were of interest to one as conscientious or new to them as Kerr, for among them he found palms and *Magnolia grandiflora*; a justicia he named 'Adhatoda ligustrums', the litchi, *Enkianthus quinqueflora* and cockscombs (celosia).

By early March 1804 Kerr had shown results, for by the East Indiaman *Woodford* and with the co-operation of Captain Warton he had sent four different kinds of peonies in 'grand growing state'. 'I have also', he told Banks, 'inquired about various kinds of plants mentioned in my instructions.' The captain had promised to care for the plants on the long voyage, he said, and he was also pleased to tell Sir Joseph of a projected move to Macao where a branch of the East India Company was going and here he hoped botanical facilities would be better.

By December in the same year he had sent two more parcels to Kew. By the plant cabin of the *Winchelsea* he sent 'the best plants I can select', he wrote. He had been given permission to collect plants in Manila and already he had explored Macao and the neighbouring islands, but this was 'explored' in the Chinese sense of the word—taken to the nursery and stock gardens and not allowed to roam an inch outside them.

By Captain Kirkpatrick of the *Henry Addington* went his other parcel.

The mention by Kerr of the plant cabin brings us to another stage in the long evolution of efficient and successful plant transportation. Sir Joseph in a letter dated April 1803 from Soho Square to David Lance indicated that this was not the grandiose affair of a special ship's-cabin-cum-greenhouse specially built on the poop deck like a low, crazy crow's nest, but a substantially built box with a three- or four-inch high wooden surround for air circulation and a removable top of triangular shape, the whole covered or uncovered depending on the weather, the waves and the spray, by an attached tarpaulin. In Lance's letter, however, Sir Joseph is playing with the idea of glass for the top. 'If in fitting up the plant cabbin, glass should become an object I would advise that two or three lights were put into it; these will be sufficient to keep the plants in order if they make the plant cabbins as light as the other cabbins in the ship.'

Alas, even with plant 'cabbins', failures were more frequent than successes. In London river or at Kew there was more often disappointment than joy on the arrival of the 'cabbins'. For although it is true to say that at Canton and Macao it would seem Banks's instructions that plants should be established in pots for some time before they were consigned to the tender mercies of the British tar and the vagaries of tropic and far from tropic weather were carried out, neither he nor Kerr realized that many of the Chinese plants were forced for a household market or that the soil they were potted in was local soil with nothing added, a heavy clay, which became either waterlogged or, if allowed to dry out, almost impervious to water. It was a hard life for plant and plant hunters!

Watching the Kerr-Banks-Kew experiment with both a discerning and favourable eye was Dr John Livingstone, Chief Surgeon to the East India Company, who had been in China eleven years when Kerr arrived. He himself was a keen amateur botanist and knew the difficulties of getting across the seas the beautiful flowers, shrubs and trees by which he was surrounded.

For the benefit of his fellow enthusiasts in his home country he gathered together, in a paper which was read to the young but flourishing Horticultural Society in London, his experiences, successes and failures. He knew, he said, that many people were surprised at the slow progress made in bringing over Chinese plants when the rarities to be brought were so well known to all.

'Many persons', he said, 'seem inclined to account for this fact by supposing that those gentlemen who enjoy opportunities of sending or bringing home Chinese plants are either ignorant of the great estimation in which they are held, or strangely unwilling to bestow the necessary attention on a subject so dear to the lover of fine plants.'

For twenty-five years, he told his hearers, he had been acquainted with the plants and the problem. One great difficulty for the plant hunter was that botany as a scientific discipline was 'extremely defective'. There was no uniformity of names, no details to be found in print about where plants grew, their uses, their descriptions, in fact no help whatsoever from books or word of mouth for the newcomer charged with the duty of seeking out new plants.

He drew attention to the Fa-tee gardens of China, saying that later in Kerr's stay access to these by Europeans was restricted to three days' visits in a month, for which a charge was made, and that the gardens were the only source for plants which were almost all placed in pots in strong alluvial clay, quite often broken into cubical pieces about half an inch in size. That was all right, he explained, for Canton where violent rains alternated with drought, 'but it is obvious that plants so prepared cannot be generally well suited for the purpose of transportation'.

Many plants in the gardens were returned from homes in the city where the gardener had contracted to supply fresh plants in bloom, taking back the old ones that had gone off. Could it be surprising that plants so treated should die on the passage to England? he asked.

Then Dr Livingstone spoke of Kerr and his experiences as a professional plant hunter. 'Infinite pains', he reminded his hearers, 'seemed to have been taken in framing his instructions. The chests and boxes formed for the reception of the plants were contrived with the greatest judgement and every facility was secured for the ready transmission to Kew of all the plants which he might wish to send there. Yet, on a comparison of the number of plants which he sent on board the Honourable Company's ships with those which arrived in good health at the Royal Gardens, it will be quite clear that he was not successful, upon the whole, nor more fortunate than the private adventurer.'

Livingstone's reasons for Kerr's troubles and disappointments he alleged could be put down to the 'want of sufficient encouragement. His salary [£100 per annum] was almost too small for his necessary wants and he consequently lost respect and consideration in the eyes of even the Chinese assistants whom he was obliged to employ.

'I have not the slightest doubt but his failure is to be attributed to the necessity he was under of associating with inferior persons, and from his deficiency of means to support himself more respectably.'

The doctor then gave a note of his experiences in plant transport. Even when he had got friends to take charge of the plants he wanted to send home they had arrived safe but died because of the delays in customs and dock handling in London river; or sickly plants removed at St Helena to feel their land legs again had been left unattended and died there; or all the plants had been received in England dead because the sailors or the captain neglected to water them. John Reeves, assistant inspector to the East India Company, had taken home safely ninety out of one hundred plants. Yet those he had sent without personal charge had died.

This led Livingstone to lay down a specific plan for the successful transportation of Chinese plants:

The plants should be collected in proper time so as to enable them to be firmly rooted in the soil in which they are to be transported to England; a proper soil to be obtained wherein they might be planted.

They should be arranged in their chests or boxes accordingly as they require frequent, moderate or slight waterings.

When on board the covers of the chests should be well closed when the spray is flying over the ship and opened at all times in temperate and fine weather; the plants should be duly watered with good water and particular attention to be paid to them from the time the ship arrives at her anchorage in the Thames until they are unloaded.

He added that plants should be potted up in proper soil at least six months before sailing.

But what a calamitous waste before ever the doctor's common-sense plans were carried out, for he calculated that for every one plant that arrived safe and sound in England one thousand had been lost.

'Plants purchased at Canton including their chests and other necessary charges cost 6s. 8d. each on a fair average; consequently every plant now in England must have been introduced at the enormous expense of upwards of £300.'

As a complete solution to this costly and disappointing task he suggested that the Horticultural Society should send a fully qualified gardener to Macao, where he would have a house and garden and native assistants. Apart from reasonable remuneration he advocated a substantial bonus on every plant 'with which he enriched the horticultural or botanical stores of England'.

The arrangements for the transportation of plants should be liberal and beneficial to the people taking part in it. Shipowners should be paid the proper freight rates for the water needed and, if possible, one person with an acquaintance of gardens should be placed in charge of the precious cargoes.

As Banks's correspondence shows, however, the traffic was not all one way and Kew regularly sent out batches of plants, particularly fruit, for establishing in Chinese soil. A list for the year 1805 from Kew to Canton contains 15 grapes, 24 plums and cherries, 24 peaches and nectarines, 20 pears and apricots, 19 figs, 12 rhododendrons and azaleas (North American probably), 34 roses, 110 various bulbs, 22 pelargoniums and 64 miscellaneous plants.

Infinite care was taken at the London end too, for a message from Aiton to Banks details how he has sent a carpenter aboard *Thames* to repair the plant cabin and a gardener to stay with the plants until she sailed; he had also told the sailor put in charge of the green cargo that he would have five guineas to himself if it was delivered safely to Kerr.

Yet success was no more forthcoming in reverse. Thomas Manning, a friend of Charles Lamb, who took a consignment over to Canton in 1806, wrote Banks from the Cape of Good Hope that after an eleven-week passage many plants were already dead and many had lost their leaves. 'I had a little trouble at first', he told Sir Joseph, 'in preventing certain officers from plucking the odoriferous leaves, but a little gentle expostulation and management soon succeeded. The first mate does not approve of having a garden on the poop at all. He says it rocks the ship all to pieces. The Captain agrees in the same story and when the beams creak in the cuddy, they turn to me sometimes and d—— the flower pots.'

In 1806 Kerr was able to tell Banks that the value of the plant cabin had been proved in at least one instance when he told him that most of the plants sent by one of the East Indiamen had arrived safely. On the other hand he had to tell of disaster to a consignment sent on board the *Hope* which were nearly all dead after suffering in a great storm at the Cape. Captain Henry Wilson, of the *Warley*, had also been most unfortunate, for the plants he had brought to exchange for Chinese plants were nearly all dead.

A letter from Banks to Kerr dated May 1806 told the sad story in reverse. 'The plants sent by the *Winchelsea* were nearly all dead,' he penned, 'but there is no blame for this on you. It seems useless', added Sir Joseph, obviously after repeated failures and disappointments, 'to send living plants unless they are in charge of a competent gardener.' And he wondered whether it would not be a good idea to engage a Chinese gardener for that purpose and pay for his maintenance and return passage.

Doing as he was told and keeping up the correspondence Kerr sent on board the *Ganges* his Manila journal and a catalogue of Manila plants. 'I have carried out my instructions on the botanical side,' he said, 'and also collected information on Chinese methods of land ownership, tenure, sale and transfer.'

Replying, Banks said he did not approve of the Manila expedition although he admitted it was justified by the result. He hoped in any case that Kerr had garnered information on the Manila linen and cordage industry, and commended him for sending fruit trees to St Helena.

It may be recalled that Banks had noted St Helena as a 'convalescent home' and halfway house for sea-weary plants from the East on his own plant-hunting expeditions with Cook, and his ideas had been put into effect there with the support and co-operation of subsequent governors and officials.

In 1807 James Drummond, superintendent, or supercargo, at Canton, wrote from Weymouth, where he had made landfall, to give some indication how this St Helena experiment was working out. He had left such Chinese plants as were sickly from their voyage to recover and left a plant cabin for their 'hospitalization' with full instructions for cabin and plants to follow by a later ship when they were sufficiently strong to make the journey.

He was pleased to inform Sir Joseph that the Chinese plants did well at St Helena and he had ordered the man in charge there, a Mr W. J. Burchell, to have boxes filled with Chinese plants sent by Kerr prepared for shipment home.

So it was that Kerr struggled on with an inadequate salary, against almost insurmountable difficulties of transport, with so little freedom of movement to seek out native plants in their native haunts, that he might well have been a prisoner. According to the pages of *The Chinese Repository*, published in Canton and later quoted by Bretschneider, all these troubles made inroads on his character. Because of his lack of an adequate salary, after three first very active years, his work and social status suffered. 'He became greatly changed. He was then unable to prosecute his work in consequence of some bad habits he had contracted as unfortunate as they were new to him.'

Yet his work was not all in vain, for despite the fact that many hundreds of plants he sent home did die, Kerr was responsible for many valuable introductions nursed back to vigorous health in the Kew greenhouses.

For the year 1804, his first year in Canton, Bretschneider notes that by the East India Company's *Henry Addington*, Kerr was able to introduce *Gardenia spinosa, G. radicans, Pittosporum tobira, Lilium japonicum* and *L. tigrinum, Nandina domestica, Dianthus japonicum, Crataegus glabra, Aster hispidus, Sagittaria obtusifolia, Begonia discolor, Pinus lanceolata, Juniperus chinensis, Taxus macrophylla* and *Kerria japonica*.

In 1805, with the aid of Captain Campbell of the *Winchelsea*, he managed to get safely to Kew *Mussaenda pubescens, Nymphaea pygmaea* and *Corchorus japonica*.

By East Indiaman *Hope* (Captain Prendergast) Kew recorded having received in living state *Gardenia micrantha, Lonicera japonica* and *L. flexuosa*. In the same year, in the *Walmer Castle* under the watchful eye of Captain Dod, arrived safely *Paederia foetida*, and by Captain Wellbank of the *Cuffreta* the following year he forwarded *Rosa banksia, Camellia sasanqua* and *Bletia hyacinthina*.

Kerr also sent plants and seeds to Dr William Roxburgh, of the East India Company's botanical garden at Calcutta, where he established *Flemingia prostrata, Vitex incisa, Hemerocallis cordata*, juniperus and arums.

So it seems that despite what Dr Livingstone and *The Chinese Repository* said about him, Kerr's work was in no small measure successful. It was certain that both Banks and Aiton were satisfied, for in June 1810 Banks wrote to tell him that the king had ordered the establishment of a botanical garden in Ceylon at Colombo and that, in consideration of his good conduct as a plant collector, he had been appointed superintendent there, a post he actually took up in 1812.

He worked hard for a year in establishing the garden amidst entirely different surroundings and climatic conditions. Here great tropical forests covered much of the island of which orchids and other tropical climbers, flowering trees and a flamboyant flora were features. Every single plant had to be sought out in its jungle haunt.

By 1813 Kerr felt sufficiently satisfied with the initial laying-out of the garden at Colombo to leave it and travel inland. He visited Adams Peak, the great 7,500-foot mountain which rises majestically over the island, and discovered many new plants, of which unfortunately no records exist. Next year, 1814, he died of 'some illness incidental to the climate'. Sir Alexander Johnston, the administrator, wrote to Banks in January 1815 to tell him of the death of Kerr in November of the previous year after a tour in northern Ceylon. Later in 1815, Banks heard of the death of yet another of his plant collectors, another floral martyr.

Richard Anthony Salisbury, himself the keenest of plantsmen and the first secretary of the Horticultural Society of London, in the first volume of the *Transactions*, 1812, had this to say:

'Among the various branches of horticulture, the managing of plants, though perhaps really the least important, is one of the most difficult and the avidity with which they are collected, as well as the permanent delight which they afford, have advanced the rank of skilful botanical gardener in some families higher than that of any other servant.' A revolution indeed!

He praised Kew too, the repository of all these hard-won rarities, as 'the grand source of inspiration in this country since the death of Philip Miller. Only the year before, 1811, he 'saw living [at Kew] more than double the number of exotic plants known to him [Miller] in 1768'.

Inset: David Douglas (1798–1834), who probably introduced more plants and trees to British gardens than any other plant hunter before or since. His main introductions were from the Pacific coast of America. *Above:* An early illustration of Fort Vancouver on the Columbia River, the base for Douglas's many incredible plant-hunting journeys. *Below:* A Hudson's Bay Company fort of Douglas's time, stockaded and tree-cleared as some provision against surprise attack by the Indians.

Above: Making a portage, a labour in which Douglas was involved so often when the rivers had to be left and all equipment carried overland to the next convenient waterway. *Below:* A winter camp such as Douglas knew so well, with rough timber cabins for the fur trappers alongside Indian tepees.

Indeed despite the troublesome times of the war with France, Kew and Sir Joseph had been fortunate in respect of Kerr and his associates in China, so far from the trouble centre, and their plant transportation had been relatively safe too, but the dangers to ship-owners generally of their ships being taken on the high seas had cut down considerably the number of plant hunters sent out from Kew.

So, coinciding with Kerr's death and almost with the impending peace of 1815, Aiton at Kew urged Sir Joseph to send out his plant missionaries to the ends of the earth once again. Almost immediately from Soho Square, on 1st September 1814, went a letter to the Government with a plea to Lord Liverpool for resumption of world-wide collecting of plants exotic, rare and as yet unknown.

It was the Banks-Kew testament admirably summing up the situation as it had been and as he hoped it would be in future.

After proclaiming the importance of Kew Gardens as superior to all others both in Britain and abroad, and how necessary it was to maintain that position, he regretted there had been some impairment due to 'the interruption of commerce during the last war or rather by the necessity of convoy, the uncertainty and delays of which had for some years past rendered the transport of living plants all but impossible and induced the King to desist almost wholly from sending out collectors as His Majesty had before been used to do.'

Banks then went on to explain in detail just how over the years he had chosen both his men and the conditions under which they hunted:

'The plan of collecting for Kew as established by His Majesty has hitherto been to employ those young gardeners educated in the gardens who showed the most inclination to and made the greatest proficiency in botanical pursuits, and were best skilled in the successful arrangements of plants in the gardens. Among the many young men who work there in the hope of being recommended to gentlemen's families as gardeners when they have learned the art, some are always to be found whose dispositions lead them to the study of botany and whose talents enable them to excel in it.

'From these the best were selected, and it is remarkable that I do not recollect one instance of a man well acquainted with the plants in the garden who did not feel an ambition to be employed as a collector.

'Although the pay of the employment was regulated more by the attention to strict economy, which all who have concern with the privy purse of the Sovereign are bound to exercise, than to the well regulated liberality which those who are paid out of the public purse experience; those who, by their salaries, do not enable them to save sufficient provision for their old age are provided with pensions of retreat sufficient to render the latter and less active parts of their lives comfortable and happy.

'The establishment of a Kew collector was, 40 years ago, £100 a year as wages. He was allowed to draw bills for travelling expenses and board wages to the amount of £200 more, but this he was never allowed to exceed, and was never exceeded without a satisfactory explanation being given. In no circumstances, as far as I can recall, has any censure been passed on any of these collectors.

'So well does the serious mind of a Scottish education fit Scotsmen to the habits of industry, attention and frugality that they rarely abandon them at any time in life and, I may say, never while they are young.'

Because of differing times, Banks now suggested that a collector should have £180 a year, out of which he could save £150 and £30 be used to furnish him with clothes and pocket money.

A free passage in one of His Majesty's ships could be expected for the collectors appointed, with messing with the warrant-officers. Governments in the colonies were instructed to supply the collectors with bullock wagons, etc., from the public store.

He himself, said Sir Joseph, if necessary, would audit the collectors' accounts sent home and certify them for the Treasury.

He put forward the names of two young men, two Scots, who were ready and very anxious to obtain the employment as collectors, namely James Bowie, who had been in the gardens four years and was aged twenty-five, and Allan Cunningham, aged twenty-three, who had worked in the gardens and as an assistant in the compilation of the *Hortus Kewensis* since 1808.

Brazil was to be their new and difficult happy hunting-ground and, warned Sir Joseph, the collectors must be directed by their instructions not to take upon themselves the character of gentlemen but to establish themselves in point of board and lodgings as servants ought to do.

He concluded by drawing attention to the importance of the commerce in domestic and exotic plants, 'supported far above its natural level by the use of growing plants in all expensive entertainments'.

By October, Bowie and Cunningham were on the high seas and did sterling work for Kew and British gardens.

But growing fast and gaining in importance as a force in the British horticultural scene was the Horticultural Society of London, who were ready to take over the collecting work of which Kew and Sir Joseph Banks had been almost sole arbiters for half a century.

6. Africa and Instructions for Plant Transportation

THERE were abroad now, in marked contrast to the years during which Banks had been almost the sole arbiter of botanical plant-hunting and the sole source of its technique, many more well-educated men with time to give to the problem of plant transportation.

Within the quickly growing membership of the Horticultural Society there were dedicated botanists and plant lovers like Joseph Sabine, Thomas Andrew Knight, John Livingstone and John Lindley, who were giving the most careful thought to the whole field of plant-hunting and were prepared to give in meticulous detail a working programme for it. A botanical traveller need no longer be sent out like a dove from the Kew ark with the hope of a successful landfall and a twig or two to show for his laborious voyaging.

We have seen, for instance, that John Livingstone had for several years sent plants home from China with varying degrees of success, in the main disastrous. But he was willing to work long and assiduously on ways and means to overcome his failures, caused, he knew, by the climate, the human element and any foreign plant's aversion to being torn out of its comfortable native heath to be shipped thousands of miles away to attempt a life in a totally disagreeable climate and country. In the paper to the Horticultural Society already quoted, Livingstone pointed out, as well as some of the difficulties Kerr had met in his attempts to send over live plants, the problems he had had with seed also, for, said Livingstone, from April to October the rain was so frequent in China that the moist air made it nearly impossible to preserve seeds. Whether they were excluded from the air or exposed to it made no difference; one way they mildewed, the other they were eaten by insects.

He suggested a method of seed preservation in which air was made dry by sulphuric acid. He had found a successful means by which to do this by placing the seed to be dried in the pans of Leslie's ice machine and carefully replacing the receiver without exhausting the air. Small seeds were thus dried in one or two days and larger ones in less than a week and were ready to travel.

If an ice machine was not to hand (not always the easiest of things to come across in the jungle!), then Livingstone suggested 'any glass, glazed earthenware or leaden vessel may be employed for the same purpose; but it is absolutely necessary', he warned, 'that the cover fit exactly and that the bottom contain at least one inch of concentrated sulphuric acid. The seeds may be placed on any kind of plate suspended on a glass stand'.

Seeds thus dried could be preserved in a vegetative state for 'any necessary length of time by keeping them in an airy situation in common brown paper and occasionally exposing them to the air on a fine day, especially after damp weather'. This method was successful, Dr Livingstone claimed, 'with all the large mucilaginous seeds. Very small seeds probably require to be kept in sugar or with currants and raisins'.

Progress was slow, however, and while long voyages and lack of technique still lost many plants (and right up to 1833 the *Gardeners' Magazine* was praising a Mr M'Gilligan, the purser on board the East Indiaman *Orwell*, who had managed to bring a few Chinese azaleas from Canton to London, as against the dismal attempts of Mr Reeve, who had previously sent home five hundred without a single live plant in England to show for his pains) there was no question but that the Horticultural Society were making some headway.

But they could do little, as Kew and Sir Joseph Banks had found, to allay the loss in human life, in the sacrificing of young, intrepid botanical travellers who would and did risk all for a flower.

While James Bowie, who did some pioneer work in Brazil and then took on where Masson had left off at the Cape, managed to survive the hazardous, dangerous and uncomfortable conditions of an early plant hunter's life, Allan Cunningham, after a spell with Bowie in South America, was sent off to finish George Caley's work in Australia, and died at Sydney in 1839 at the comparatively early age of forty-eight.

The Horticultural Society found themselves just as unfortunate and recorded in the preface of the fifth volume of their *Transactions* that by 1824 they had lost by death two of their first three collectors, John Potts, who had gone to Bengal and China in 1821 and had died in October of the following year, having outlived his return but a few weeks, 'having contracted a disease in the execution of his duties'. Then there was the melancholy news to tell of John Forbes who, as a young man of twenty-six, went out to the east coast of Africa in 1822 and died at Senna in the August of the next year while making his way up the Zambesi River.

Yet men, it seemed, were eager and ready to undertake the almost superhuman tasks which plant-hunting in foreign and unknown countries called for. The next to answer to the call was George Don. He was a Scot from Doo Hillock, Forfar, brought up in his father's nursery gardens, later seeing service with Messrs Dicksons' nursery in Edinburgh, then in London at the Portman nursery before obtaining employment at the Chelsea Botanical Garden, where he became foreman under Anderson. He it was, at the age of twenty-three, who was chosen by the Horticultural Society in 1822 to hunt in three great continents and to scour the island-studded seas between.

Now there were detailed instructions available for any such collectors, collated, catalogued and precise. John Lindley, then assistant secretary at Chiswick, the garden of the Horticultural Society, was willing and able to draw up a brief for any collector for any country. He went into print with *Instructions for packing living plants in Foreign Countries, Especially Within the Tropics and Directions for their Treatment during the Voyage to Europe.*

In these instructions precise details are given for a most up-to-date plant cabin, now called a 'portable greenhouse', which was proving reasonably successful for the safe transportation of plants from overseas.

It certainly showed the tenacity and grimness of purpose of the early botanical travellers who, on the death of George III in 1820, despite the loss of literally thousands of plants sent from overseas had, it was reliably estimated, been responsible for not less than 6,746 rare exotics introduced during his long reign of fifty-nine years.

Lindley in his paper was able to point out that the traffic in exotic plants had become of great importance, so that it was most necessary that both plant hunters and plant receivers should understand where they had so often gone wrong in the past. This, he thought, could be attributed 'to the insufficient manner in which the packages were originally made up'.

He did not blame the poor, untiring, often desperate botanical traveller for, he explained, 'the insecure modes of packaging abroad do not arise from any indisposition on the part of those who prepare to give them all necessary care, nor from any in-difference as to their fate; but entirely from not considering sufficiently the various accidents to which plants on ship board are exposed, and the improbability that they will experience, even under the most favourable circumstances, the care and attention which they require.

'In vain are lives and property risked in attempting to transfer the vegetable beauties of other countries to this, if the same pains which were devoted to procuring them be not continued in their subsequent management. The idea which seems to exist, that to tear a plant from its native soil, to plant it in fresh earth, to fasten it in a wooden case and put it on board a vessel under the care of some officer, is sufficient, is of all others the most erroneous and has led to the most ruinous consequences. Perhaps', he con-tinued, 'beyond anything else, it is necessary to take care before plants are finally prepared for their voyage their roots be well established in the pots in which it is intended they should be transported.

'With any herbaceous plant this requires only a short space of time; but for such as are shrubby or of hard woody texture a period, in many instances, of not more than two or three months is absolutely necessary. The attention of gentlemen residing in hot countries within the tropics cannot be directed too strongly to this fact, which if alone neglected, must either destroy entirely, or very materially weaken, the effect of any attention which otherwise may be bestowed.

'I would recommend that square wooden boxes be used for the plants instead of earthenware pots, not only because the former are less liable to be broken, but also because they are lighter.

'When the period for embarking them arrives, they should be placed in wooden cases, the tops of which must be capable of being opened and should slope both ways like the roof of a double greenhouse. These cases must be furnished with a tarpawling, fixed along their tops and sufficiently large when unrolled to cover them completely so as to protect the plants from being damaged by the salt waters dashing over them in rough weather.

'It cannot be expected that heavy cases should meet with very gentle treatment on ship board, and it is certain they will be handled in a rough manner by watermen, carters and custom house officers after they have arrived in port.'

He suggested dovetail joints and iron binding for the corners, for he had actually seen boxes holding fine collections with the sides of the cases beaten in and the pots inside broken to pieces.

Then Lindley came to that so difficult part of plant travel, the actual voyage. His advice was that the person in charge should be briefed with implicit instructions: 'Never to exclude them [the boxes] from air and light in fine weather, unless to protect them from the cold as the vessel makes the land, and after she is in port, or during high winds or especially when the seamen are washing the deck, but in foul weather to close the lids down and unroll the tawpawling over the latter to exclude the sea spray effectually.'

If salt spray ('saline particles', John Lindley called them) did get on the leaves then as soon as possible this had to be removed with fresh water and a sponge!

Watering must depend on what water could be spared from the ship's ration, but the mould should at least be kept moist, he advised. To prevent waterlogging, half-inch diameter holes should be drilled in both case and pots.

Monkeys and paroquets on board ships were also a hazard, said Mr Lindley, and a strict guard should be kept against their attacks. So that no amount of shaking would throw the soil out of the pots, the pots should be made square to fit accurately into the bottom of the case and fastened with crosspieces of wood.

The soil should also be covered with coarse moss which should be kept in place with criss-cross pack thread or slender laths. This would not only help to retain the soil in the pots but the moisture also.

For special plants there were special methods and for the new, rare orchidaceous or 'air plants' then the boxes could be made of trellis work provided with crosspieces of wood inside to which the plants, on the bark or moss on which they grow, could be securely tied and the space between filled loosely with moss. In such cases the box lid should be nailed down.

Bulbs would travel best, advised Lindley, in paper or canvas bags or dry sand. In the soil of all the boxes 'any woody or bony seeds or capsules should be buried'.

Four cases like those Lindley advocated had been sent from Mauritius and the plants received in excellent condition. The details for making the boxes were given by Lindley. They should be of stout inch board, 3 feet high, 4 feet long and 1 foot 8 inches wide. The sides were to be straight up to 20 inches then sloped like a greenhouse to a ridge $2\frac{1}{2}$ inches wide. The lid, which opened both ways from the middle, was of wooden bars 2 inches wide and 2 inches asunder, under which were fixed panes of stout coarse glass.

It was this kind of instruction, come by after years of bitter experience and disappointment, with which the new men were armed as they left London river for all parts of the world.

And now that the Cape and Australia had been well plant-hunted, the tropical coasts of Africa, that great continent full of such legendary floral wealth, was next to be botanically explored, and it was George Don who, on 4th January 1822, set sail in H.M.S. *Iphigenia* for that task. And what an itinerary had been set for him, what a programme—or was it a programme or a blitz? For in a matter of fourteen months he was to search for plants in six different countries in the white man's grave on the west coast of Africa, in six of the main islands of the Atlantic, and to land at four places on the Brazilian seaboard and quickly but thoroughly do a botanical skirmish on Manhattan Island, North America, before returning home. This expedition must have been the forerunner of the present-day American tourists doing Europe in eight days!

It was all to be undertaken, particularly the Gold and Ivory Coasts—malarial, snake-infested, climatically dangerous as they were—without any of the advantages of modern drugs and medicines for combating tropical ailments and the depredations of insect and reptile life, specially designed clothing, dehydrated or compressed food packs and vitamins.

But then men like George Don were young, eager, full of keenness to make a name for themselves in the botanical world, even if it were but for a plant named after them, and it must be said the botanists sitting comfortable at home gave precious little away to mere gardeners who simply found the plants—Kerr did get his 'Kerria' but Don, despite his Herculean labours, got but *Memecylon donianum*, a species of 'glabrous trees or shrubs unknown to cultivation in this country', said Nicholson about sixty years later.

When George Don set out from London in the November of 1821 he carried with him a portfolio of instructions most carefully drawn up by Joseph Sabine, the Society's secretary. They were unequivocal, demanding in the extreme, carefully detailed and put the young botanical traveller in no doubt as to his social status or the work he was expected to do as he read his almost overwhelming rota of duties for a plant hunter 'on the western coast of Africa, part of South America and the West Indies'.

'On this enterprise', the rigid, curt briefing ran, 'you will consider yourself under the immediate command of Captain Sabine [Edward Sabine, the secretary's brother] to whom you will refer on all occasions when you want advice and assistance and you will attend to whatever directions you receive from him.'

He was told that he would be right under the thumb, too, of the *Iphigenia*'s commander, Commodore Sir Robert Mendo, who would tell him when he could go ashore, and woe betide him if he was not punctual in his return for the ship's boat once he got ashore.

Then came his mission directions: 'The chief object of your mission is to collect, transport or bring home for the use of the Society, seeds or plants of the different vegetable productions to be obtained in the countries you visit, whether found in a wild or cultivated state, such as are likely to be useful as fruits on account of their first importance and next to take those plants which will be esteemed in our gardens for their beauty or singularity.

'The fruits you will find will be all, of course, natives of hot climates, but these the Society are particularly desirous to obtain, you will therefore be particular in your description of them as well as noting and recording every circumstance relating to their habitat if in a wild state, and in their cultivation or their treatment when in gardens.'

He was reminded that he was furnished with all the equipment for making a herbarium, and requested to collect plants and seeds for exhibition in the Society's rooms which had to be 'as perfectly formed as possible' and packed dry in boxes.

'You will, of course,' the memorandum went on, 'gather dry specimens of the plants of each country you visit. Your collection must not be confined to single specimens. It is desirable that you should bring or send home several of each specimen you meet with and you will be particularly careful to place a note with the several specimens of the time, place and situation where they were gathered.'

It was not necessary for him to name everything he found because, warned Sabine, that would be a waste of time seeking out the names when he could be well employed on other duties.

'Whenever you are not immediately engaged on your own particular pursuits you will render all the assistance in your power towards the formation of a collection of natural history in other subjects besides those of the vegetable kingdom.'

This was practical work, but there was literary work to do too for, inexorably, the Society's secretary requested, 'you will be particularly careful to write me by every opportunity that occurs and number the letters progressively, keeping copies of them.

'You will keep a fair journal of all your proceedings and observations and make a copy of the same from time to time in the smaller book supplied to you for the purpose and you will send home the parts of the copy whenever you are able to do so.

'Your journal should be made as ample as possible. It must contain the details of every day's proceedings as well as notes and accounts of all you can see.'

The secretary had not finished yet, for if Don did not happen to meet with any of the Society's corresponding members on his travels then he was to act as agent, seek out suitable persons, enlist their services and sign them up.

On the preservation and packaging side of the business it was clearly apparent that times had changed, for Don's instructions from Sabine told him that it was presumed he was skilled in the packaging of plants and only reminded him that he should avail himself of 'every good conveyance that offers to send home whatever you have collected'.

The secretary did deign a little advice on seed transport, saying that the differing methods, which he did not specify, should always be tried, for what might fail with some might well succeed with others. Larger seeds were known to survive a long voyage, he said, if bedded in moist earth and then closely packed up. Specimens of fruit could be preserved for exhibition at home by putting them in spirit in bottles well closed.

A last admonition told Don he could make nothing on the side and that 'everything collected by you during this voyage is exclusively the property of the Horticultural Society and you have neither power nor permission to give or send to any individual whatever article which shall be collected by you'.

His notes and journal too were the absolute property of the Horticultural Society, he was reminded. Coming full circle on the venture, Sabine requested Don to write to him from the first port of the British Isles he reached on his return. There was to be no time for a quick reunion with relatives and friends for the weary traveller, who was strictly commanded that he should remain with his collection until they were safely deposited on shore or transmitted by land to London. Then he himself 'as expeditiously as possible' had to get himself to headquarters 'to report the results of your voyage and to assist in the arrangements of the things you have brought home with you'.

This then was Don's bible, his manual of flower-hunting, a tall order enough in itself. He also found himself charged with a miscellaneous array of equipment supplied to him and debited to his account.

The inventory is an interesting one and contained Swartz's *Florae Indiae Occidentalis* in three volumes, Aublet's *Histoire de Plantes De La Guiane Françoise* in four volumes, Sweet's *Hortus Suburbanus Londinensis*, Persoon's *Synopsis Plantarum* in two volumes and Bullock on preserving birds and taxidermy; a box for stationery, four folio books for his journals, a box of wafers, a bottle of ink, pieces of indiarubber, two quires of foolscap paper, three reams of brown paper for the herbarium, four balls of string, a trunk for the herbarium, a dozen ink powders, two boxes of bottles, one and a half gallons of preserving spirit, eight pruning knives and a pocket compass.

Then Don had to kit out at a cost of £36 7s. 10d. His itemized bill to the Society shows a Mr Low paid £1 2s. 6d. for preparing boards and £4 5s. for two boxes. He paid 11s. 11d. for glass bottles, bladders and corks, £1 7s. for a trunk, £1 8s. 2d. for knives and scissors, £1 13s. 6d. for a magnifying-glass, 2s. 8d. for two large bungs, £2 16s. 10d. for camphor, etc., camphorated spirits of wine cost 17s. 4d., stationery £12 14s. 7d., canvas for making bags 9s. 9d., 7s. 1d. for cotton and wool, £5 for an insect box, a guinea for preserving powder and £2 10s. 6d. for books.

These then were the preliminaries of the tour, which actually started for Don on 13th November 1821, when he left London on the overnight coach to Portsmouth and spent next day, not kicking his heels and waiting to board, but 'visiting the smaller gardens about the town where the *Medicago arborea*, myrtus and laurustinus (viburnum) were here finer than I have ever seen before'.

This, of course, was the nineteenth century, but travel by ship was not one whit surer or speedier than Banks, Masson or Nelson had found many years before. It was the 17th of November when Don went aboard, but it was not until 4th January that *Iphigenia* could get away, and what a time the young gardener had had before they sailed the high seas!

By 22nd November they had only reached Weymouth, and already the Chelsea foreman gardener had found life at sea vastly different from his bothy and his garden, as he confided in his journal ('much exhausted by sea sickness'), so that he welcomed a trip ashore to Portland Rock with Captain Sabine on a minor plant hunt for *Euphorbia portlandica* without success, but did find *Iris foetidissima* in the hedges.

December 6th saw them off Torbay, which they reached on the 19th, and on most days until the 23rd Don explored the Devon countryside for plants, finding and recording *Cistus rubia* and *Cotyledon umbilicus* on the walls.

On Christmas Eve Don, on his way back to ship board, put off in a small boat but found the sea so rough 'we were nearly swamped in the attempt and we got to shore again with great difficulty'—his first baptism of the waves.

This was the start of a fantastic initiatory adventure for Don and the several officers and midshipmen ashore with him. The same rough seas that nearly swamped Don's boat were too rough for the *Iphigenia*, who had to cut her cable and run for the open sea. So on Christmas Day began a quite ridiculous and mortifying chase which swept all thought of Christmas dinner and festivities out of their thoughts.

The small party left Brixton by boat to try to catch up with their ship, which they learned was now anchored at Plymouth. They got as far as Dartmouth by two o'clock in the afternoon, hailed a pilot boat, hoisted their own small craft on board and put to sea. Next day, about four in the morning, Don wrote: 'We arrived off Plymouth and went on shore to have some breakfast.' An officer went to seek help from the admiral, who put Don and his unfortunate friends on board the schooner *Pygmy* to go in search of the *Iphigenia*, which they heard was now actually at Plymouth. When *Pygmy* anchored there on the 27th it was only to hear that their ship had returned to Torbay. Then the sea was too rough for *Pygmy* to venture out of harbour and by the 29th Don was desperate. This was a shocking start so, he wrote, 'I and one of the midshipmen made up our minds to walk to Torbay, a distance of about 32 miles. We left about 10 a.m. and proceeded on our journey. About 3 we arrived off Totnes, a distance of 24 miles from Plymouth, but the day being so wet we considered it most advisable to stay all night'.

The next day they hired a conveyance and, arriving in Torbay about 10 a.m., hired a boat and at last caught up with the *Iphigenia* on 30th December. The last day of 1821 they weighed and, picking up the officers who had come on later in *Pygmy*, they put out to sea. Bad luck was still with them, however, and unfavourable weather in Plymouth Sound kept them until 4th January of the New Year.

By 11th January of 1822 George Don had really started the job he was sent to do, and in subtropical Madeira for four days got his plant-hunting bearings by browsing about Funchal and one day climbing to the peak of Pico Ruivo, coming face to face with the climatic vagaries of foreign parts which all botanical travellers from England, unseasoned and completely untravelled as they were, found both strange and uncomfortable.

Climbing out of the heat of the seashore up the Pico Ruivo on horseback, he arrived at 4 a.m. as far up the route as the poor beast could stagger. On foot he set off to reach the topmost peak, but at 5,000 feet found his sunny island changed into an Arctic landscape as he plunged through one and a half feet of snow and a temperature so near freezing as makes no matter. He noted the plants on his way, recording them as nothing new or unusual. The journey down was 'most dangerous, among rocks, difficult places and dangerous precipices'. It was midnight next day before he reached safety.

By the 17th he was at Teneriffe, and on the shore there collected two or three species of centaurea and 'spent the day intensely botanizing in a temperature of 69 degrees', which contrasted uncomfortably with the 39 degrees he found on the peak of Madeira.

A signal gun from the ship sent him hurrying back so that the commodore could catch the wind, but it was an advantage of short duration, for *Iphigenia* was becalmed for several days until the 24th, when Don sighted the Cape Verde Islands away on the horizon. It was not until two days later that he landed at São Tiago, only to find the island was so 'completely parched up that there was hardly a green leaf to be seen'. He collected some seed, however, and next day, before breakfast, set off to climb the nearest mountain (George Don had a besetting passion for mountains; maybe due to his Scottish blood or just a hunch that any plants he found there would be hardier or more suited to the English climate than the tropical finds of the lower regions). He found nothing to remark and next day sailed for the west coast of Africa, which was sighted on the 31st off Cape Verde. They passed Goree Island on their way to the mouth of the Gambia and on 3rd February he got ashore for the first time on the African continent. He landed at Gambia, and the same night recorded having collected ipomoea, *Plumbago zeylanica* and *Capparis floribunda*. Early next day he spent 'laying in the specimens I had collected' before setting off to see a garden. 'On coming back I hired a canoe, but the river was too strong and the natives too weak; we were drifting fast down the river and I had to hail the ship for a boat which was sent and we got aboard.'

This was just a foretaste of the dangers of the profession he had chosen; already he was finding Africa, its climate, its black men, its flora and its tropical luxuriance a vastly different world from the mundane routine of the Chiswick garden. This was to be underlined even more markedly two days later when, having spent long, peaceful days on board arranging what specimens and seeds he had collected, the ship anchored off Roxa on the tip of Portuguese Guinea. The next morning he and some other members of the crew went off by boat to the shore. 'As soon as the crew landed', he wrote, 'they were overpowered by the natives armed with bows and arrows which obliged the boat crew to retreat.' It was a nasty experience for a gardener armed with a trowel who had never seen a bow and arrow mob of wildly shrieking natives black as the ace of spades and splashed with war paint and little else. However, this was a British ship and the natives were no lasting deterrent. Back they went to the shore 'to look for a [slave] vessel up the river', armed to the teeth this time.

No plant hunting here for Don, for *Iphigenia*'s captain weighed after satisfying himself that there was no slave vessel lurking upriver, but it was obvious now to Don why the natives had been so ferocious; it had been a case of mistaken identity. The natives, terrified of pirate slavers, were not to know that this was a ship covetous of nature not of man.

Hugging the coastline *Iphigenia* was now bound for Sierra Leone, not without a nasty incident, however. When off Cape Verga she grounded with a horrid shaking of the whole ship. Fortunately, after an agonizing wait for the non-sailor, the tide refloated them and they made Freetown on the 18th February.

Don got ashore the following day to look for lodgings, for Sierra Leone, according to his brief, was to be his principal happy hunting ground. The Governor, he found, was away and, trying for other lodgings, he found the rent so 'immodest' that he went to the ship and stayed with the gunners. Two days later, however, he heard that the Governor had made all arrangements for him to stay on his own farm about a mile from Freetown, so next day he brought ashore his plant boxes and equipment for a determined onslaught on the West African flora.

'The Governor lent me his mule to carry me to his farm,' he wrote, 'and on my way I saw pineapples in the hedges'—a rare sight for a man who had almost certainly spent many English winters keeping up the heat of bark stoves to make sure the few sickly pines in them would be preserved. At the farm he was delighted to see the glory of hibiscus and clerodendrons.

Here was floral fascination, here was a luxuriating wild garden beyond the rosiest dreams of the most skilled of hot-house gardeners. Compared with those poor sun-starved specimens under glass, here, against a backcloth of red ochre earth and dense greenery of mountain slopes, was a picture of floral colour and form so different, so unusual, as to seem incredible; the silken white tassels hanging from the rose apple tree, the clerodendron blooms like branching red coral, the brilliant purple blossoms of pineapples like miniature hyacinth blooms peeping from each diamond segment of the fruit. Large yellow cactus flowers filled the hedges, while the brilliantly hued cannas at their feet shouted their sanguinary message. The sensitive plant, with delicate pink blossom and shrinking foliage, stood on a carpet of what looked like earth-bound dog roses. In the forest around the whole scene was one of incredible floral and natural confusion as the clinging climbers of startlingly blue flowers mixed with wild vines and a host of other parasitic creepers criss-crossed and crossed again to bind the trees together in wreaths of liana and blossom. There were scarlet capsicums, the scarlet and orange faces of poincianas (the flower fence), and the great white and scarlet streaked trumpets of amaryllis all combining in a display which, to a gardener from northern climes, was a floral paradise.

His first night ashore amidst the rolling, luxuriant tropical forest which climbed the

Sierra Leone mountains and formed a strange background to his temporary home was not too comfortable. 'I was kept awake by the howling of wild animals,' he wrote, 'and with mosquitoes.' There were leopards and wild boar in the woods around so that trips farther inland meant hiring native guides who could follow spoor and warn a poor unsuspecting gardener in time that hungry and angry wild beasts were around.

So it was that the next day, with two Kroo men to carry all he should find, Don tried to push his way through virgin country to the coast, but found that nature was not so accommodating, for 'the woods were so thick and tangled with pineapple undergrowth, the spines of which could gash a man cruelly', that he had to confess himself beaten.

On the 25th the tropical humidity, which was far, far worse than the atmosphere of his hottest stove house at home, began to tell on Don so that the climb up the hill to the Governor's farm from the coast found him 'strangely fatigued'; but this was only the beginning of a day in which he set about felling trees for the epidendrums in their frondy tops. As the sun got higher so Don became weaker and found the going hard and painful. This was in a valley to the south-west of Freetown where, despite the punishment he was taking, he 'found many curious plants by the side of a rivulet'. There were other hazards to plague him, for 'this place was so invested with snakes which make it dangerous to walk in the long grass. Two of the snakes I saw were very large, the colour of one was yellow, that of the other was green'.

Despite this he collected seeds and bulbs and managed to reach the farm before dark, all in. This was no white man's country in 1822, as George Don found next morning when he woke with a fever. He fought against it to get up and go to Freetown where a ship was in harbour for England, so he had heard, and here was 'an opportunity' he had been so strictly instructed not to lose.

He arranged matters to his satisfaction, went back to the farm and spent the next two days packing, wrapping and sorting to get off to the Society his first collection boxes packed with assorted plants, with epidendrums, and *Elaeis guineensis* (one of the many palm trees) seed sown in the layer of mould covering the bottom of the boxes. In another two boxes he had packed seeds and herbarium species.

Another opportunity arose on 19th March to off-load his green treasure, when he sent more boxes. In No. 1 box 'was a strange sort of pepper growing in the loftiest trees, a curious fern growing upon the largest trees, a narrow-leafed coffee; osbeckia, a beautiful plant with a large blue flower, growing in low parts near Freetown (it would be a great acquisition to nurserymen as it is a tub perennial which would likely keep dry all winter), a very curious orchidaceous plant (a parasite here), there is no doubt but you will be able to grow it in a flower pot, heliconia, with a yellow flower, costus, clerodendron (red and white), ipomea and pothos'. Fruit and seeds in bottles were packed in other boxes.

Back in the forests on 20th March Don cut down more trees to get at the orchids seeking air and sunlight in their tops, walking eight miles to do it and finding on his way 'a beautiful shrub having exactly the appearance of a persian lilac and also having the same scent'. Magnificent and gaudy specimens of ipomoea he found too, before returning in the evening 'famished with hunger and rather feverish with great difficulty in breathing'.

After resting he was off again on a twelve-mile trek and came back well loaded, so much so that he had to spend a day in Freetown ordering new boxes; his harvest was outstripping his packaging capacity. On his way home the tropical climate showed its fangs, with a threatened tornado which made Don run for the shelter of the farm.

Now that it was nearly the end of March he decided to make a complete list of the fruits he had both seen and collected, with a full description of their nuts, seeds and pods.

On one day, setting off before dawn, he did not reach the safety of the farm again until well after 1 a.m. The jungle of thick, clustering trees and undergrowth played havoc with his sense of direction and for hours he was lost, try what rough-hewn path he would for, as he told his diary, 'there were many paths and only one leading out'.

On the last day of March he experienced a tornado, when at about two in the morning he was awakened with a crash of thunder and the most vivid lightning without interruption for the course of an hour.

The first day of April found Don climbing the Sugar Loaf mountains after an early start at 6 a.m., when he recorded finding those gloriously coloured hothouse subjects ixias and caladiums, as well as salvias.

A longer trip next day took him thirty miles from Freetown to York for a few days' stay. By the seashore there in the swamp forest and among the creeks he walked twenty-four miles in the day to collect two hundred bulbs of *Haemanthus multiflorus*. Coming to a deep river it appeared his plant hunting had come to an end, but natives directed them 'to the shallowest part'. Don's party were told they would have to strip and did so, carefully putting the piles of clothing on their heads, and what good fortune they did, for the 'shallowest part' came up to his neck as with trepidation he waded and pushed his way through the swirling waters to continue his work on the other side.

Another day he spent wandering about the savannah type bush, where the grace of oil palms and other trees of the same family spreading over the brightly coloured, lush, tropical vegetation made every inch of the way a joy to behold, although all manner of black and red ants, giant cockroaches as well as the veil of mosquitoes caused him much distress. The last day here he paddled down the river in a dugout canoe, to pick up a curious species of caladium and a beautiful race of exotically coloured foliage plants he had seen in his wanderings. He managed to dig up one or two plants and, having set off downriver about 5 a.m., arrived back at his base 'craving for breakfast at about 1 p.m.'.

The following day, 6th April, he rode back to Freetown to make a start of packing up his opulent finds. He managed to fill five boxes, one with living plants, one with specimens, one with seeds, one with bulbs and the last with insects. He needed yet another box for seven or eight types of passifloras. Among the living plants so carefully packed in wooden pots at the bottom of his plant cabins he listed 'osbeckia, bletia, limodorum, smilax sp., begonia sp., dracaena (a beautiful species this last, he recorded), acrostichum, stemodia, chlorophytum and 20 different species of epidendrum, all of which are strangers, and bulbs, arums, gladiolus and haemanthus'.

April 10th was a day 'of great flurry, the ship was going. I got a man to carry down boxes from the farm to Freetown and on April 11 went on board the *Pheasant*'. Later John Lindley was to mention plants brought home alive by the *Pheasant*.

In the meantime our plant hunter spent a day 'arranging things in my cabin'. It must have been a weird sight, with books, boxes, drying papers, dried plants, bulbs, bottles and Don! After two months' stay in Sierra Leone *Iphigenia* was moving on for the next stop, Cape Coast on the Gold Coast. But for ten welcome days there was a respite as the ship tacked down the Ivory Coast, still a place of slaves, pirates and bloodshed. This gave him time to write up his diaries and journals, to dry out his herbarium specimens, see his seed kept free from mildew and tend his boxes of living plants on the poop deck.

They dropped anchor on 21st April at Cape Coast under a frightening sun, anything up to ninety in the shade and madness to walk unprotected in the open.

Despite his warning bouts of fever previously the climate could not deter Don from getting ashore to hunt on the lagoon-covered shoreline fringed by a hot, damp jungle of palms, tropical undergrowth and a wealth of equatorial flora which he rejoiced in. 'Went out to the bush', he wrote, 'where there is plenty of *Vinca rosea, Stachytarpeta jamaicensis*, various sida [*abutilon*], *jacca* [breadfruit], amaryllis and *Brassia coccinea*.' Too numerous were the prizes here to collect in one day of plant hunting, so another day was spent collecting the seeds of a 'curious palm tree, a species of elaeis, bulbs of amaryllis and roots of jacca'. The tropic sun, combined with the enervating humidity of this white man's grave, was too much for Don, who complained of 'too much heat' and a 'severe headache' which sent him back to the ship.

Next day he kept away from the unmerciful sun-beaten shore, spending the daylight hours in his cabin packing up a box of centaurea and amaryllis.

Towards the end of the month, on 27th April to be precise, Don sailed for Accra and 'had to land in flat-bottomed canoes because the ship's boat could not take the surf'. He was hurled through the crashing waves by sure and strong-armed native oarsmen at 5 a.m. to take up his lodgings in Accra fort, and had to run this hair-raising gauntlet every time he wished to visit the ship. Here were many 'strange and curious plants', he noted, and added: 'The country here is beautiful, the trees and shrubs are so regularly dispersed that one would from appearance think they had been planted.'

'This morning [the 29th] I opened the boxes which I had packed at Cape Coast and put in the tuberous and bulbous roots I had collected the day before and in the afternoon went out a different way and came across *Gloriosa superba*; the species which I collected is probably different from that of New Holland.'

He was fortunate again here with his newly won natural wealth for he heard of a schooner which was sailing for England in a day or two and managed to get his precious box on board for Mr Sabine.

On the last day of April his botanizing was varied with bird shooting so that he could add to his natural history collection, but he also managed to collect seed 'of a curious tree with pinnate leaves, fruit in a cluster, small and coloured red'. He spent the evening on board arranging the seed and specimens he had collected and marked the start of May by going inland to Little Popo in Togoland, a small village luxuriantly hemmed in by a beautiful stand of *Elaeis guineensis*.

Still another port of call for this indefatigable plant hunter, this time Widah in Dahomey, with two unusual incidents to mark the days, one, which must have been a salutary shock to him, when one of the marines who had been ashore with him in Sierra Leone died of the fever he himself felt in his bones. The other incident meant fresh meat for all as the crew caught a shark, with the subsequent rich red steaks on the gunners' mess bill of fare.

Now *Iphigenia* turned from the west coast, cutting a diagonal course across the Gulf of Guinea to make for St Thomas Island (São Thomé, one of 'the pearls of the ocean' as the Portuguese named it). Here the ship anchored off St Ana de Chaves. Ashore Don found himself in a natural tropical hothouse. The climate was equatorial, with a heat and a hot damp air unhealthy to man, but to nature an unexcelled promoter of the most unusual luxuriance of vegetation. Here was an island of great scenic beauty, of virgin tropical forests, an exciting admixture of arboreal and floral magnificence, an island of great trees, of palms, of tree ferns, blossoming shrubs and climbing plants all interwoven to form a picture of vivid, colourful enchantment.

There was trouble at first for Don in getting permission from the Portuguese Governor to land, and another member of the crew, the master, died and was buried at sea. For the first two days they could go only as far as the town, where Don saw and described the teeming native market full of gaily dressed natives whose baskets were piled high with soursops, bananas, limes, guavas, papaw, coconuts and pines. The same evening *Iphigenia* was hit by a tornado in harbour; the ship's cable had to be cut and she ran for open sea to weather it safely; but next day the air was still as they beat their way back to the coast to land at Man of War Bay, where Don 'saw a house that he had been told was uninhabited but on going there found it full of soldiers sent there by the Governor' to stop Don or anyone else 'using instruments for observation'.

Despite the antagonism of the authorities he tried again the following day, 20th May, and got some four miles inland, 'but dry grass, seven or eight foot high, and no path rendered it very difficult to travel here. I was very disappointed when I arrived back on board', he wrote, 'as the appearance of the Island promised something more interesting.'

But Don would not have been the tough Scot and determined plant hunter his masters knew him to be if he had not tried again, and next day he walked three miles and 'in a moist thicket by the side of a rivulet, found a pancratium, a new species I hope, but not in flower, and a species of mirabilis and a curious species of dioscorea with lobed leaves'.

While another day Captain Sabine skulked in a house taking observations, Don, almost as a cover, went off in a southerly direction into the luxuriant forest where 'on my way I met with a beautiful tree about 100 feet high bearing a fruit about twice the

Portions of a letter sent from Bengal to the sixth Duke of Devonshire at Chatsworth House, Derbyshire, by John Gibson, Joseph Paxton's young plant hunter.

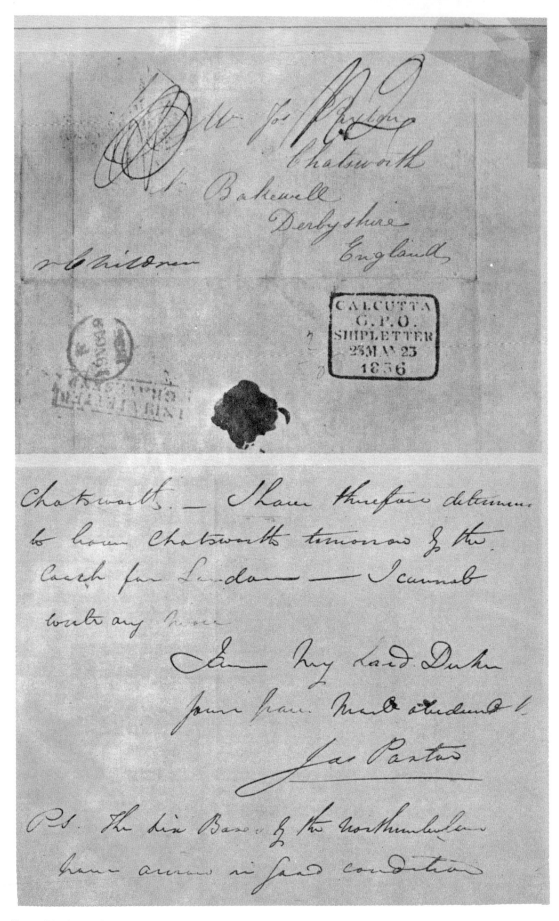

Above: Ship's mailing system as used from Calcutta in the days of the East India Company is shown by this cover of a letter from Gibson to Paxton. *Below:* Paxton's impatience to see Gibson's plants which had just arrived at London docks can be seen by the closing lines of his letter to the Duke of Devonshire.

size of a man's head, the seeds of which the natives boil and eat, also a beautiful her-nandia. I saw several trees 120 feet high, pandanus [screw pine], and the pancratium I had found the day before I saw in flower and proved to be a white crinum. I had great difficulty in getting back as there was no path. Returned on board about seven but not without my seeds, specimens, papers and myself properly wet through owing to the great surf on entering the boat'.

A ten-mile trip, still in a southerly direction, took him into thick rain forest next day. 'The country here is quite covered with tree,' he recorded. 'I have been quite in a thicket all this day where I saw many trees of *Pandanus candelabrum* and plenty of the fruit I mentioned the day before called "jakansie" [one of the breadfruit family?] by the negroes. Here I saw great herds of monkeys.'

Another day he pushed his way through the steaming heat and forest to be rewarded by a sight of several new arum lilies, and, with a Negro and two marines for company, he struck out south-west and 'travelled about three miles among long grass which was very fatiguing but met with nothing particular except a trailing species of cleome. After we had passed through the grass we entered a thicket and travelled until we were quite fatigued, particularly by thirst so that we were obliged to chew the leaves of a species of adiantum which grows plentifully here. On our return, just as we got out of the forest, we came across a beautiful shrub covered in white flowers and got some coconuts and quenched our thirst, returning home in the evening very much fatigued'.

A further day he spent locating and digging up the roots of the crinums he had seen previously and managed to bag about a dozen. Coming back from this trip he walked along the beach to St Ana, a distance of about ten miles, noting that some parts of it were 'covered with a beautiful species of ipomoea and a dolichos, which were common', he said, 'to the sea beach throughout all parts of tropical Africa so far as I have seen'.

A busy day on the 30th saw Don pushing and hacking his way by the luxuriously overgrown side of a rivulet through palms and jakansie trees with monkeys screeching and flying in the tree tops before him with a deafening clatter. Here he 'saw many strange ferns, peperomia, an acanthacious plant, hemionitis, and "safu" trees'. The country was low and moist. The last day of May he spent trying to cut down some of the stately corypha palms both for seed and to see if any parasitic orchids were hiding up in the great crowns seeking the sunshine, but found the wood so hard his hatchet would not pierce even an inch into the trunk.

With the onset of June it was back to his old love as Don set out from the lowland and swamp to clamber some eight miles to the top of the Pic (7,000 feet), being re-warded for his pains with 'a fine species of laurus resembling a cinnamon'. Great herds of monkeys and paroquets made the tree tops alive with the clamour and flashing colours, while below in the half-forest gloom Don noted two curious species of convolvulus and 'two species of japicera'.

A severe pain in the chest confined Don to his bunk in the plantation house he had made his temporary plant-preparing store—but only for a day, for with two marines next day he set off in an easterly direction, and 'after we had travelled several miles in the natural forest, and after crossing the first range of mountains, we arrived at some beautiful plantations which are composed of the following: bananas, plantains, a great quantity of cassava (manihot), several trees of safu and jakansie, with two or three immense trees of bombax, as well as guavas, limes and oranges, and a few trees of mangoes. I also saw here one bush of pine, but it was very slender, which I suppose is owing to the heat. On my return I saw a strange species of costus about 12 foot high with scarlet flowers and a very curious bulbous plant with round plicated leaves but it was not in flower'. Two further days he spent collecting seeds of many of the plants he had seen, and traded with the natives for others, as well as for some young plants of *Pandanus candelabrum*.

On the 6th he went in search, with a guide, of the 'Cinnamon of the country'. They set off early in the morning, did sixteen miles in four hours, passed 'over several ranges of mountains' and collected a few plants of cinnamon. On the way back he met with 'a very curious species of banisteria and likewise the Christmas bush of Sierra Leone'.

After still another day in the wood, as he chose to call these tropical jungles, Don, with 'a marine and three blacks, set out for the peak of St Thomas. We did not get many miles before the blacks left us, and I and the marine proceeded on our journey. Breakfasted at the Villa de Gualaloupe, a small village composed of 20 houses, after which we proceeded again. About 3 we were not able to proceed any further on account of the forest becoming so thick we were obliged to give up the idea of even being able to reach it from this quarter. I met with a beautiful specimen of celosia. The monkeys are numerous', was his written verdict of the day's outing.

For two days he sorted seeds and specimens for packing and planted two boxes of live plants. Another box was full of seeds and specimens and another of bulbs, with some of the fruit of *Pandanus candelabrum*. In one matted parcel was rolled up carefully one branch of the pandanus and in another two bundles of fruits of the corypha palm.

Among his live plants were orchidaceous ones as well as moraea, laurus, *Pandanus candelabrum*, pothos, costus, 'jakansie' and ipomoeas.

On the 11th he set out, with help, to carry the boxes and matted bundles to St Ana by boat, some nine miles. He delivered them to the acting consul and directed that they be sent home on board the British ship *Eclipse*, after which he returned to base, got the rest of his kit together and boarded *Iphigenia*.

Three days later at sea, the debilitating conditions of the Slave Coast and St Thomas Isle took their toll. He was seized with a violent fever which, by the time the ship reached Ascension Island on 25th June, had carried off the marines who had been on shore with him and left Don a weak, poorly man. It was 6th July before he was to comment: 'Able to walk a little these four days past and I am getting stronger every day.'

A chance offer of a mule on that day saw his indomitable spirit rising to the challenge. He tackled the peak of Green Mountain, the huge elliptical crater some 2,817 feet high which dominates this lava-covered island, for it was not in the steep ravines, lined with masses of barren lava, that there was life; it was on this green peak that any hope of plant-hunting lay. He wrote: 'I left the ship about 9.30 and started for the mountain about ten. The distance is about seven or eight miles, the road is good and level for the first four miles, but the last three or four miles is almost perpendicular. On my way for the first four miles saw nothing but *Portulaca oleracea* and a species of euphorbia.'

As he clambered higher so the flora differed and became more varied, and he listed polycarpia, physalis, *Asclepias curassavica*, hibiscus, ipomoea, oxalis, lycopodium and asplenium.

On 8th July his fever returned as severe as ever, and on the 9th *Iphigenia* sailed for South America, the voyage and rest restoring Don's health, so that when they anchored at Bahia in Brazil by the 29th he was able to go ashore immediately, and in 'pleasure grounds on the outskirts' saw for the first time the true breadfruit tree *Artocarpus incisa* and *Magnifera indica* (the mango tree) as well as *Eugenia jambos*.

Here was new and exciting territory indeed. From what few botanical skirmishes had previously been made the plant hunter knew this was terrain with a most flamboyant and unique flora. It was a country famed for the rarest of orchids and the most colourful and unusual specimens of plant life, although they were hidden away in dense jungles or in the fastnesses of huge river valleys or defying the hunter on soaring mountain peaks.

Don, of course, with the time at his disposal, was essentially and primarily a coastal plant hunter, in the deltas and luxurious woodiness of the river mouths and the mountain foothills which ran down to the Atlantic coast. He was to hunt under damp tropical climate conditions again where the fever of the natives, now better known as malaria, lurked in every pool of stagnant water. In fact it was only the second day of his stay in Bahia that fever struck Don down again and worried him. 'These attacks after a little fatigue call for caution in venturing on shore,' he warned himself.

Two days he spent in making sure the British Consul knew what he was up to and that his safe conduct on plant-hunting expeditions was arranged with the authorities. It was from the Consul's, where he stayed after the preliminaries had been gone through, that he ventured some three miles out of the town, where he saw orchidaceous and ageratum species. But an even more beautiful sight was in store, when he came to 'moist meadows covered with iris in flower, and a species of *hypoxis*, both with yellow flowers'. Several days of rain stopped a full measure of plant discoveries for Don, but he managed, between the heavy downpours, to collect seeds of melastoma and to dig up roots of adiantum and a large species of begonia.

With a slackening off of rain on 5th August he walked three miles from town to meet 'with a beautiful malvaceous plant'. 'A little further on, in a grove in a moist place, I found a curious sort of orchid with yellow flowers and also many curious ferns. On my return collected specimens of a beautiful clematis with flowers white and fragrant and another plant about six inches high profusely covered with red flowers.'

On the 7th *Iphigenia* weighed anchor and was off again, 400 miles up the Brazilian coastline, for the next port of plant-hunting call, Pernambuco near the equator. It was to be a short stay at the 'Venice of Brazil', but Don went on shore immediately and travelled over the bridges linking the three towns into the country where he noted 'sensitive mimosa, pontederia, also a copper coloured flowered *Exacum guineensis*, and a species of calceolaria, one of which has a beautiful dark blue flower. This country', he added, 'is very low and marshy'. It was a short stay, however, and that night they weighed anchor and sailed up coast again for Maranhao, making this island port on 20th August. Here there was to be more opportunity for Don to botanize on shore, so that his first job was to attempt to find lodgings, but he had to settle for accommodation at an inn.

Next day, the 23rd, he set out early: '. . . I and a man I had hired to carry my specimens on board. I saw many species of palms, many of them very fine, two species of cocus trees and met with many other curious and beautiful shrubs which are not yet in English gardens. In a thicket of low growing trees I found two species of amaryllis but not in flower, which I collected several bulbs of each sort.'

A marsh about six miles from Maranhao was the object of a daybreak start to find many different species of melastoma and other marsh plants.

By canoe upriver with a 6 a.m. start was another excursion to search for trees of 'Castanea de Para [chestnut] and *Bertholetia excelsis* [Brazil nut]'. He wanted to see the last in flower, 'a very desirable thing', he added, 'as it is not known', but found only one tree of 20 foot in height without flowers or fruit. He saw nothing else particularly so shot some birds to add to his collection of fauna.

Returning with the stream he had time to notice the huge groves of mangroves which clustered and bent low their cathedral-like pillars wherever the banks were low and swampy; but when the banks stood high above him they were crowded with stately and fanciful palms among which he recorded two or three species of eugenia, several of banisteria with beautiful yellow flowers and, growing under their protective shade, two or three different kinds of begonia with red flowers. In a different direction next day he roamed the forest again, seeing for the first time the enchanting *Taligalia campestris* and, turning and twisting their evergreen way through the jungle trees, the immense waxy golden yellow trumpets of *Allamanda cathartica*. The rain from the mountains came to spoil the day in the afternoon and footsteps were retraced, but to what a depressing homecoming. 'The windows of my room had been left open and the room was full of water. My specimens and seed perfectly wet which caused a great deal of trouble and rendered many of them useless.'

Despite the setback, or because of it, next day Don set off well before daybreak intent on penetrating as deep as he could into the hinterland before dark. He pushed through the forest, through the jungle-clad hillsides, some fourteen miles, much of the way by the side of a rivulet, on his way discovering a very large scitamineas plant with a flower stem about 20 feet high, the leaves larger than that of a plantain resembling *Urania speciosa* (Syn. *Phenakospermum madagascariensis*) and on the paths many examples of exacum and plenty of *Taligalia campestris*. A tiring day, he recorded, so the next day was a little easier for him with a programme of seed and specimen sorting in the forenoon and a stroll by the sea in the afternoon among hundreds of carolinea in flower. The day after, too, he set off along the seashore before striking inland for five or

Penstemon ovatus (*left*) and *Oenothera lindleyii*
(*below*) are two of the hundreds of hardy plants
David Douglas introduced from the Columbia
River district of the Pacific Coast of America.

six miles, collecting both seed and specimens of many rich and exotic flowering plants, he saw, among which were 'byronimas several species, allamanda, carolineas, turnera, a beautiful species of hibiscus and a trailing plant with large yellow flowers'.

A long forage next day, with a guide and a man named Smith, saw Don toiling twelve miles upriver, pushing their canoe through mangrove swamps so that dark had almost fallen when they reached base in a luxuriantly tropical jungle scene with a strange medley of sound as a background: howling monkeys, croaking frogs, an insect chorus and the eerie jungle sounds of falling vegetation. Next day in a difficult assault course over marshy ground, but a botanical treasure house where nature lavishly displayed her teeming vegetation, he squelched around among magnificent stands of melastoma. Growing profusely on little elevations from the festering fungoid-covered marshland were all manner of palm trees from which he collected seeds and specimens.

It was now 2nd September as Don collected together and packed his treasures of yesterday and sent them to town by canoe with their guide, whom they were glad to get rid of on account of his condition: 'He had not been sober for an hour since he left town.'

As the two men remaining pushed their way through the walls of lianas and of grotesque, twining climbing plants on the hardly discernible path, which needed matcheting at times to clear the barricading over- and undergrowth, in dark mossy earth he found several species of violas. He found also, to his delight, the pathways clothed all the way with various species of banisteria decorated with glorious clusters of long, scarlet, trumpet-like blossoms of the bignonias, with *Hosta coccinea* and several species of eugenia, those relatives of the clove family whose evergreen flowering trees and bushes show all manner of colours and shades in their blossoms. Some were in flower, observed Don, 'which had a noble effect'. It was breakfast time next day when they reached base.

Another day was spent turning specimens and seeds on the drying papers, packing some in bottles and papers, and digging from their native earth some young palm trees a mile or two away from his camp. He was not able to find enough palms of the right kind, of the right height and age to fill one of his boxes, but he knew they must be filled if they were to have a chance of surviving the long voyage before them, so another morning he pushed some miles into the jungle to get some more, which he was able to plant up in his box that afternoon. Another box he planted with some 'of the finest shrubs I had seen here'. Next day he felt feverish and weak and, on 6th September, he sailed, confiding to his diary that he was still 'weak and feverish'. The mosquitoes and his own conscientious hard work and long day in the jungle had been too much for him. Once more it was to be the rest and a fortnight or so of sea air that brought recovery, for *Iphigenia* was now sailing for Trinidad.

They were becalmed on the 17th within sight of the island, and next day they were driven back by the current in a vivid thunderstorm, so that it was not until the 19th that they anchored off Port of Spain. Don went ashore with an introduction to David Lockhart, an ex-Kew gardener and superintendent of the Botanical Gardens behind the

Governor's residence, some few miles out of the town. Seeing he was going to stay here some days, Don sent the boat back to the ship for his gear, but it returned without it, so he put up at an inn for the night. Although he was down at the wharf before daylight next day, it was seven o'clock before the ship's boat hove to and it was eleven before he could get off to meet Lockhart fully equipped for his botanical gold-mining in Trinidad, where the gardens had already showed him a paradise of tropical colour and form in the blood-red shock of *Amherstia nobilis*, in *Tecoma spectabilis* with its huge bouquet of golden yellow flowers, the graceful date palms and many more luxuriant and unusual forms of the family.

The following day Lockhart and he climbed to the top of a range of hills 'about six miles distant', and Don wrote excitedly of the hedges round the plantations which were all *Haematoxylon campechianum*, the log wood tree. In the beautifully verdant woods clothing the hillsides overlooking the gardens and the whole of the beautiful Gulf of Paria were the tall red and orange coloured banana-like leaves of *Heliconia bihai*. He saw many new ferns to delight his collector's eye and also noted *Cerbera thevetia* (*Thevetia nereifolia*) with saffron yellow flowers and shining leaves, and the stinging *Illairia crepitans*. These were busy days as with Lockhart he climbed up the Maraval valley by roads shaded with many different varieties of palms, among which were *Cocos fusiformis* (the coconut palm) and *Elaeis occidentalis*. On the lower parts of the hillsides were growing *Areca catechu* (the betel nut tree), *Bactris minor*, a prickly palm, *Ludovia funifera* (*Carludovia funifera*) many species of melastoma and the noted flesh-coloured flowers of *Blakea quinquenervia*, hundreds of curious ferns and the slender climber with its yellowish white flower heads, *Mikania scandens*.

All this wealth needed a day at base to arrange and collate, and while many seeds he had taken were drying, he took the opportunity to put in spirits many of the unusual fruits he had found.

This was only a day's respite, however, for on the 25th he and Lockhart were out again to the south of the town searching in another valley where 'I met several curious plants, particularly a very fine fothergilla. On the top of the mountain at the termination of the valley I got several epidendri but here it began to rain which made us retreat to the rest house, but before we could reach shelter we were completely wet through'.

One day he hired a boat for Chaguanas, some twelve miles west of Port of Spain. It was mid afternoon before he landed; it had rained hard all the way and it was still raining, so he stayed the night with the local commandant. Next morning early he went to the woods near to a place which had been cleared by the cutting down of the forest, and what a floral sight met his eyes! 'These trees were covered with parasitical plants; many very curious epidendri I collected here.' The country here was low and wet and the glorious erythrinas shaded the plantation, he said, but not enough to protect him from the torrential thunder rain, which drenched him to the skin before he retraced his steps.

As a change and a rest from footslogging he took canoe upriver; he might just as well have walked, for the tide was too low even for the canoe to float, 'and we were obliged to push the canoe for two miles in the mud'. It was late afternoon when he got back, but not too late to stop this untiring man after a bite to eat setting to and carefully packing a box of epidendrums.

Fortunately too next day he was able to get his boxes down to the wharf and on board a ship which sailed for England that day. In the plant cabins were 'helicona, *Maranta capitata*, scitamineae, another three different sorts of maranta, *Ludovia scandens*, pothos (a very curious plant), *Ruellia tuberosa* (with large blue flowers), *Millettia speciosa*, apios or arachacia with about seven, all different, species of epidendri, each species tied up separately'. It was a full day following during which he and Lockhart on mules travelled to the valley of the Maracas where they arrived at the plantation house just after midnight.

On the first day of October the two of them set out for Las Guevas, a distance of twelve miles, to see a plantation manager, 'and here we had to pass over a large mountain range seeing many strange plants, particularly ferns, some of the most delicate film ferns'. Above them on the well-clothed valley sides, beautiful blossoms of the bignonia and mucunas twined their bizarre colours like low fireworks among the ferns and mosses, while ardisia and aphelandra dotted the landscape with blossoms. When they were about to descend from the high ground above the sea coast it began to rain and thunder. 'We were four or five hours in the rain before we could reach our destination,' he wrote, 'where we had to borrow clothes.' Here they were told it would be impossible to reach the top of the highest mountains above Las Guevas, and to climb to the top of all mountains near by seemed a necessity in all Don's itineraries.

The rain this season, they were told, was almost perpetual on the summit, so a very disappointed Don had to content himself with the lower hunting ground, of which he said: 'The country here is very beautiful. The mountains are high and covered with wood the summits of which are almost always hidden in the cloud, and in the valleys are most extensive cocoa plantations.'

Walking to the beach on another day in this area he was rewarded by finding 'a curious pancratium', and, wanting to see more of this scenic and floral beauty, he hired a boat to take him to Little Maracas; but it rained all the way, forcing them to land and make for Port of Spain. They found they had to climb two steep mountains to get there so that it was well after dark when they arrived, leaving their hunters' traps before walking on to St Anns, which they reached about 2 a.m.

On the 3rd he spent the day arranging his seed haul; and next day, instead of robbing Trinidad of her natural wealth, took a step to add to it by going on board his ship, and from his store bringing back for Lockhart to plant in his garden two or three plants of *Pandanus candelabrum*, one of jakansie and one plant of *Heritiera heterophylla*.

On another day with Lockhart to a valley about eight miles north-east of Port of Spain they saw 'a beautiful blakea'. It was an early start the day following, for the two to scale a mountain to the east of the port on the right of the valley of Maraval, when Don got a salutary taste of the startling weather changes that can occur in the tropics within an hour or two, as he wrote: 'We had just reached the top when it began to rain very severely which obliged us to return. The valley on our way here proved dry but on our return it was inundated in some places a foot deep.' This was a miserably squelchy journey, but after a rest he was off again in the evening light three miles up the valley 'to see the vegetable butterfly in flower. [Most probably the strange orchid *Oncidium papilio*.] It was beautiful,' he enthused, 'and is the colour of *Herreria tigrida*, the leaves of which are light coloured with dark spots'.

By next day, the 8th, Don's ship was ready to sail, but heavy threshing rain kept them at anchor for that day and the one after. In a last desperate bid to beg, borrow or filch a plant of the vegetable butterfly Don spent another day ashore, but had to come back empty-handed.

From the 10th to the 17th, when they anchored at Port Royal, Jamaica, Don had his sea rest disturbed by plant cabins, drying seeds, plant specimens hung from his bunk space and a garden on the poop deck to watch and tend daily.

The day after *Iphigenia* dropped anchor he was ashore in one of the wherries for Kingston, about seven miles from the ship, seeking out two people who could help him and to whom he had letters of introduction. Unfortunately they were not there, and in a miserable rainstorm he hired a canoe to be paddled back to the ship.

Now it was rain, rain, rain for two whole days. Don could do nothing but spend the time on board, attending to his live plants and keeping the damp out of his drying seeds and specimens. Whether George Don knew or not he had hit the rainy season for Jamaica, but rainy season or no rainy season two days were more than enough for anyone like Don to kick his heels in new territory, and on the third day, taking the rain in his stride, he went ashore and hired a mule to ride six miles beyond Kingston. On his way he saw hedges of bromelia species and noted particularly a cereus with twelve angles as well as the grace and grotesqueness of such trees growing most luxuriantly as tamarindus, the bottle-shaped bombax, trees of the laurus family, 'Pasco' (Pascuita), papaya (*Carica papaya*) and, with delight, hedges covered with a flower which at a little distance looked like fields of ranunculus or buttercups in flower. It was, he found, *Tribulus maximus*.

One day he spent moving lodgings from Kingston to Port Royal, as the former had proved too dear for his pocket. The first day at Port Royal he stayed indoors as the humid heat had brought on a slight fever. Next day, probably thinking that the sea air would do him good, he hired a boat for Port Henderson in Green Bay, noting that the banks of the roads were covered with curious species of cacti, some grotesquely large, others small and beautifully contrived, many in gaudy, garish bloom, two species of cereus with ten or twelve angles as well as various 'opunti, *Guaicum officinale* [*Lignum vitae*], cistus, acidoton and zygophyllum'. Beyond the road to Port Henderson on the way to Spanish Town the valleys were covered with *Mimosa desmanthus* and cacti in plenty, along with many other succulent plants. 'Among all plants here there is none equal in beauty to *Tribulus maximus* which clothes the edges of roads and also low sandy places with a complete sheet of yellow.'

Botanizing between Port Henderson and Spanish Town occupied his attention for the next four days, when he noted a magnificent species of bauhinia, of the showy, colourful Ebony family, and collected seeds and specimens of bauhinia and cacti.

This job done to his satisfaction, he spent a day preparing to climb 'to the highest point of Port Royal mountain', and to do so left early next morning about six, landed at Kingston and started his mountaineering to pitch his camp about a hundred feet up the mountainside before dark.

Next day, 1st November, he noted the thermometer stood at 45 degrees and 'found it exceedingly cold' as he set out, which made him all the more active as he climbed with a will to reach the peak at 8 a.m., a height of some 4,600 feet. 'Here I gathered many curious epidendri which I think would stand the greenhouse (in contrast to the stove) as the thermometer must sometime be as low as 40 degrees.' Another peak in his bag, Don went forward to meet a Dr Gordon at Coldspring where 'tree ferns and magnolias' were a delight to the eye in their green and coloured lushness on the six to eight miles to the doctor's house. Next day he visited 'old Mr Wiles, the former superintendent of the Jamaica Botanic Garden. The same person', Don noted, 'that went to Captain Bligh for the bread fruit'.

The following day he visited the Botanic Gardens and, on coming down the hillside on his return, 'the road being very bad, the horse stumbled down which pitched me a considerable distance down the hill which bruised my right hand very much and threw one of my fingers out of joint'.

'November 4, my hand much swelled,' he wrote, 'and so painful I could not venture to herbalise, so I returned to Kingston, hired a boat and went on board.'

During all next day, despite his injured hand, he turned his specimens on their drying papers and tried out a new way of packing up epidendri, 'in such a way', he said, 'as I think they will carry home safely'.

On 6th November the ship and Don sailed for Grand Cayman, which they reached by the 11th, and dropped anchor off Georgetown. Going ashore he found nothing particular, but the country was so infested with mosquitoes that 'it was scarcely possible for a person to stop even for a few minutes to gather anything'. This for a man with a fever just under his skin waiting for a mosquito to puncture was not a happy prospect, but a risk and probably a waste of valuable time, so *Iphigenia* took Don's advice and sailed for Cuba, anchoring off Havana on 21st November.

As soon as possible Don was ashore, hiring a coach to take him to see Antonio de la Osa, at the Botanic Gardens, who showed him round, 'although he could neither write nor speak English, but I had permission to select seeds and specimens'. Another day he spent on the outskirts of the town, from where it is highly probable he filched a much guarded specimen of the true tobacco plant (*Nicotiana repanda*).

This was a quick survey indeed, for on the 27th they were bound for New York. He was fortunate once more in his dispatch arrangements, for when he learned that the *Vittoria*, in convoy with them, was bound for England on the 29th he packed boxes of epidendri and bulbs to sail with her. He listed for the boxes other orchidaceous plants and bulbs, including catasetum, angraecum, amaryllis, pancratium, *Swietenia mahogoni*, ipomoea and *Limodorum inflatum*.

December came in with a north-wester bringing heavy seas, lashing rain and hours of anxiety for Don with his precious plants in the miniature poop deck garden now in danger of breaking adrift, and of being lashed with cold and rain in conditions so cruelly different from their own warm tropical homes. 'Got my boxes out of the chains', he wrote, 'and placed them on the lower deck where I am afraid they will not survive long as the place is too close; but there is hardly anywhere, if they are not killed by the cold they must inevitably damp off and, in any other part of the ship, they would not survive one day on account of the intense cold.' Here was a plant collector's dilemma indeed, but New York was on the ship's itinerary—he was only a gardener after all— so on the ship ploughed through the ever-increasing cold with its hothouse treasures to reach Staten Island on 9th December. The tropic sun, tropic heat, tropic rains and tropic sunshine were now a glory to remember and vicariously bask in, for the cold increased as they neared the North American coast and, on 9th December, when they anchored off Staten Island, Don could only write the brusque but revealing words, 'Very cold'.

Next day he left on the steamboat for New York, a thrill after the waywardness of sail. He visited a Mr Hogg, about a mile outside the city, who had a small nursery there. He seems to have stayed with the kind Mr Hogg, who took his British plant-hunting friend to the 'neighbouring fields' where he saw *Pothos foetida* and *Grontium aquaticum* growing. Cold, with severe frost, were the conditions next day which confined Don and his new found friend to the town, but in the evening 'went to a meeting held every Saturday by the literati of New York and was introduced to Dr Torrey who produced a catalogue of plants growing within 30 miles of New York'.

The Sunday he spent profitably with Mr Hogg on a visit to the 'Old Botanic Gardens where I saw the old greenhouse with slated roof. The garden is 20 acres surrounded by a wall; vinery on one side and on the other a stove with the glass broken. The ground is lying waste and has the appearance of a common field'.

But Don never let an opportunity pass, for from the debris of the old garden, he recorded, he picked seeds of *Inosteum perfoliatum* and a lonicera with which he was not acquainted.

A little farther out, where, he was told, a field contained most of the plants to be found on the island, 'I collected *Pyrola umbellata* [*Chimaphila corymbosa*], *P. rotundifolia, Aquilegia canadensis*, anemone, *Halectroides pensylvanica, Goodyera pubescens*, opuntia, *Michelia repens* and *Hepatica americanum*. The only shrubs I could make out here were *Hamamelis virginica, Kalmia latifolia* and azaleas. We should have got some roots of *Erythronium americanum* and *Hypoxis graminaei* [*erecta?*], but the frost was so severe that it was impossible to pierce the ground in any part'.

The next day he spent with Hogg and Dr Torrey seeing a 'botanical library and a herbarium of New Zealand plants and also looked through a herbarium collection by Le Comte'.

On 20th December he went out to Flushing, Long Island, to a garden belonging to a Mr Prince. 'Not to be compared', was the English gardener's dry comment, 'with English nurseries.' Returning to New York in heavy snow, followed by severe frost which kept him more or less confined to the city centre, it was the 23rd before he went off with Hogg to dig up roots where the snow was deepest, and succeeded. Another day of 'severe frost set in', and on Christmas Day he celebrated the occasion by working. 'Went with Mr Hogg', he wrote, 'to see some small greenhouses belonging to one of the merchants in the town, but nothing in them', he commented, 'but a few common flowering plants.'

On Boxing Day Don received a plant box from Mr Prince and ordered another box to be made for the few plants he had collected with Mr Hogg.

On the Friday he packed up his New York plants and next day attended the Literati Society meeting, and on Sunday hired a boat to take him and his boxes back to Staten Island and the ship.

On the last day of 1822 he had to sit down and pen a dismal and disappointing story in his journal. Here they were, having batted round the tropics, crossed the equator, boiled in heat, been bitten to death by mosquitoes, having felt the deleterious damp heat of the African and South American shores; and now 'frost continues,' he wailed, 'so that I am afraid I shall not be able to keep a single tropical plant alive. The boxes of plants on the lower deck seem already to feel the effect of the frost. There is not a place in the ship but water will not freeze in a few minutes'.

The year 1823 opened with Don travelling back to New York to collect a few seeds from Dr Torrey, who accompanied him to see if they could 'collect seeds of a yellow honeysuckle, but the plant was dead'.

On the 15th Don sailed for England after a job well done, during which many scores of living plants and scores more of specimens and seeds had been sent home success-fully. He had a last dismal task before he wrote finis to his journal on reaching Spit-head early in February 1823; that was to record that the New York frosts had killed off the whole box of living plants from the Isle of St Thomas, and another box containing live plants with nuts of the same plants buried in the mould had also perished in the severe New York winter of 1822.

The plants Don had sent home, and those he had brought with him, created a furore in the horticultural world. There was excitement and delight at the rare and unusual natural wealth he had collected from the two great unsearched continents and the many islands he had visited. Only a month after he had returned to Chiswick Gardens to help propagate his seeds and tenderly nurture his tropical beauties, to inure them to English winters in the stove houses there, Joseph Sabine, the enthusiastic Horticultural Society secretary, had given to the members a paper on the tropical fruits Don had found. Many of the plants were 'hitherto unknown or undescribed', said Sabine.

He went on to outline these thrilling discoveries. There was a 'Negro peach' (*Sarcocephalus esculentis*) which had been raised from seed in the stove house and had the flavour of a strawberry; an African custard apple (*Anona senegalensis*) and Monkey

Bread (*Adansonia digitata*), an oblong shaped fruit which tasted like gingerbread grown on in a bark stove from a live plant. There was also a locust tree (*Inga biglobosa*) a beautiful tree when it blossomed with its compact heads of fine vermilion-coloured flowers engulfing the tree. This had been grown on from seed sent in pods. There was a cherry called 'country cherry', and described from a specimen of fruit sent back preserved in spirit. Seeds were also sent of Monkey Apple (*Anisophyllea laurina*) but they failed to germinate, although Don's description was exciting with the fruit, he said, 'pigeon egg size, red on the sunned side, yellow on the other and with a taste between a nectarine and a plum'.

Then there were plants sent and reared of country grape (*Vitis cassia*), black and acid tasting, country currants, which Don had described as having berries like those of the elder and growing in the mountains. A large fig (*Ficus brassii*) grew freely in the stove from the spirit-preserved fruit. The guava (*Psidium pyriferum*), greenish yellow and red inside, was grown from seed.

Seven different plums were part of the vast harvest: yellow plum (*Spondias myrobalanus*), grey plum (*Parinarium excelsum*), the latter grown on from seed, a gingerbread plum (*P. macrophyllum*), pigeon plum (*Chrysobalanus ellipticus*), yellow pigeon plum (*C. luteus*), sugar plum (sweet and agreeable) and a black plum (*Vitex umbrosa*).

The list went on: sweet pishamin (*Carpodinus dulcis*), a climbing shrub with a fruit like a lime, sour pishamin (*P. acidus*), the mammee apple (*Mammea africana*), which on a lofty tree grew its fruit twice as big as a man's fist, the butter and tallow tree (*Pentadesma butyracea*) with a fruit with turpentine flavour grown from seed sent home.

There were two African apples, 'long-leaved star apple' (*Chrysophyllum macrophylea*) and the obovate-leaved (*C. obovatum*), *Tonsella pyriformis* with fruit shaped like a bergamot pear and a flavour rich and sweet. A kind of pomegranate was described by Don, as was a cola tree (*Sterculia acuminata*), the seeds of which were used as a substitute for quinine. He had sent here also a specimen of the velvet tamarinds (*Codarium acutifolium*) with seed-pods which when cut yielded a farinaceous substance with an agreeable acidy taste. The seed-pods of another variety were also sent with pods a brown colour. The pineapple (*Ananas comosus*) Don reported, grew vigorously and wild.

As a means of contrasting Don's quite amazing work in the relatively short time at his disposal, Sabine quoted fourteen fruits recorded by Dr Afzelius, of the Africa Company, who had resided in Africa for several years, which were also recorded by Don, but he had also sought out and collected another seventeen never seen at all by the resident doctor.

Don himself in 1824 wrote of 'rare and beautiful plants' which were 'all of them deserving of being cultivated in our stoves'. He added a most important rider: 'Several of them I have been so fortunate as to introduce into this country in a living state'— fortunate indeed, almost epoch-making in the history of exotic plant introductions.

'Many of the plants', he said, 'could be seen growing in the gardens of the Horti-cultural Society at Chiswick.' He listed, among others, *Clematis grandiflora, Crathaeva fragrans, Gardenia coccinea, Arum compressum, Cassia conspicua*, many of a beautiful climbing shrub family, *Combretum*, 'profuse and brilliant', five clerodendrons, *Gomphia reticulata, Ochna multiflora*. He loved his flowers too, as could be seen in his descriptions: '*Clerodendron splendens*, one of the greatest ornaments in Sierra Leone mountains, climbing, many-flowered, particularly at extremity of the branch, deep scarlet colour with yellow filament and bluish anthers.' There was *Rondeletia febrifuga, Smeathmannia laevigata, Spathodea campanulata, Tetracera potatoria*, aletris, bletia and strophanthus.

When John Lindley, assistant secretary to the garden, some time later gave more details of Don's floral harvest the picture glowed with tropical colour and romance as Society members read their descriptions or in the gardens saw, with covetous eyes, the glorious colours or curious forms of the specimens themselves.

There was *Pergularia sanguinolenta*, grown from seed sent from Sierra Leone. 'A magnificent plant, *Marica sabini*, sent from St Thomas with leaves three feet high, ultramarine flowers three inches across like a giant iris and also from Sierra Leone, *Chlorophytum orchidastrum, Ipomoea paniculata, Phylopsis longifolia* and *Ocymum febrifugeum* (the fever plant by which the dangerous fever of the coast could be alleviated).'

In the family *Orchidaceae* plants were sent of *Angraecum luridum* (Sierra Leone), *Eulopia guineensis* and *E. gracilis* (Sierra Leone). *Pancratium patens* had been grown from bulbs collected by Don in Grand Cayman, and the true tobacco plant, *Nicotiana repanda*, had been successfully grown from seeds sent from Havana, as was *Prockia crucis* sent from the same island. 'From Maranhão on the Brazil coast came a curious species of sensitive plant (*Mimosa polydactyla*), another orchidaceous plant *Catasetum claveringi*, smelling of honey,' from Bahia, and also from the South American jungle of the coastal strip a large honeysuckle having a flower spotted with purple. Exceedingly rare, recorded Lindley, was *Polystachys puberula* from Sierra Leone, with flowers in a close panicle, bright greenish and orange. Another plant from Havana was *Zephyranthes rosea*, which arrived safely to be described by Lindley.

Crinum revolutum was sent as a bulb from Maranhão and in seed form came *Sarcocephalus esculentus* from Sierra Leone. Another seed success from Brazil was *Passiflora obscura*.

A rich, rare harvest indeed, and from Don's successes and his failures it can be seen that plant hunters generally were finding transportation hazards could be overcome to quite a considerable extent by careful packing, by the use of plant cabins for live plants and germinating seeds, and the careful preparation and packaging of seeds to travel in a viable state. There was also the tremendously important factor involved of ships' captains and officers, who were now willing to take both care and a pride in the bringing home safely of their precious vegetable cargoes. It may be it was now worth their while, not only for a purely mercenary advantage, for there was social gain to be won when people in high places were waiting at London river to take over some rare foreign plant to grace the new hothouses and stoves they were building on the big country estates.

It was patently obvious that the final secret had not been entirely probed in this long and vexed problem of how to bring a living exotic plant many thousands of miles over land and sea to a temperate country. The whole question was still too much dependent on the human factor which, combined with extreme climatic vagaries, could still result in all the difficulties, dangers, hardships and zeal of a plant collector's work being brought to naught in a matter of hours.

There was another important factor too, that of the actual money needed to mount such an expedition as that of George Don. Fortunately for us, Don's account forms are still extant and show in quite vivid detail the way this money went as your itinerant plant hunter sailed the seven seas in search of floral beauty.

When Don returned to the Society he had to present his detailed balance sheet for the whole of the fifteen months' expedition. The complete sheet, minus the thirty-six pounds odd he had been paid for his kitting out before embarking, came to £415 7s. 5d., a tidy sum indeed, which included Don's wages at one pound a week, except for the actual time he was engaged in either travelling or plant hunting (from 13th November 1821 to 7th February 1823) when his wages were for '64 weeks and four days at £2 a week' giving a total of £129 2s. 10d. While preparing for the trip from 6th August to 12th November he received one pound a week for fourteen weeks, which made his total of salary paid £143 2s. 10d.

His itemized balance sheet makes fascinating reading, giving a vivid insight into the cost of living for a globe-trotter nearly a hundred and fifty years ago.

His bill presented to Sabine, the Society's secretary, ran:

	£	s.	d.
Wages	14	0	0
Outfit and specimen boxes	42	5	2
Wages plant-hunting	129	2	10
Expenses on voyage	89	9	10
By salary from 8th February 1823 to this day 7th February 1824 (52 weeks at £1 a week)	52	0	0
Same from 8th February to 30th October (38 weeks at £1 a week)	38	0	0
Rope for chest		2	6
Stage to Portsmouth	1	10	0
Coachman and guard		4	0
Porter		1	0
Refreshments		2	0
For bed and bedding	5	9	0
Crockery		14	0
Three pairs of coarse gloves		6	0
On joining gunners' mess	6	0	0
From being left behind at Brixton	5	6	3

	£	s.	d.
Peak Truro			
Paid for hire of horse	1	6	0
Washing sheets and towels		4	6
Sierra Leone			
Man for drying papers		10	0
Refreshment		5	0
Man for carrying baggage, etc.	1	10	0
Guide		2	6
For messing with the Governor's Gunners from 25th February to 11th April	4	12	0
Ascension			
For mules		5	0
For wood for boxes at St Thomas	7	10	0
For nails		5	0
Maranhão			
Canoe hire		5	0
Canoe hire		14	0
Interpreters	1	0	2
Jamaica			
Man for carrying plants		2	6
Horse hire to ascend peak of Port Royal	4	19	0
To man for loan of spade		1	0
New York			
Dinner, supper, bed and board		4	6
For three weeks' board and lodgings at 4–6 per dollar	4	10	0
Man for cleaning cabin, drying papers and other aid	1	9	0
Portsmouth coach to London	1	5	0
Coach and guard		2	0

While George Don was busily working out his expenses and the Society was weighing in the balance the horticultural value of the mission, the decision was made to send off into the wilds another young Scotsman—David Douglas.

7. Trees into Landscape

THE advent of David Douglas and a miscalculation in international affairs led the Horticultural Society to fix their botanical eyes on an entirely different floral target from that which had attracted the stay-at-home botanists and their botanical travellers in the past.

For fifty years or more Kew, and later the Horticultural Society, had had no thought but for exotic flora and tropical fruit, as if the lure of the tropic sun and the vegetative luxuriance it drew from the earth had so dazzled them that they had no eyes for the hardy and the half-hardy inhabitants of the plant world.

Despite the difficulties, first of transporting these sun-drenched daughters of nature, and the even more difficult task of keeping them alive once they had, if fortunate, arrived here, the fascination, the witchery of the flamboyant and rare had been too strong. Great ranges of conservatories, hothouses, stoves and greenhouses had arisen to house these tender treasures, whilst a large, extremely skilful band of garden crafts-men had been trained in their nurture and maintenance.

When Douglas was first taken on by the Horticultural Society in the spring of 1823 the Society's ideas still ran exotically and sunwise, for his intended employment was in China, but the disturbed state of that country at the time made it necessary to abandon the design. So as an afterthought, as a matter of expediency, and so as not to leave Douglas unemployed, it was conceived 'he might be more usefully employed in bringing from the United States such plants as were wanting in our collections, particularly fruit trees'.

Douglas was the first botanical traveller to plant hunt assiduously and systematically in a temperature comparable with that of the British Isles, and the fact that on the American and Pacific seaboards climatic extremes and vagaries did not present unsurmountable problems, either in transportation or survival, gave a zealous and enthusiastic man a reasonable chance of success.

And Douglas was nothing if not zealous and enthusiastic. He was another in the long line of hard-working sons of the soil; dour, self-reliant, full of confidence and sheer guts.

He was born at Scone in Perthshire in 1798, the second son of a stonemason, and had his first practice in footslogging, an attribute he was later to need so much, with a daily journey of six miles there and six miles back to school at Kinnoul. Young David showed his mettle early, being described as 'self-willed with a determination amounting to obstinacy and a contempt of the schoolmaster's thong'.

His love of nature was early apparent in his liking for fishing and bird-nesting rather than school, and of rambling over his native hills, where he sought out and brought home as pets all manner of birds, including owls and hawks.

Before he was eleven he left school to be a gardener's boy in the nursery garden at the Earl of Mansfield's Scone Palace, where his master Beattie had occasion to say of him, his high spirits and his quarrels with the other bothy boys: 'I like a deevil better than a dolt.' It was obvious Douglas was a good learner, for after seven years at Scone Palace, during which time he had been appointed first gardener in the forcing and kitchen garden, Beattie recommended him to Sir Robert Preston, at Valley Field on the Firth of Forth, a garden noted for its fine collection of exotics.

Douglas joined the staff there in 1818 after having spent the previous winter months at a private school in Perth revising his arithmetic and other subjects. At Valley Field, where for the last twelve months of his two years he was foreman, Sir Robert recognized the young gardener's worth and gave him the run of his most extensive botanical and garden library.

From Valley Field he went to the Glasgow Botanic Gardens under Professor William Hooker, who encouraged him and took him to the Highlands to assist him in collecting material for his (Hooker's) *Flora Scotica*.

In the spring of 1823 Hooker, having been consulted by Joseph Sabine about a suitable person as botanical collector to the Horticultural Society, unhesitatingly recommended Douglas, who at twenty-four entered the service of a society to which he was to bring almost incredible horticultural gains and honour.

Despite the fact that Sir Joseph Banks in one of his last letters to Kew had suggested an increase in the old rate of £100 a year for botanical travellers to £180, the Horticultural Society, according to Don's account, had stuck to £100, so that even in the 1820s Douglas was certainly not taking the job for the money, and indeed, so far as one can read between the lines in his letters and journals, never had any. His contemporaries wrote soon after his death: 'He barely got a living at the best of times and was often in the most distressing circumstances.'

His plant-hunting brief from the Society was short and simple, with a most notable exception: the sending of live plants was not stressed—his job was to collect seeds as well as to procure specimens of trees and plants not in cultivation or not described.

John Lindley, gardens clerk at Chiswick, was in process of drawing up a pamphlet for all the Society's collectors, and there is no doubt that Douglas would have had the benefit of this thorough-going document. It told collectors that if they found wet seeds they must dry them before wrapping in brown paper and be sure to place them in dry, airy parts of ships or, if the seeds collected were from tropical countries, then they had to be placed in a vessel or a bottle wrapped in dry paper. The larger seeds of fruiting trees and berrying shrubs were to be cleaned of their pulp and wrapped in paper unless they were oily in nature, when their wrapping had to be clay. Cuttings of fruit trees should be stuck into a lump of well-rendered moist clay before being packed in moss. Bulbous or tuberous rooted plants had to be dried out until all moisture from the outer coat was evaporated and then treated as seeds.

No time was lost in getting Douglas seaborne, and on 3rd June 1823 he left Charing Cross by coach for Liverpool and the eastern United States.

He arrived at Liverpool about tea time and discovered that his ship did not sail until next day, so straightway he found his way to the Botanic Gardens to study North American plants. Next morning, the 5th, by 6 a.m. he was aboard the *Ann Maria*, bound for New York, but she was unable to clear the river, so back went Douglas to the gardens to study American plants again. On the 6th, with two tugs to haul her down the Mersey, his first voyage had started. 'Most people were seasick because of the tremendous seas,' he wrote, adding: 'It was not until the 10th we saw the Welsh mountains from the mouth of the Mersey.'

The 26th June was his twenty-fifth birthday and he noted nostalgically: 'Market day at Scone.' It was July before they sighted Newfoundland, in heavy seas and gale force winds that tore their sails. The rough weather followed them, slowing down *Ann Maria*'s progress so that ship's rations ran short. 'Every person on board now became uneasy,' wrote the young gardener. 'The ship's crew were out of tobacco and many of the passengers who found for themselves were out of provisions, so that there was nothing but passengers buying and bartering, etc., which made good sport. The sailors, chewing their tobacco, dried it and then smoked it again.'

Whether New York was ultra fashionable in 1823, or whether Douglas had spent more on his equipment than on his clothes, was not certain, but by 5th August when they arrived in New York and he wanted to go ashore he was told he could not possibly go in the clothes he was wearing, and had to spend a sixpence or two to get decently rigged out.

In a quick botanical skirmish in New York he made a tour of 'all the vegetable markets in the neighbourhood' before going forward to Albany, where of Mr Van Ransaleir's garden he wrote: 'A large space of ground occupied as a pleasure or flower garden which is a novelty in America, as little attention is paid to anything but what brings money or luxury for the table.'

By 8th September he was on his way to Canada by stage coach to Utica, but '70 miles on the bad road and the jostling reduced me so much I was obliged to give up coach and take a canal boat'.

At a more leisurely and comfortable pace he now made for Rochester, some sixty miles away, where he changed to stage coach again for Buffalo and Lake Erie, which he reached at midnight on 12th September. He pressed on next day, facing a sixty-hour steamer passage on the lake to Amherstburg.

It was 6 a.m. on 16th September on an early excursion into the woods that American natural scenery first got hold of him. 'This is what I might term my first day in America,' he wrote. 'The trees in the woods were of astounding magnitude. The soil in general over which we passed was a very rich, black earth and seemed to be formed of decomposed vegetation. On the south side of the town near the margin of Lake Erie the soil is of a reddish cast and produces fine crops of indian corn, and, now for the last few years, I learn they have cultivated cob with great success and accordingly, as the general opinion goes, it will form an article of great importance to the Canadas at no very distant period.'

He went on to describe the trees and some flowers of which he had collected seed— liatris, helianthemum, solidago, asters, eupatorium and veronica. One oak tree, he noted, did not grow a branch until forty feet high. 'I cut some branches, leaves and acorns with a shot from my gun.'

Trouble, to dog Douglas all his working life as the sparks fly upwards, came early with a French horse which could not understand the English word of command, and later, when Douglas was up a tree collecting seeds, his cart driver and guide took his coat with all his notes and 19 dollars, his copy of Persoon's *Synopsis Plantarum* and a small vasculum (his collecting case). Left high and dry he put his seeds in his necker-chief and had to hire another man to take him back to base, where he had to borrow a coat as there was no tailor to make him one.

Returning on the Detroit steamer to Buffalo they ran into a storm so violent it carried off one of the paddle wheels with a frightening roar and rending of wood and metal, causing almost complete chaos in the engine-room and some most uncomfortable moments on deck too.

It was obvious that even a dedicated plant hunter such as Douglas could not miss seeing the pre-eminent natural sight of Canada and America—the Niagara Falls—but with a typical Scots gardener's comment he remarked: 'I am like most who have seen them, sensitively impressed with their grandeur, but particularly with a red cedar which grew out of the rocks on the channel of the river. I picked up an astragalus and a viola.'

From Niagara another long jaunt took him right back to the coast and Philadelphia, where he visited the home of his eminent predecessor old John Bartram, and saw in his garden a cypress 90 feet high and 23 feet round planted by John himself at eighty-five years of age, while his son Willie held the tree firm. Then he took coach for Bordertown to South Amloy in New Jersey. 'But the coach broke down taking two hours to repair and to make up for lost time they raced the horses to do 29 miles in 3 hours.'

He retraced his steps to New York, from where he crossed the Hudson to seek sarracenias, and got them too, but only after 'going up to the middle in a swamp'.

By 12th December he was ready for home after this short botanical reconnaissance and brought all his collection over the Atlantic himself, arriving in London with his North American finds on 10th January 1824. He had made a profitable choice of fruit trees, oaks and other plants in the nurseries of New York and Philadelphia.

'This Mission', stated the Society report, 'was executed by Mr Douglas with a success beyond our expectations. He obtained many plants which were much wanted and greatly increased our collection of fruit trees by the acquisition of several sorts only known to us by name.'

There was not much time for Douglas to rest on his laurels, however. The Horticultural Society were hard taskmasters, and for one so eminently successful as a collector there was much more work to do. It was said of Douglas that he spent eighteen hours a day during his short respite from travel in perfecting his art, and less than six months after his first homecoming he was on the London coach again, this time for Gravesend and bound for the Pacific coast of America on board the three-masted brig *William and Ann*. Influential members of the Society had arranged that their collector should be under the patronage of the Hudson's Bay Company both for his travelling arrangements and his home on the Pacific coast.

It was inevitable that Douglas would run into trouble quickly and on only his second day at sea his ship struck 'the shivering sands near the Nore and beat about dreadfully for an hour taking in fourteen inches of water in the hold which, fortunately, the pumps held to an inch' and they sailed on. He spent the time recording thermometer readings, reading up his botany books, baiting or shooting birds, dredging for seaweed, for zoophytes and phosphoric creatures, skinning birds, studying Linnaeus and language dictionaries.

Fifty-seven days out of Liverpool and the date 3rd August reminded Douglas that it was exactly a year since a raw garden hand had landed in Staten Island. The brig had cast anchor at Porto Santo in Madeira, where the gardener exclaimed, 'Is there anything more agreeable to the feelings of a prisoner than liberty?' as he scuttled ashore to seek out the native vegetable markets to see what offered. There he noted the vines, the different varieties, their taste, where they grew and how they were pruned, jotting down the vegetables he had seen, including yams, cabbage and cayenne peppers.

Near Cape Verde Islands 'it was 86 in the cabin with all air on' and, with a rising thermometer to watch, he crossed the line on 9th September, Neptune calling as usual. This was a reasonable diversion far better than the sea provided a few days later, when it constantly broke over the whole ship and gave no one on board, and certainly not Douglas, any sleep.

Very soon this was forgotten in the glory of Sugar Loaf Mountain, the magnificent prospect of Rio harbour, where on 28th September Douglas got his first sight in their natural haunts of some of the rare and difficult exotics he had cared for at Valley Field. In the rich, luxuriant countryside around he saw many of the bizarre orchid family, and richly ornamental marantas, begonias and gesnerias. A sight for a connoisseur was his when he noticed seventy magnificent orchids on a wall at Botofogo nailed up on bark. He spent twelve days roaming the botanically rich foothills and plains around Rio, noting six fine days to the rest wet, but collecting many fine orchids and bulbs and a new species of gesneria he called Sabina, after his master in London. Fortunately he was able to pack them and dispatch them for England before he left, obviously because of their very nature—orchids and gesneriads—in a dry state.

Taking his many other botanical specimens aboard after a farewell dinner given to him by some friends of the Horticultural Society, Douglas was caught in a torrential downpour as he got into the ship's boat. He got wet but his specimens were kept as dry as might be, since he wrapped them in his coat and vest. There were some two hundred of these plants which, even with his precautions, took days to dry out on the ship, keeping him busy for quite a time.

Cape Horn now loomed ahead like a bad dream in everyone's thoughts, and Douglas, the greenhorn, remembered all the stories he had heard of ships lost, of innumerable miserable days spent trying to round this ships' grave; nor was he cheated of his misery, or his thrills, as for ten days the brig lurched and wallowed. 'The motion of the vessel was so great,' he wrote, 'the waves frequently breaking over it, there was no sleep and the watch was completely worn out with fatigue.' The cold was insupportable and there was a piercing rawness in the atmosphere.

At Juan Fernandez, apart from his seeing the only white man there, William Clark, 'a modern Robinson Crusoe', he collected seventy-eight plants, including ferns, tree ferns, escallonias, hypericum, berberis, lobelia, silene, euphorbia, aralia and verbena.

Christmas had passed, they had dined on a goat given them by Clark, and now on 10th January he had the 'glory of stretching legs' once again, at Chatham Island. For three days he was able to go ashore two or three hours each day on this but recently discovered, richly vegetated pinpoint in the Pacific, noting that the birds flying among the trees and tree ferns were so tame they perched on his head and on the end of his gun. Whether or not such easy game was cricket he killed forty-five of nineteen genera and skinned them all for specimens, but unfortunately lost the lot because twelve days' rain followed, when drying them was just impossible. The same thing happened with the 135 plant species he had collected, although he did manage to save the seeds of about forty, including a giant cactus and gossypium.

They had hit a rain belt now and on Sunday, 16th February, Douglas recorded so much rain fell that the ship's crew collected five tons of it in sails, enabling them all to have a washing day and more to drink.

This was the only advantage, for the rain was accompanied by weather both boisterous and frightful for six weeks. 'Here we experienced the furious hurricanes of North America in the fullest extent and a thousand times worse than Cape Horn.'

They were so at the mercy of the elements that, although on 2nd April the *William and Ann* was but some thirty-six miles from the mouth of the Columbia River on the Pacific shores of America, they were blown 170 miles out to sea and it was not until the

7th they were able to enter the river mouth, Douglas taking the soundings as they crossed the bar, 'and thus my tedious voyage of eight months and 14 days from England terminated'.

This great river, backed by mountains snow-tipped and forested with a million pines, was to be Douglas's highway to the floral wealth of north-west America. Sailing into Bakers Bay with the great, steep, 700-foot cliffs of Cape Disappointment rearing above them they heard no answering shot to their gun salute from Fort George, the Hudson's Bay Company depot, and anchored the night in the mouth until morning light, when 'the relief of standing still in quiet waters was a magic thing', wrote this weary gardener. 'We spent the evening with great mirth and at an early hour to sleep, to sleep without noise or motion, the disturbing attendants of a sea voyage. With truth I may count this one of the happy moments of my life. As might be supposed to enjoy the sight of land free from the excessive noise and motion of the ship was to me truly a luxury.' Poor man, he did not know it, but it was about his last taste of luxury on this vast continent.

Next morning he set foot on American soil. 'The first plant I saw on stepping ashore at Cape Disappointment was *Gaultheria shallon*.' There it was growing in abundance, covering the rocks with its beautiful roseate flowers. Coming down to the sea, and extending as far as the eye could see so that the whole country appeared to be one continuous forest, were the great pines, under whose gloomy, dense cover was a luxuriant growth of native flowers. Douglas noted them—many varieties of American currant, the ribes, beautiful trilliums, plants of *Rubus spectabilis*, of the *Smilacinae*, of tiarella and heuchera in flower. He landed at Fort George, and, spending a few days exploring its surroundings, found that what had appeared unbroken forest broke up into lush meadows and verdant swamps where willows arched the streams and American brambles lit up the scene with the mixed coloured beauty of their flowers. Two days after he had stepped ashore he saw his first redskin and noted 'his compressed forehead, his copper beads and the shells and bits of copper through holes in his nose and ears'. He noted too the grimy state of his first native, saw the high cheekbones and the grease-smeared queues of jet-black hair hanging over his shoulders under a large sugarloaf hat, saw the rough robe of marmot skin, a tattered shirt and blanket not even decently covering his body and made a mental note that these would be the people with whom he would be sharing the wilderness of forest and lakes and fast-flowing rivers for the next few years.

There was a river journey of about eighty miles to the new Hudson's Bay Company depot, Fort Vancouver, but it was not until mid April that a party was got together for the voyage; meanwhile he collected seeds in the neighbourhood.

Then on the 19th Douglas made the first canoe journey of the many hundreds he was to make in his plant-hunting career, and a strange, frail craft it must have looked as the birchbark-covered vessel tossed like a cork on the swift-flowing Columbia, manned by six Indians, the stern and bow men and the inside paddlers. By the time it held passengers and crew, and Douglas's kit, largely drying papers, canisters and boxes, a bundle for clothes and blanket, the canoe, with its mere six inches of freeboard, looked dangerously near to sinking before the start. But Indian canoemen were skilled, day and night meant little to them, the voyage was the thing and at 3 a.m. on the 19th Douglas started upstream for his depot base.

He soon learned how much sleep one might expect on these journeys, for he found his bed was the barely wide enough bottom of the canoe, which was beached on a sand-bank in mid stream for a short siesta. Swift, strong strokes took them through the wild scenery of pine forest and mountains, high cliffs, low swampy plains, the rock-strewn picturesque route of the river, the 'mad river' as the earliest pioneers had called it. For the first time he realized the tremendous botanical treasure which was his for the taking, for in the deep, gloomy recesses of the forest and dotting the plains he saw one and then another huge stand of pines running through all the greens to the blues and silvers, with their pyramidal grace, their balsamic scent, and beneath them the flowering shrubs, the flowers, which all piqued his collector's appetite.

They reached Fort Vancouver just before midnight when he was given a tent home in this new Pacific Coast outpost of the company, where a heavily built wooden stockade fence surrounding the fort, itself having a wooden look-out tower at each of the four corners and a heavily barred entrance gate, indicated danger in territory that overnight could change from the peaceful to the unfriendly and distinctly hostile.

Next day Douglas met the company official under whose auspices he was to travel and in the daylight noted the details of the fort itself, with its great log-built hall where, in the height of the season, fur trappers, both whites and Indians, brought their natural wealth for exchange into money, food for the next rough months upcountry, ammunition, clothes and equipment. He noted too the long, low log-built warehouses, the shops of the merchants and the cabins of the officials all built round a barrack square for self-protection.

Probably to familiarize himself with native ways Douglas soon left his tent for a lodge, an Indian style tent of poles covered with deerskin. For a short time he made botanical excursions in the vicinity of the fort to acclimatize himself to the strange, rough, almost primitive life he could see he would have to become accustomed to if he was to travel any distance in this wilderness of forests and natives, of mountains and rivers, where the only pinpoints of civilization were small fur-trading posts hundreds of miles apart amidst thousands of miles of unexplored territory bordered only by the great barrier fence of the Rockies on the one side and the Pacific on the other.

Being the hardy, dour Scot he was, of 'undaunted courage and singular abstemiousness', as Professor Hooker said of him, Douglas found he could rough it and enjoy the experience, for on 16th August, just over four months after he had stepped ashore, from a hut 'made of the bark of *Thuya occidentalis*', he confided to his journal how he spent his days and nights in the wide, open spaces: 'On my journeys I have a tent where it can be carried which rarely can be done; sometimes I sleep in a canoe turned upside-down, but most commonly under the shade of a pine without anything. In England people shudder at the idea of sleeping with a window open. Here every individual takes his blanket and, with all the complacency of mind that can be imagined, throws himself on the sand or under a bush just as if he was going to bed. I confess at first, although I always stood it well and never felt any ill effect from it, it was looked on by me with a sort of dread. Now I am well accustomed to it so much that comfort seems superfluity.'

The tenderfoot was already the old stager, and during this toughening up period he collected avidly, finding 139 shrubs and flowers in and around the fort, and 295 on a visit to Menzies Island in the middle of the Columbia River. Included in his finds, where it grew on the margin of springs round the fort, was *Mimulus moschatus*, the scented musk.

He had already in June made a trial run, as it were, for the long, arduous and dangerous journeys he knew lay before him, when on the 20th of the month he went up-river by Indian canoe to the Great Falls by the Multnomah River and Grand Rapids, pushing, paddling, poling and cordelling their craft through the narrows, between the sandy islands and shoals, through strong, rock-strewn rapids, amidst magnificent scenic beauty of forest and huge, black, precipitous rocks, one of the Great Beacon, reaching 800 feet into the sky; from some of the sheer cliffs above the foaming river-bed watercourses hurled their precipitous cascades. This really was a 'mad river'; the pioneers had been right, for Douglas soon found it was a thing of contradictions: here running vastly wide and smooth-flowing and there roaring and racing through the narrowest of black rock tunnels or descending in a race of rapids, whirlpools and eddies. It was a journey of some two hundred miles at a time when, as he knew, the Indians were hostile, but it was a memorable botanical journey for Douglas as he pushed up-country against the snow-swollen current. Scenic changes were immense, from the rugged steep banks clothed with gigantic pines to dreary wasteland. But he found *Clarkia pulchella, Calochortus macrocarpus, Lupinus aridus*—at one stretch of the voyage he saw the grandeur of *Lupinus polyphyllus* covering immense tracts of low-lying land growing up to 8 feet in height—*Scilla esculenta, Acer macrophyllum, Mahonia aquifolium, Berberis glumacea, B. nervosa, Arbutus menziesii, Spiraea ariaefolia, Collomia grandiflora*, penstemons, leucophyllums, *Bartonia allicaulis, Brodiaea grandiflora, Purshia tridentata* and *Nicotiana pulverulenta*.

On 19th July, with one Canadian and two Indians, he set off by canoe from base to the ocean to look for a tuberous-rooted cyperus, and spent twelve days searching for it without success. On the trip he experienced the misery of rain in the forest and on the river, recording with feeling: 'Now I have a little idea of travelling without the luxuries of life. Only two night of my stay on shore were dry; before I could lay down to sleep my blanket drying generally occupied an hour. For food I lived on small trout and young salmon, and this, with a basin of tea, a small piece of biscuit and now and then a chicken I managed to live very well.'

Life was just as full of incidents when he retraced his canoe journey to the fort. An Indian chief with whom he had become friendly, and who called him the 'Grass Man', built him a log-cabin within his own lodge, 'but the immense number of fleas' the chief seemed to have built in with his logs forced Douglas back to his own devices, though whether he was safer outside the lodge or in it was difficult to say, for while he stayed with his Indian friends several tribesmen were killed and others wounded in skirmishes. One night was particularly disturbing to a peaceful, sober Scot. 'In the evening', he wrote, 'about 300 men of war in their war garments were dancing the war-dance and singing death songs,' and what a fearsome sight and ear-splitting ceremony it was, with the glare of the heaped-up fires making real red Indians of the horribly ochre-lined braves with eagle feather headdresses, carrying bows and arrows, tomahawks, bone knives dangling from their wrists, all exciting themselves by dance and voice into the extremes of violence to be wreaked on their enemies. The braves showed their prowess with bow and arrows by throwing grass hoops into the air and shooting their arrows cleanly through the centres. Douglas himelf, who boasted of his skill with a gun, let them see his magic and shot a bullet an inch from a mark at 110 yards, then sighting an eagle on the stump of a tree at 45 yards, took a stone to flush it and shot it on the wing. This did not altogether satisfy the demanding braves, so he took his own hat, threw it as high as he possibly could into the air, and shot the whole brim away before it fell.

Next morning looked to Douglas as if a battle was really going to break out. 'Seventeen canoes carrying 400 warriors made their appearance, but for the present hostilities were suspended, and I returned to Fort Vancouver,' making the comparative safety of this stockaded depot on 5th August.

When he had time to reflect on the life and the career he had embarked on he knew that danger, hunger, extreme fatigue, were to be his daily companions, yet there were great compensations. At Grand Rapids, again on his way to exploring the Multnomah River, where he first came across that magnificent monarch of the forest, *Pinus lambertiana*, though he could gather no perfect seeds of it as it towered 300 feet above him, he wrote with a note of ecstasy of his picturesque surroundings: 'The scenery is grand beyond description; the high mountains of the neighbourhood, which are for the most part covered with pines of several species, some of which grow to an enormous size, are all loaded with snow. The rainbow from the vapour of the agitated waters which rushes with furious rapidity over shattered rocks and deep caverns producing an agreeable, although at the same time a somewhat melancholy, echo through the thick wooded valley, the reflections from the snow on the mountains, together with the vivid green of the gigantic pines, form a contrast of rural grandeur that can scarcely be surpassed.'

On another canoe trip with a Canadian and an Indian chief to Grand Rapids, Douglas was able to realize for the first time how difficult and precarious canoe travel could be as a raging, rapid current with a high wind behind it whipped up the waters so high it was impossible to see from canoe to canoe. At times the conditions were so frightening they had to run for shelter into relatively peaceful creeks.

Some of the long portages were a mile or two miles long and often in narrow defiles which, as they laboriously tracked along the waterside, made them sitting ducks for any hostile Indians sheltering unseen in the dense gloom of the enveloping pines. There they would be, struggling, as they said, uphill and downhill, among a confusion of rocks, gullies and thick mud from end to end. They were journeys obstructed all the way, by land, by water and by Indians, all hostile.

Yet whenever this remarkable young gardener had time to sit by his camp fire he would muse after some long and hazardous journey into the unknown on just how comfortable by contrast was camp life where he could buy for a few pence a 35-lb. salmon, taken straight from the rapids by the Indians, who spent their summers here fishing. 'How little the value from that in England where the same quantity would fetch £3 or £4 and in crimped salmon, as it is termed by those acquainted, is the refinement of dishes as I have it cooked under the shade of the lordly pines or rocky dell far removed from the abodes of civilized life. It is very wonderful the comfort, or at least the pleasant idea of being comfortable in such a place, surrounded by multitudes of individuals who perhaps have never seen a white person before and who, to judge by their appearances, are very hostile. The luxury of a night's sleep on a bed of pine branches can only be appreciated by those who have experienced it.'

This was a fragment culled from his diary on the trip to Grand Falls, for he continued: 'Our route was now over a barren plain, scorched by the sun, fatigued and groping our way through a thick forest, crossing gullies, dead wood, lakes, stones, etc., I was so much worn out by the fatigue and hunger that three times I crawled, for I could hardly walk, to a small abandoned hut. I had in my knapsack one biscuit.'

'The third and last time [he had to make the hut for rest] I was not so bad with hunger, but very weak. I killed two partridges and put them in my kettle and went to sleep.'

Next morning he woke under the balsam-scented air of the pines to a domestic tragedy. The fire during the night had burned his kettle bottom out and there was no vessel for tea-making or heating water in any way until this ever resourceful man screwed the lid out of his tinder box and boiled the water for his tea in that. 'Tea,' he said, 'which is the monarch of all foods after fatiguing journeys.'

Having by now had some experience of the Indians, whose territory he constantly travelled in, and who still, if they had ever seen one before, did not like the white man or his intrusion into their hunting grounds, and, if they had not, looked upon him as an enemy on sight, he had a word to say about the 'noble savage'. 'The natives are inquisitive in the extreme, treacherous and will pillage or murder when they can do it with impunity.'

Already those who knew him in this neck of the woods had a name for him. It was Olla-Piska, which in Chinook meant 'fire', because, as Douglas explained, he drank what the Indians thought was boiling water but was only effervescing salts. His own canoe men thought he was a bad spirit because he drank boiling water (tea) and lit his pipe with a burning-glass. When they saw him spectacles on nose they placed a hand on their mouth, a gesture of dread and astonishment.

Still on his trip to Grand Rapids he had another taste of climatic variance when a day's trek took him nineteen miles across a barren plain of pure white sand without a drop of water, with the thermometer at 97 degrees in the shade, and where he suffered much from the heat and the intense reflection of the sun from the sand. He could scarcely tell the state of his feet in the evening, as the heat of the day had raised all the upper part of them in one big blister.

His list of plants for the trip, every one of them now a common inhabitant of our garden borders, included penstemon, phlox, erigeron, hypericum, arabis, echium, campanula, scutellaria and veronica.

At his base from 6th to 18th August he wrote up his journals and his botanical notes as well as sorting, labelling and drying out the plants and seeds he had collected.

On 19th August in a small canoe manned by a Canadian and the Indians he went southwards to the Multnomah River against many rapids necessitating long, tiring portages and, where it was impossible for the loads to be humped and the canoe carried on slings round the heads of the crew because there was no beach to walk on, they had recourse to cordelling, as with rope they hauled their frail craft and its necessities of life through the rapids and whirlpools.

This was only a short trip for Douglas, who was back in camp on the last day of the month. Indefatigable Douglas—by 5th September he was off with a canoe and an Indian chief as sole companion to Grand Rapids. 'The first time a white man had made the journey without a guard,' he wrote with some pride, 'as the Indians were hostile and had already ambushed a boat and killed its men.' This was at the falls, on the portage where, from the beginning of the fur trade, the white man had always been at the mercy of the Indians, and many were the tales at Fort Vancouver Douglas must have heard of death and destruction which had taken place at Great Falls portage and other rapids and at the narrows on the Columbia. The old Pacific Company of John Jacob Astor could point to dozens of men lost, and the North Western Company, with whom the Hudson's Bay amalgamated, lost more scalps at portages than in any other of the dangerous and numerous hazards of a fur trapper's and trader's work.

But Douglas was fortunate this time. He got through the portages without trouble, and with his Indian as his only guide went on a three-day trek to the mountains. 'The way was rough, over dead wood, detached rock and rivulets. I left my blanket and took as provisions three ounces of tea, one pound of sugar and four small biscuits. . . . Our path being so dreadfully fatiguing, climbing over the shelving, detached rock and fallen timber, night closed in on us before we had reached the summit. I killed a young or half-grown brown eagle on which we fared and with a little tea made in an open kettle and drunk out of a bark dish and with a good fire we passed a tolerable night without any lodgings. Previous to lying down I took the precaution to dry all my clothing which was soaked with perspiration from the violent exertion of the day.' It was worth while, for he had found the new pines, *Pinus nobilis* and *P. amabilis*, and in the tobacco pouches of some Indians seeds of the remarkable large pine *lambertiana*, which he had seen before, although the seeds were of no use and he found no more on that trip.

That night he slept with his feet to the fire, but found this was no antidote to the cold of the summit, having to get up four times to walk briskly round the fire to get warm enough for sleeping. The following day he reached his base at the falls, 'faint and weak; my feet suffered so much on the three days' journey that I was totally unable to prosecute my fatiguing researches without taking some rest'.

When he retraced his steps and reached Fort Vancouver there was exciting news. A boat from England was in the Columbia estuary. An overwrought Douglas strove with might and main to get his seeds and specimens ready, but so hurriedly and excitedly did he get on with his packing that on the eve of leaving he wounded his knee severely on a rusty nail on one of the packing-cases so that he was unable to travel. From 4th to 22nd October he was laid up with a swollen knee joint and a most painful abscess. But he packed up sixteen large bundles of dried plants, a large chest of seeds, one of birds and quadrupeds and another of Indian dress, and sent them downriver with instructions to the captain to put the seeds in an airy position in the ship and to keep all his cases above the water line.

This was a most mortifying experience for Douglas, robbed, it seemed, of seeing the only real friend he had, John Scouler, who had accompanied him to Canada, and who was on board. On 22nd October, however, he heard the ship was still in the mouth of the Columbia so, weak as he was, he arranged with Alexander McKenzie of the Bay Company and four Indians to speed down the river, some eighty miles to the sea, starting after supper at 10 p.m., expecting to arrive before daylight two days later. But there was a most difficult swell on the river so that it was impossible to take a midstream course; hugging the bank was the only way and here they struck a concealed stump, splitting the canoe from end to end. There were hurried repairs, fresh gumming and new pieces inserted on the bank, and the paddlers sped on through the night. At nine next morning they arrived at the seashore, only to find the ship had sailed an hour before. A bitterly disappointed Douglas made work his solace and determined to visit Whitby's Harbour on the mouth of the Cheeheelie River.

There was one bright spot in this adventure; he did meet an old Indian who had spoken to Scouler of Douglas and who agreed to accompany him to Whitby's Harbour. Near disaster followed on disappointment, for when crossing the wide, fast-flowing estuary mouth to Bakers Bay the canoe was overturned in a violent storm and, although it was recovered, Douglas lost all his possessions but a few ounces of chocolate he had in his pocket. Then, making Cape Disappointment, they had to drag and carry the canoe four miles through woods, over rocks, stumps and gullies. He camped one night at the Cape, and he found his knee paining him severely after the exertions of the day. Another desperate situation arose next day when he found no salmon at an Indian village where he fully expected he would be able to replenish his larder, so he made all speed to Cape Foulweather existing on the few ounces of chocolate he had managed to save. It was a forty-mile journey along the coast, and on shore at the Cape he met with a hurricane wind, sleet and hail. The Indian was sent back with the canoe, for food was non-existent and a sixteen-mile portage had to be made anyway.

With the coming of darkness a camp was made, while the hurricane rain and sleet continued unabated. Douglas wrote that he was twice obliged to move camp as the sea rose so unusually high. 'We had no protection save what a few pine branches and our wet blankets afforded and no food. We had very little fire on account of the wind and the rain.' He later told Scouler in a letter that he and Mr McKenzie were three days in their miserable shelter, and as he could not get out to shoot they fared most scantily. Scantily was right, for he collected and then ate the berries of *Arctostaphyllos uva-ursi*, but managed to save the seeds of an erigeron, of '*Helonias tenax* and a fine large fruited carex'.

'Long before daylight we were ready to leave Cape Foulweather, which name it totally deserves, and we walked along the sandy beach 16 miles to Whitby's Harbour for fish' (they had been two days without food), the journey taking them from 4 a.m. to 6 p.m., but on their arrival they found the village deserted and there was still no fish. 'Our prospect not in the least bettered we remained here several days, faring scantily on the roots of *Sagittaria sagittifolia* and *Lupinus littoralis*, and, from continued exposure to the cold and rain and the want of proper sustenance, I became greatly reduced.' To help to restore his strength Douglas built a booth of pine branches and grass and made a fire at which they dried their soaked blankets, sitting as near to the fire as they could to drive the chill from their bodies. His knee was now so painful that he had to rest throughout the whole day. Fortunately just a little before dusk he felt slightly better for the rest and went out with the gun and shot five ducks with one shot. He cooked them, only to find he had lost his appetite after so much privation.

'So soon as the weather permitted us we made a large fire to attract the notice of our guide's friends residing on the other side of the bay and they sent a canoe for us.'

After a few days' rest, on 7th November, he started the ascent of the 'Cheecheeler River' in a canoe with an Indian guide, who asked him to shave him so he would look like one of King George's chiefs, and he obliged. The three of them, McKenzie, Douglas and the Indian, pushed sixty miles upriver in deluges of rain in an advancing season which cooled his botanical ardour and determined him to give up any further canoe voyaging that year. He embarked, paid off his canoe man, and at an Indian village bargained with another Indian to carry his baggage on horseback to the 'Cow-a-lidsk River' (Cowlitz River), a journey of some forty miles which extended over two slogging days, for they were forced to climb higher into the gloomy, almost impenetrable forest as heavy rain all the way had brought flooding to the creeks, rivulets and lakes in their path. Twice it was found impossible to scale the hillsides or find any other way across the flood water except by stripping off and, with precious bundle on head, swimming for the farther shore. Again food became scarce and Douglas, with bitter disappointment, had to see his berries and seed collected with so much hardship and pain disappear down the throats of himself and his companions to keep body and soul together.

At Schachanaway a chief of the Chinook Indians lent the struggling, hard-hit men a canoe, a few roots, some dried salmon and a goose so they might reach Fort Vancouver by the quickest way, down the Cow-a-lidsk River to its junction with the Columbia and then by that fast-flowing stream to base. On 14th November the two miserable men,

Douglas almost out on his feet and McKenzie ill with food poisoning from the roots he had eaten, launched their canoe at 5 a.m. At midday they camped on an island grounding the boat on the high tide and on a six miles an hour current. When they were ready to leave Douglas found 'I had not the strength to launch the canoe on the ebb, so we had to wait for the high tide again to refloat it and at last later in the day came to the roaring Columbia', where, hoisting his blanket and a coat as sail, they bore merrily down at a spanking rate and reached the fort just after noon on the 15th, after an absence of twenty-five days, 'with hardly a specimen or seed to show for my efforts and during which I experienced more fatigue and misery and gleaned less than in any other trip I have made in this country. I had suffered so much', he wrote, 'from my last trip that there was little hope left for me being able to do much again for this season, at least in botany'.

So it was that until the year's end he watched, in an infirm state, the rains and fogs of the Columbia winter season from his lodge. This man so dogged with ill luck was to receive another bitter disappointment before 1825 ran out.

On 18th December he heard with joy that the Express—two boats and forty men— had arrived at Fort Vancouver from Hudson Bay, having left the Atlantic side on 21st July. The two long canoes with their singing paddle crews were heard and seen seven miles away descending the river in great style. The landing stage was crowded; almost everyone in the depot had come out to meet these bearers of news of friends and relatives, of parcels from home and letters, news of how the world outside was doing and a few little luxuries for Christmas; but there was not a single letter or parcel for Douglas. 'I was given to understand', he bitterly complained, 'that the Express left Hudson Bay before the arrival of the ship. I left London the May before so that if Mr Sabine did write to me the letter will remain on the other side of the Continent till next November. I was exceedingly disappointed.'

On Christmas Eve the rain fell so heavily 'my bark hut was completely inundated with 14 inches of water in it so on Christmas Day I removed into the half-finished house of Mr McLoughlin on the trading post'.

His knee was still troublesome, preventing his joining a little party which took to the woods on horseback for an airing on the festive day.

On Sunday, 1st January 1826, David Douglas as befitted a true Scot celebrated the New Year. He took stock and summed up his own personal position in his journal. 'Commencing a year in such a far removed part of the earth, here I am nearly destitute of civilized society, there is some scope for reflection.

'On New Year's day in 1824 I was on the Atlantic on my way to England, 1825 between the Island of Juan Fernandez and the Galapagos in the Pacific. I am now here and God only knows where I may be next. In all probability if a change does not take place I will shortly be consigned to the tomb. I can die satisfied with myself. I have never given cause for remonstrance or pain to an individual on earth. I am now in my 27th year.'

This was a low, pessimistic mood indeed for a young man; but the crisp air and brilliant sunlit snows, the pleasant anticipation of a Columbian spring, the scent of pines in the air, the spurling, roaring ebullience of the great river between its hundreds of miles of scenically beautiful banks, drew from him a much happier response a month or so later.

Time had dragged during the first two months, although he did record having spent his time observing birds and noted that he had seen the silver-headed eagle, the magpie, the wood-partridge, the grouse, the pheasant, the jay, the large brown eagle, many owls and geese. Geese—they were reminiscent of his journeyings, for on creeks and lakes in the hinterland they had risen from the water in their tens of thousands, blacking out the sun. Spring was near and it was a totally different Douglas now who wrote to the Horticultural Society to tell them of his plans. The Society's were that he should return that year. This was unthinkable. Douglas was in thrall to the north-west with its breathtaking scenery, its challenge of thousand of miles of unexplored, untrodden territory with its teeming wealth of flowers, shrubs and trees all set against a background of the limitless pines and the great overlording snow-covered mountains.

'From what I have seen myself', he penned, 'of the upper country towards the head waters of the river [Columbia] and the boundless track contiguous to the Rocky Mountains I cannot in justice to the Society do otherwise [than stay a further year]. If not approved then may I be pardoned?'

He pointed out that he was incurring little expense during autumn and the seed harvest. If there were expense 'then most certainly will I labour for this year without any remuneration if I get only wherewithall to purchase a little clothing'.

The extreme distance he hoped to travel was about eight hundred miles to the north-wards in the Walla Walla, Spokane and Kettle Falls districts, and he hoped to reach the Rockies by August.

This programme decided, he cleared his affairs at Fort Vancouver and packed up the remainder of his specimen plants, seeds and birds to send to England on the first ship which would arrive.

He collected 102 lb. of seed and drying papers ready for his long inland trek, later having to complain of the huge stock of paper he was compelled to carry with him on all his plant-hunting expeditions, for quite often some of the necessities, and all the luxuries, of life had to be left behind.

Monday, 20th March 1826, and Fort Vancouver friends waved him off as two boats and fourteen men, including Mr M'Leod and a party bound for Hudson Bay, left the landing stage for the interior.

By the second day the party had reached Grand Rapids, and by the third day the Indians, six miles below Great Falls, were seen to be restless. The canoe party was being watched keenly through the forest trees; there was much coming and going of Indian runners and much noise of dancing and war songs in the night. The Great Falls portage, narrow, long and difficult in course, had always been a danger spot for the white man and his native guides as he struggled to get his canoe hauled by line through the turbulent waters or carried by head string over the rough uphill and downhill path.

There was no sleep for any one of the party as they sat by cocked guns at the portage camp. In any case it would have been impossible to sleep had all been quiet as the camp site was so steep that no tents could be pitched. So while Indians prowled around the camp hidden in the jet-black cave of the forest Douglas pressed mosses and wrote letters.

Next morning the small party found itself surrounded by '450 savages who, judging by their appearance, were anything but amicable'. A guide acted as interpreter and tried to persuade the chiefs to go away, but this was no good. 'We set off, however,' wrote Douglas, 'but found the Indians were troublesome at the Fall portage, for they had collected to pillage the boats. They got some tobacco and tried to get us to camp the night on shore once again. They threw water on our gunlocks and would not allow the boats to be put into the water.'

There was now a howling, shrieking mob, 450 against fourteen, with all the advantages to the mob on their own well-known territory with limitless shelter behind them, while the white man had a few feet between them and the roaring river itself snarling past its rocky outcroppings. It was an ugly situation and, said Douglas 'as Mr M'Leod was putting his hand on one of their shoulders to push him back a fellow immediately pulled from his quiver a bow and arrow and presented it at Mr M'Leod. As I was standing on the outside of the crowd I perceived it and, no time to be lost, I instantly slipped the cover off my gun, which at the time was filled with buckshot and invited him to fire his arrow then I should certainly shoot him'.

Then a Kyeuse chief and three of his young braves came on the scene and settled the trouble 'as they like white men'.

The chief then accompanied the two canoes up the river until they camped the following night. 'He was 6 ft. 6 in. and the finest figure of a man I have seen. I was King George's chief or the Grass Man and so I bored a hole in the only shilling I had, which has been in my pocket since I left London and, the septum of his nose being perforated, I suspended it to it with a brass wire. A ceremony which afterwards proved a seal of lasting friendship. Later, after smoking, he returned to his Indian village, but we could not sleep and had to keep a guard.'

Douglas then settled down to write to Dr Hooker to tell him excitedly of his discovery of the new pinus, the sugar pine (*P. lambertiana*): 'I rejoice to tell you of a new species of pinus, the most princely of the genus, perhaps even the grandest specimen of American vegetation. It attains the enormous height from 150 to 220 feet with a circumference of 50 feet and the cones are from 12 to 18 inches long; I have one which is 16½ inches long and which measures ten inches round the thickest part.' He also mentioned in passing his domestic problems. 'My stock of clothing is very small,' he told Hooker, 'being reduced to two shirts, two handkerchiefs, my blanket and cloak and no stockings.' It was impracticable to carry much more, he explained, since the papers for pressing and drying specimens and other necessary tools of his trade—thermometer, barometer, canvas bags for seeds, etc.—'formed a burthen of considerable bulk'.

As the party pushed farther northward the cold began to have its effect on Douglas, who complained that he was almost benumbed as he trod the rough paths by the river. On the 28th the party arrived at the Walla Walla establishment of the Hudson's Bay Company, where the river was lined with the gracefully contrasting weeping willows with green grass below. It was a pleasurable sight after the huge, dark and columnar pines, so there was a short halt here until 30th March when Douglas went forty miles upriver to make camp at Priest Rapids on 1st April. Here he wrote to his old friend Dr Scouler telling him of the mishaps and misfortunes which had led to his having missed him in the mouth of the Columbia the previous year. He told him how ill he had been at that time so that he could hardly crawl into his tent and how 'my eyes which, always weak, have lately been much impaired; and though I have felt no pain or inflammation yet they have become so dim that I can hardly use the gun which I could formerly do with considerable advantage'.

Although it was April, by the time he had progressed very far up the Okanagan River he found snow from three to five feet deep. He took to horseback, a good thing for a man with no stockings to do, also avoiding a circuitous canoe journey to arrive at the junction of the Spokane with the Columbia on 11th April, where he packed up notes, plants and seeds for Mr M'Leod to take forward to Hudson Bay and home.

Then with his own small party he pushed forward higher up the Columbia another ninety miles to Kettle Falls by canoe against a rapid current through steep-sided gorges, graced but darkened with towering pines. The sides of the river were so steep that camping was a problem, sleep being grabbed in the canoe in mid channel. This proved too cold a way of resting, so at 4 a.m. one morning Douglas left the canoe and managed to walk the next forty miles on the narrow trails skirting the river, except in three places where because of the steep and precipitous rocky banks he had to take to the river again to pass.

On 22nd April he arrived at Fort Colville near Kettle Falls where he 'walked about', as he put it, for several days; indeed he did so most diligently, for it was the ninth day of May before he struck out northwards, towards the mountains now heaving their snowy heads into the far-away blue of the horizon, on a 120-mile reconnaissance, taking with him two horses, some dried buffalo meat, a little tea and sugar; one horse carried the provisions, the other his blanket and papers. He managed to obtain the services of two guides. But even horses were of no avail when it came to river crossings where on one occasion he had to make 'the trip twice, one with my papers and gun the other with my blanket and clothing and holding my property above water in my hands'. It was a 30-yard swim at a temperature of 40 degrees. He was nearly half an hour in the water and was so benumbed with cold when he struggled out that he had to call a halt and build a great blazing fire of pine branches to warm his frozen marrow before he could continue. With a start long before breakfast and the prospect of some home comforts at the end of the journey he set off on 11th May for 'the old establishment at Spokane'. By seven o'clock he had reached the summit of the last range of hills, and just before noon was received 'by Mr Finlay who, with his family, had no food, having lived for the last six weeks on roots of *Phalangium* or *Camassia esculenta* and a species of black lichen growing on pine trees'.

This was no comfort, and to make matters worse Douglas found his flintlock damaged. Fortunately the only man who could mend it within eight hundred miles was in camp. He could speak only French but he managed the essential job, Douglas giving him 'one pound of tobacco, the only thing I had to give'.

Returning after a day's scouting from the Spokane depot he suddenly felt very cold, and on reaching camp found he could not sleep for a severe crippling pain between the shoulders. There were no doctors here so he 'dried his blanket and spare sheet, had some tea and set out before 4 a.m. on foot, driving the horses before me thinking that perspiration would remove it which it partly did'.

Another day he botanized in the hills, finding himself so fatigued in a temperature of 86 degrees 'that I sat down under a pine and went asleep not waking until 4. I was 20 miles from camp and had a six hours journey over rough country'. His day had resulted, however, in the finding of a white and yellow ribes, a new pine (*Pinus ponderosa*), *Penstemon scouleri*, *Claytonia lanceolata* and *Erythronium grandiflorum*.

He left the area on 5th June by canoe on a river swollen with mountain snow-melt to 600 yards wide and so rapid 'that the canoe shot like an arrow from a bow'. He refused to shoot the Thompson Rapids in their wild, roaring, foaming uproar of water, and walked; they had come ninety miles in eight hours—some current!

Making for Walla Walla now, he killed a rattlesnake in a temperature of 92 degrees in the shade, and on 8th June, 'having had little sleep since leaving Kettle Falls I thought of indulging six or seven hours at least so I laid on the floor of the Indian hall, but fleas woke me so I had to sleep among the bushes, but here were ants, one three-quarters of an inch long, so did not sleep after all'. He did himself some good, though, by getting 12 feet of tobacco from the Indians, which gave him vital bargaining power for guides, a canoe or food.

By 10th June he was back at Fort Vancouver to find that at last he was remembered; there was still no letter from his master Sabine, 'and even though I did not hear directly from my own friends', he wrote, 'I now for once in my life enjoy and relish the luxury of hearing from England. I pored over my two letters until midnight, and although I had not slept for 12 hours in the 15 preceding nights I was so excited I never slept'.

A 4 a.m. start next day, on a short trip from camp, found him at noon without water and extremely fatigued, for wind-blown sand and the reflection of the sun on it had played havoc with his eyes so that he could scarcely distinguish an object at ten yards' distance.

Troublesome eyesight or not, on 16th June Douglas made ready for another extended trip, this time southwards, 150 miles to the Blue Mountains and Grande Ronde in Oregon. He met with trouble again when a 'herd of rats ate all my seeds and carried off my razor and soap brush. One was in the act of carrying off my inkstand. I lifted my gun (which is my nightly companion as well as day and lies generally alongside me, the muzzle at my feet) and gave him the contents. He was ten inches long with a tail seven inches long'.

He was travelling with an Indian guide and a party of French-Canadians and Indians of mixed blood and speech. His means of communication with this motley crowd were complicated indeed. 'I explained to an Englishman my intended route who translated it in French to his Canadian interpreter who told the Indian in the Kyeuse language.'

The Indian guide before taking on this job asked what his reward would be, as his family had been starving for two months. Douglas told him a scalping knife, a small piece of tobacco and a strip of red, coarse cloth. A boy of twelve called the Young Wasp also accompanied the party to help the interpreter. Walking thirty-five to forty miles they came to snow and camped at 1,500 feet under the summit of a mountain. From this camp Douglas set out to reach the tip which was 'difficult and exceedingly fatiguing on soft snow with snowshoes, but when within 100 feet of the top found a hard crust of snow'. He reached the top at 9,000 feet above sea level. At about 5 p.m. with a tempera-ture of 26 degrees, 'I had not been three-quarters of an hour than a tremendous storm broke. Thunder, lightning, hail and wind. The heavens were in a blaze'.

He managed to get down safely but considerably shaken to have been caught up in the fury of the elements, and on arriving at camp found he could keep no fire in. 'My clothes were so wet I stripped and rolled in my blanket. At midnight I woke with the cold. My knees would not work so I scoured myself with a rough towel. The storm abated so I made a good fire and could not resist to make a basin of tea and revived. If I have any zeal,' he wrote miserably, 'for once and the first time it begins to cool. But I slept until 3 a.m.'

When he wanted his guides to follow him over the ridge next morning they refused. They said the Snake Tribe would kill them and steal their horses, so it was back to base. Here Douglas was determined he would go over the ridge and get the guide to go too. 'I was going to give him a little corporal chastisement to teach him but he escaped.'

Left high and dry, Douglas had nothing for it now but to make his way back to the Columbia. He suffered much pain from inflammation of the eye. 'Read or write I cannot but in the morning without pain. That which had gratified me most was a beautiful peony [*P. brownii*] the only one of the genus in America with a flower that is dark purple outside and yellow within, blooming on the very confines of the perpetual snows. *Lupinus sabini* covers the country for miles with foot long yellow spikes.'

On 10th July near the junction of the Lewis River, after he had canoed on a twelve-mile-an-hour current and travelled fifty-five miles in two days with only one incident to mar the trip, he came across a party of white trappers from the coast. He told them how an Indian had stolen his knife and how he got it back. 'I paid him and paid him so well with my fist he will, I daresay, not forget the Man of Grass for some days to come.

'I cannot describe the feeling which seized me after travelling in the society of savages for days together and can but speak a few words of their language, assuredly the face of a Christian, although strange, bespeaks friendship.' The white men were doubly welcome, for they had brought him letters, among them the long-awaited one from Sabine. 'To say I was happy would only convey but a fair idea of the rapture of hearing from you,' he wrote later. Meanwhile he told his journal emotionally: 'I am not ashamed to say I rose four times from my bed during the night to read my letters. Before morning I might say I had them by heart. My eyes never closed.'

Encouraged and heartened, he was in high spirits and was off upriver again to the forks of the Lewis and Clarke River, about 150 miles from the Columbia. It was not the cold or the effects of snow glare which caused him trouble on this trip, but heat—a temperature of 108 degrees in the shade. 'The only difference to a desert of Arabia was that there was water here.' The general fare was horse-flesh, for fish was scarce, but when he offered his Indian guide the horse-meat he found he wanted dog.

In the last week of July Douglas decided to try the Blue Mountain country again, with Cock de Laird as a guide and companion. After travelling through the night he made camp at sunrise and lay down to sleep. 'I was not asleep for more than two hours when I was awakened to take on the profession of soldier. The interpreter had had a handful of hair torn out and an Indian Chief being told off went away and brought back a posse of braves some 73 strong. On arrival at our camp we with our guns cocked and they with every bow strung we stood to arms and demanded if war was wanted. "No," was the answer; "we only want the interpreter killed and as he is no chief there could be little ill done."

'Surrounded by a powerful armed party our position was not an enviable one, but the cool way we looked on these proceedings had a good effect on these persons.'

Naturally Douglas did not want to sacrifice his interpreter and, after a day spent present-giving, haranguing, peace-pipe smoking and dancing, peace and order were restored.

On the last day of July he set off with Canadian hunters and many horses for Spokane, on the way being obliged to cook with water from stagnant pools full of lizards, frogs and water-snails. From Spokane he carried on to Kettle Falls and arrived there on 5th August. After two months upcountry he took stock to find that his personal possessions were one shirt, one pair of stockings, a nightcap and a pair of old mitts. He had lost all his seeds, his notebook and his knapsack when his horse slipped and threw him head first into a river.

On the first day of September he heard there was a ship in the Columbia bound for England and, since he now had at Kettle Falls a collection of 120 species of seeds, he arranged to be passed from one Indian tribe to another overland to the sea, a distance of some two hundred miles, 'Little Wolf' going with him to act as interpreter and smoother of his path.

But there was trouble before he could start, for the Cootanie Indians arrived, war was declared on another tribe in the neighbourhood and it was several days before pow-wows and long talks brought peace.

'Here I am', he sighed, 'in the midst of savages, naked, some red, black, white and yellow with bows strung, muskets charged; war caps made of Calumet eagles' feathers

Combretum grandiflorum (left), Zephyranthes rosea (right). George Don hunted the coasts of Africa and South America for the Royal Horticultural Society. *Zephyranthes* he found in Havana and the tropical house climber *Combretum* in Sierra Leone.

were the only particle of clothing they had on. One chief shot at another, someone hit him on the nose and there was a real rumpus, harangue and clamour.'

His plan for a short, but in the circumstances much more dangerous, overland trek was abandoned and he made for the Okanagan River 250 miles away, to make the canoe journey via that river and the Columbia's circuitous and tortuous route. Before he embarked he added to his personal wardrobe an old straw hat, a pair of deerskin trousers and a few pairs of moccasins.

His Indian guide, to whom he could not speak a single syllable he understood, took him overland to the Okanagan. Douglas had a tent with him, but after the first forty-five miles of gruelling forest trailing he was too tired to pitch it.

At the Okanagan he took to canoe and descended the whole chain of the river to the mouth of the Columbia, a distance, he calculated, of eight hundred miles which he paddled in twelve days, six hundred of them being in an Indian canoe. In the narrows between the Great Falls his canoe was wrecked 'when I lost the whole of my insects', some of his seeds and his pistols. He was carrying on his back some of his seeds and specimen papers, but to add insult to injury he had to pay the old Indian for the loss of his craft. Acting as steersman, Douglas arrived at Fort Vancouver with hands blistered from the exertion at four in the morning on 30th August. He had managed to collect some more seeds and got these off in the ship bound for England.

There was little rest as for the next three weeks he prepared for a journey down to North California, as he called it, and on 20th September he made for the Umpqua river in present-day Oregon, the horses doing ten to sixteen miles a day. One day he did a twenty-four mile forced march to get quickly through hostile Indian country, and found himself overwrought and his toes cut badly with the undergrowth.

He pushed through thickets of *Pteris aquilina* and *Rubus suberectus*, but found that because of the strain he was having to rest every thirty or forty yards. On a mountain stretch of the trail his horse rolled from the rough, narrow track, so for safety he transferred his plants, wrapped in a bearskin, from the saddle to his own back. He must have looked a curious creature with his tattered deerskin clothes, old straw hat and his big, bulging bearskin pack, for 'Indian children scattered at my sight in the lodges', he said. To cross a river he made a raft, tearing his hands in doing so, with the result that he could not use a hatchet to blaze the trail for days afterwards. He found it cold on the mountains, having only one blanket to wrap himself in for sleeping and a piece of deerskin to lie on. One day he fell into a gully and injured himself and had to use an eighteen-year-old Indian guide to help him along. His horse was unsaddled and Douglas's own burden transferred to its back as he plodded along with his gun and a stick to help him. His left foot had been injured so he had to bleed it to feel a little better and enable him to carry on his march.

By now he was reduced to one meal a day, and the night of 25th October, he wrote later, 'was one of the most dreadful I have ever witnessed. Teeming rain made a fire impossible, at midnight my tent blew down' so he rolled it round his wet blanket and himself and tried to sleep. Sleep—that was a luxury he was not to have: 'Every few minutes the immense trees falling produced a crash as if the earth was cleaving asunder which with the thunder peal on peal before the echo of the former died away and the lightning in zigzag and forked flashes had on my mind a sensation more than I can ever give vent to, my poor horses were unable to endure the violence of the storm without craving of me protection which they did by hanging their heads over me and neighing. Wringing wet through I exerted myself so much as to throw myself into a violent perspiration to rid myself of cold, fatigue and aches and pains.'

Looking for new pines one day he came across the *Pinus lambertiana* cones which he had found earlier but had lost when forced to escape in a hurry from hostile Indians.

This tree, the tallest pine in the world, excited Douglas. It was while he was seeking cones on a walk from his camp that an Indian came out of the dense forest and, seeing Douglas, immediately strung his bow. The Scot, seeing this, put his gun at his feet and offered the aggressive brave some tobacco and a few beads, then drew him a picture on the forest floor of the cones he wanted.

'Letting the Indian lead the way lest I shall never be able to tell my friends myself about my tree,' he came across one of these monarchs of the forest crashed to the ground. Measuring it he found it was 57 feet 9 inches round the trunk and 245 feet high.

'The huge cones (on the growing trees) were like small sugar loafs in the grocers' shop. I took my gun and was busy clipping them from the branches with ball when eight Indians came at the report of my gun. They were all painted with red earth, armed with bow and arrows, spears of bone and flint knives and appeared to me to be anything but friendly. I endeavoured to explain to them what I wanted and they seemed satisfied and sat down to smoke, but had no sooner done so than I perceived one string his bow and another sharpen his flint knife with a pair of wooden pincers and hang it on the wrist of his right hand which gave me ample testimony of their inclination. To save myself I could not do by flight and without hesitation I went backwards six paces and cocked my gun and then pulled from my belt one of my pistols which I held in my left hand. I was determined to fight for life. As I as much as possible endeavoured to pre-serve my coolness and perhaps did so, I stood eight or ten minutes looking at them and they at me without a word passing until one at last, who seemed to be the leader, made a sign for tobacco which I said they should get on condition of going and searching me some cones. They went, and disappearing I beat a quick retreat. How irksome is such a night to me. I can't speak a word to my guides, not a book to read and constantly in expectation of attack and the position I am now lying in is lying on the grass writing by the light of my Columbia candle, namely a piece of wood containing resin.'

It was a dangerous way home too. Indians were round the camp, there were fires in the forest and Douglas had to hide in the bushes, firing at noises and shapes in the dark. He got back in twelve days of hard labour with great misery and hunger in rain and in cold. His legs gave him great pain 'but what gave me most pain was my nearly total loss of my collection crossing the River Sandiam'.

He reached Fort Vancouver on 20th November. Again it was but a short respite from his floral foraging, for on 9th December he went the eighty miles downriver to the sea, meeting high tides that smashed his canoe and nearly drowned him as he lay sleeping in the bottom. A friendly Indian solved one problem for him with the loan of another canoe, but he came up against a food shortage and desperate hunger. Luckily seven buttons from his coat and a hatchet secured him a bit of fish.

Christmas Day saw his return to the fort a sick and spent man. Until February of 1827 he spent the time recuperating, getting back his strength by reasonably regular meals and rest from either canoeing or hacking his way through untrodden, dense woodland. Now for Douglas it was a wait until the snows melted, for his next journey was to be his longest yet, from coast to coast, from the Pacific to the Atlantic, from Fort Vancouver to Hudson Bay and then, he hoped, home.

Already his journeyings for plants in the north-west as he totalled them up were prodigious. In 1825, from April to the end of the year, he had covered 2,105 miles of tortuous, previously untrodden tracks; the following year he notched up 3,932 miles, during March and April covering 620 of them from Fort Vancouver to Kettle Falls, 414 from the junction of Lewis and Clarkes River and 490 from the Okanagan back to base. In September, October and November from the Columbia to the Umpqua River was a trip there and back of 593 miles.

Now he was essaying a trip as the crow flies of over 1,650 miles, but, as Douglas and the trappers had to go, well over 2,000.

His friends of the Hudson's Bay Company saw he was kitted out, 'fine ye ken', for the journey—a suit of bright red Royal Stuart tartan with coat, vest and pants. In this quaint outfit he set out on 20th March to make the journey by foot, horseback and canoe. The first stage to Fort Colville on Kettle Falls he did on foot in twenty-five days, botanizing as he went in the deep fir woods and in the bare sandy plains skirting the rivers, creeks and lakes in his path. Part of the way he was forced to take to the river after eleven days on his feet as his feet were so painful and blistered that the blood ran from them as he walked. But this was only for a day and a half.

At Fort Colville he rested a short time before, on 18th April, he set off to face the stage in which he would have to cross the Great Divide in order to go over for the first time into the other watershed—over the Rockies. He made for Jasper House in the Rockies, a 350-mile trek, and as he set out by canoe snow was beginning to fall. Nine days later he fetched up at the Rockies portage, the boat encampment as he called it, having made his way against strong currents, stretches of treacherous rapids, on one of which the river fell so sharply over a short stretch that all the combined strength of the crew were needed—two guides in the canoe with poles and seven hauling on the line along the shore—to get the heavily laden boat up into the quieter river above. Douglas carried his own kit along the portage; he could not risk losing his possessions again. This was in swamp ground 'about three miles long, knee deep of water and covered with rotten ice through which we sank more than a foot down at every step we took'.

It was about this time that to walk at all he had to have recourse to what he called 'bear's paws' (snowshoes), for the snow was from four feet to seven feet deep, but he found himself falling head over heels, as this was footwear he was unused to. Frost and cold made the trek uncomfortable too so he made a pair of stockings out of the legs of and old pair and took the skirts of his coat to wrap round his toes. This little bit of comfort did not secure his feet, toes or ankles against the chafing of the rough straps of the 'bear's paws' and made his walking miserably painful, but 'otherwise', he said, 'I am well and comfortable at nights lying down in a deep hole or pit among the snow or on a couch of pine branches with a good fire at my feet.

'The snow was four to six feet deep in the higher spots, the ravines or gullies unmeasurable and towards noon becoming soft I sink as I ascend two steps and sometimes slip back three, the snow shoes twisting and throwing the weary traveller down (I speak as I feel) so feeble that lately I move among the snow like a broken down waggon horse entangled in his harnessing weltering to rescue myself.

'On arrival at camp one gathers a few twigs and makes a fire, two or three procure fuel for the night and as many more gathering the green soft branches of *Abies balsamea* or *Tsuga canadensis* to sleep on, termed "floring" the house, each hanging up his wet clothing to the fire and arranging his load for the ensuing day that no time may be lost. In the morning we rise, shake the blanket, tie it on top and then try who is to be at the next stage first.

'Dreamed last night of being in Regent Street, London, yet so far distant. The temperature is at minimum 2 degrees and at maximum 49.'

Douglas and his companions found themselves frequently going off the trail as they were not able to see the blaze marks on the trees because of the height of the snow. They had to ford rivers two or three times a day, and in the mornings and evenings there was sufficient frost to freeze the clothes on their backs.

One morning, after being at the highest point of the route, while the rest of the party camped Douglas felt 'I must scale a peak. I set out alone sinking up to the middle, the labour of ascending being great beyond description. Came on, about one third of the way from the summit, a mountain of pure ice. About 5,000 from the base there is 1,000 feet of perpetual snow and about 1,250 feet of ice with a thin covering of snow. It took me five hours to climb. I descended in one and a half using snow shoes as a sledge at 500 to 700 feet a minute.

'I stayed 20 minutes at 18 degrees on top. The sensation I felt is beyond what I can give utterance to. Nothing as far as the eye could perceive but mountains such as I was on and many higher, some rugged beyond description striking the mind with horror blended with a sense of the wondrous, a sense of the Almighty. The aerial tints of the snow, the heavenly azure of the solid glaciers, the rainbow like hues of the thin broken fragments, the huge massy icicles hanging from the perpendicular rocks with the snow sliding from the steep southerly rocks with amazing velocity produced a crash and grumbling like the shock of an earthquake, the echo of which remained in the valley for several minutes.'

While Douglas and his party covered some thirty miles in the Rockies in long, arduous days one bright spot for him was when he captured alive a young eagle, and, managing to make a rough sort of cage, carried it with him hoping to make a present of it to the Zoological Society of London. After this thirty miles of ascending and descending the pine- and snow-covered scenic beauties of the Rockies he reached level country and navigable river travel once more. Here ice and fast snow-water currents in the headwaters made canoeing dangerous and difficult, yet despite this he reached Jasper House on 7th May.

There was only a short rest here and then a 4 a.m. start on Shanks's pony to make for Lesser Slave Lake and then on to Fort Edmonton on the Saskatchewan River. To cross a shallow lake on the way the party had to chop down trees to make a raft; at another river crossing the current was so patently violent and fast running that they sent a strong swimmer across well roped. When he got to the other side he hauled the rest of them across the turbulent waters one by one. There was some bad going on one stretch in swamp condition where 'we often sank up to our middles in mud and water'. Just after one of these slimy encounters Douglas heard a howling of sledge dogs in the distance and, knowing this meant strangers 'and being all over mud I returned half a mile to a small lake, stripped and plunged myself in and then comforted myself in a clean shirt which I carried on my back in a bundle'.

Meeting the owner of the sledge later he commented: 'I was most kindly received by Mr John Rowland, who had supper prepared for me of fine moose deer steaks which were most acceptable after a walk of 43 miles through a most wretched country without having anything to eat.'

It was well into May now, and on a Saturday evening at the fort 'some one brought a violin and we had to have a dance in his honour. I could not do less than endeavour to please by jumping for dance I could not'.

From Edmonton he took to canoe again, and had not travelled far when an empty canoe was seen. Shots were heard not far away, and guessing there was trouble Douglas left the river and plunged into woodland in the direction of the shots. He found a Mr McDonald gored by a wounded bull. The poor man had been thrown into the air and was senseless. A quick check showed Douglas—who was often known to the Indians as Dr Douglas, for he invariably carried a few drugs and a sharp knife for rough surgery with him—that he was badly injured, 'having literally opened the whole back part of the thigh to the bone'. He found that the beast's horns had gone through the pouch, coat, vest, flannel and cotton shirts, bruised the skin and broken two ribs. 'He was bruised all over, but had no other part materially cut,' said the amateur doctor, 'except the thigh and his left wrist dislocated. My lancet always in my pocket like a watch I had him bled and his wounds bound up. When he was carried to the boat I gave him 25 drops of laudanum and procured sleep and sent him off to Carlton for a doctor if there was one about.'

Douglas himself was now making for Norway House on the tip of Lake Winnipeg via the Saskatchewan River, Carlton House, Cumberland House and the lake. Naturally he collected specimens and seed throughout the whole of the journey; and said himself there was never a day on this extraordinary journey when he hadn't to change the drying papers, rearrange his seeds and dry out plants whatever the night.

One of the lovely evergreen shrubs he found, its branches gracefully festooned with twelve-inch-long furry catkins, was one he named for Nicolas Garry, the secretary of the Hudson's Bay Company who had acted as father and mother to him during his stay —it was *Garrya elliptica*.

He was now within reasonable sight of his destination—York Factory on the north-west shores of Hudson Bay—which he reached on 28th August after having canoed part of the way with Franklin the explorer, an exhausted and rather poorly man whose eyesight, never too good, had become worse with snow blindness caused by his travels through the Rockies. He had canoed and trekked some 2,900 miles.

Yet when Douglas left for England on 15th September 1827, despite his sickness he had a great thought to sustain him: he knew he had eclipsed in every way any expectation of success his patrons Sabine, Hooker and the Horticultural Society could ever have had of him in their wildest botanical dreams.

He had sent during his almost three-year stay, and was taking with him now, the floral wealth of a vast continent which was to transform in a few years the English garden scene. It was good he had these sustaining thoughts, for a severe storm in Hudson Bay almost cost him his life on two counts, starvation and drowning, and so much was he weakened by the experience that he was confined to his bunk for almost the whole of the voyage home.

When he did arrive at Portsmouth on 11th October he found his fame had gone before him. In London botanical and scientific circles he was treated as a hero and lionized in their society. So much had his hunting success impressed the learned societies that he was elected a fellow—a very rare honour indeed for a mere Scottish gardener—of the Linnean, Geological and Zoological Societies without fee.

Some part of his time now was spent in the Horticultural Society's gardens helping to arrange his specimens in the herbarium and attending to the propagation of his many hundreds of seeds. Part of the time he spent studying surveying under Captain Edward Sabine, his patron's brother; he also wrote several papers for the societies he had been made a member of, but his successes in the field had been too resounding for any employer ever to let such a man rest on his laurels. In the preface to the *Horticultural Society's Transactions* for 1830 his work was well summed up and his fate sealed when, writing of the plants in the Society's gardens, the writer says: 'In the ornamental department the most extensive and valuable of these collections is unquestionably that formed by Mr David Douglas. Of the species thus introduced about 120 have been raised in the gardens of the Society and after having abandoned the multitude of those which present no other interest than of botanical curiosity, 130 species are now growing and nearly the whole of which have been furnished to the Fellows and to the principal public gardens . . .

'The peculiar value attached to these plants which are hardy enough to bear our climates without any protection in winter, many of which are also distinguished by their great beauty, had induced the Council to engage the same indefatigable collector to undertake a fresh expedition to the same country with such additional means and assistance as the difficulties experienced by him in his former journey had rendered necessary.' He had proved such an apt pupil at surveying that the Colonial Office also commissioned him to map the new territory he would travel in, setting him up with instruments as well as paying some of his salary.

So it was that, two years almost to the day he had returned, he was setting out again on 26th October 1829 under Hudson's Bay patronage once more for the Columbia River via Cape Horn and the Sandwich Isles. He reached his old base, Fort Vancouver, on 3rd June of the following year. The rest and the sea journey made a new man of him. With a little Scotch terrier at his side now he made two journeys into the interior immediately, one in a southerly direction, the other to the east where he made the glorious discovery in the mountains just south of the Columbia cascades at 4,000 feet of the stately *Abies amabilis*, standing 150 feet and clothed to the ground with graceful, sweeping branches; and went on to discover *Abies grandis*, another of the giant, majestic firs of north-west America with an elegant feathered sweep of branches of foliage. In October he dispatched three chests of seeds to London, but towards the end of 1830 travelling, he found, became more and more dangerous. The Indians were hostile, the tribes were warring with one another, and there was bad blood and hatred towards the white man largely caused by some unscrupulous fur traders who had, unlike the Hudson's Bay Company people, given the brave a taste for strong liquor, very often defrauding him into the bargain and getting rich hauls of fur for little or nothing. There was also raging through the Indian territory 'a dreadful intermittent fever' which depopulated whole villages, 'dead bodies being strewn in every direction on the sands of the river'.

So it was that a lone white traveller like Douglas, with but a little terrier at his heels and a single Indian guide as companion, was easy game for any Indian with a hatred of white men, and there were hundreds such.

It was actually 10th December when Douglas decided fate and fortune were against him on his beloved Columbia, and he left for California. A few days before Christmas he was making his way from where San Francisco now stands to the Spanish settlement at Monterey, where he made his base at a monastery and planned a series of excursions into what has been called a botanical paradise. He intended to return to the Columbia in the summer of 1831. As at that time there was no shipping going north and no other transport he stayed on in California, going as far south as Santa Barbara and San Diego. Douglas was now a well-seasoned professional traveller and plant hunter and the Californian hinterland was an Aladdin's cave to him. It was here that he first came across the giant redwood trees, and he was the first botanist to describe them in their titanic immensity, their almost unbelievable natural splendour and the miracle of their hundreds of years of growth. It was here in their shady depths and fertile outskirts he was able to write home saying he had found twenty new genera and 360 new species of flowers, shrubs and trees, one of them being *Abies nobilis*, probably the grandest of the silver firs, towering 300 feet above him and furnished with deep, glaucous green branches from towering top to the pine-needled carpet whence it rose.

Spending three weeks in the Shasta Mountains in a forest country containing little else than this conifer giant, Douglas wrote: 'I could not cease to admire it.' He found too the herculean *Abies menziesii* with its characteristic whorled branches, as well as *A. douglasii* (now unfortunately renamed *Pseudotsuga menziesii*), the Douglas fir from which the flag-staff at Kew is made, an almost fabulous tree with its ruler-straight trunk soaring 200 feet to the sky without a single branch or blemish before fanning out in a beautiful crown of foliage, with a trunk ten feet round at a height of four feet from the ground.

After nineteen months in California Douglas tore himself away, having dispatched his Californian treasures to England. These included new mimulus, clarkia, colochortus, phlox, gilia, collomia, heuchera, oenotheras, penstemon and poppies as well as hundreds of cones of the pines he so delighted in—he wrote to Hooker: 'You must think I manufacture pines at my pleasure.'

On 18th August 1832 he boarded a forty-ton ship for the Columbia via the Sandwich Isles, of which journey he wrote at the time: 'Who could have thought 40 years ago of passing more than half the great basin of the Pacific in such a craft?' It was a nineteen-day sail to the Sandwich Isles. Douglas stepped ashore at Honolulu hoping to climb the volcano there, but an attack of rheumatism laid him low. While he was nursing his aches and pains he was most distressed to learn that his first friend and patron, Joseph Sabine, had resigned from the secretaryship of the Horticultural Society to avoid a scandal involving embezzlement. Feeling that his old master had been wronged he took a most decisive step and resigned his official connection with the Society in protest before he left Honolulu. He decided in future that his seed collections would be shared at his discretion between his first patron, Dr Hooker of Glasgow, and the Horticultural Society. From the islands he shipped nineteen large bundles of dried plants in two large chests, together with seeds which were placed in the captain's own cabin at Douglas's request. After a short stay to recuperate and get over the shock of the Sabine affair he took ship for the Columbia and Fort Vancouver, which he reached on 14th October.

From the fort he made a few short excursions at the end of the season round the fort and up the river, but did not start out on any large-scale hunting expedition until the February of 1833, when he went to Puget Sound in present-day Washington State, returning in mid March.

With only a few days' rest after this trip—most of it taken up with preparations for the next—he set out again on 19th March to explore the Fraser River and surrounding country up in British Columbia, the most northerly and least accessible region he had yet attempted. 'The country is certainly frightening,' he wrote; 'nothing but prodigious mountains to be seen.' His equipment for the trip was 5 lb. of tea, 5 lb. of coffee, 25 lb. of sugar, 15 lb. of rice, 50 lb. of biscuits, a gallon of wine, 10 lb. of powder, 10 lb. of ball, a little shot, a small silk fishing net, some angling tackle, a tent, two blankets, two cotton and two flannel shirts, a handkerchief, vest, coat and a pair of deerskin trousers, two pairs of shoes, one pair of stockings, twelve pairs of moccasins and a straw hat, a ream and a half of paper, several Indians, ten or twelve horses and 'my old terrier'. He spoke too in his journals home of the Indian plague which, praise be to God, had passed him by, but had laid low 140 Hudson's Bay people.

From what little we know of this daring and adventurous trip it is certain that it was a botanical success, but, alas, in canoeing down the river later in the year his frail craft hit a rocky islet in the Fort George canyon and he lost journals, all his personal possessions, his surveying instruments and four hundred specimens of plants and an innumerable collection of seeds. 'A disastrous day for me', he chronicled, 'on which I lost, what I may call, my all.' He was fortunate to escape with his life, for he was washed unconscious over the cataract and into a whirlpool below where, luckily, his canoe man managed to drag him ashore.

In November of that year he had travelled as far back as California from where on 11th November, from his tent pitched on the hills of Ferba Buena, somewhere in the region where San Francisco now stands, he wrote of the call of Honolulu with its tropical sunshine and waving palms, so vastly different from his gloomy pines and dim-lit forest ways. It was a call he answered, for three days before Christmas he arrived there. A short rest, and on the 27th he left for Byron's Bay (Hilo), Hawaii, and on the second day of 1834 set out to climb the volcano Mauna Loa. His letters showed he was revelling in the tropical vegetation as he wrote of trees covered with giant creeping and climbing plants, especially of tillandsias and of the graceful and stately tree ferns. Even here though it rained (he told his friends), so that there was mud in the chinks of the lava in which he sank up to his knees.

On the higher parts of the mountains he gathered a fern identical with '*Asplenium verida* of my own native country, a circumstance which gave me inexpressible pleasure and recalled to my mind many of the happiest scenes of my life'.

He climbed the volcano and into the awful pit of the crater, frightening himself almost to death as he nearly burnt the shoes off his feet, gave himself a headache and parched his throat; but he was delighted despite all this to record a temperature reading of 195·5° in a fissure. On coming down he took some cooling medicine and slept soundly.

He went back to Honolulu after a three-month stay spent climbing round the volcanoes of Hawaii, but returned to his enchanted island in July, when again the fascination of the two great volcanoes—Mauna Kea and Mauna Loa—held him in their thrall. On 12th July he dismissed his guide and with his little terrier by his side and a trusty stick in his hand, he set off across the north side of Mauna Loa—and fell into a pit into which a young bullock had already fallen.

Some hours later a passing native saw his feet in the pit and, looking closer, saw a body covered with dirt and rubbish. The native ran for Mr Gurney, a friend with whom Douglas had spent the previous night, who hurried back to see what help he could give to the happy traveller he had set on his way in the early morning. He shot the still alive and raging bullock and, with native helpers, got the broken body from the pit. The natives carried it, covered in a bullock hide, twenty-four miles to the shore and then in a canoe to Hilo's mission post.

'Could it be he?' the missionaries asked. 'The face was covered with dirt, the coat, pantaloons and shirt considerably torn, the hat was missing. On washing the corpse we found it in a shocking state; there were ten to twelve gashes on the head, a long one over the left eye, another rather deep just above the eye and a deep one behind the right ear. The left cheek bone appeared to be broken and also the ribs on the left side, the abdomen was much bruised and also the lower part of the legs trampled under the bullock's feet.'

Near to the pit the terrier and a bundle were found, so that it appeared that Douglas, who had once told a friend he would face a bear in a thicket but that the sight of a bullock grazing in a field was to him more dreadful than all the terrors of the forest, had been unable to control his curiosity, had laid down his bundle some few yards from the pit, had ventured to the edge to look in, had stood on the unstable sides which, giving way, had avalanched him into the pit.

At Honolulu on 4th August was buried David Douglas, aged thirty-five years, probably one of the most successful plant hunters the world of botany has ever known. Today his grave is unknown, and a memorial stone placed against the wall of the native church at Kawaiahao is scarcely decipherable.

The monument, which was subscribed for by botanical friends and admirers, reads: 'Here lies David Douglas, born in Scotland in 1799 who, being an indefatigable traveller, was sent out by the Royal Horticultural Society of London and fell a victim to science in the wilds of Hawaii on the 12th day of July, 1834.'

In his native village of Scone a monument (now in poor repair) subscribed for 'by the lovers of botany in Europe' says of him:

'In memory of David Douglas, a native of this parish, who from an ardent love of science and a desire to promote the improvement of botany visited the unexplored regions on the banks of the Columbia and southwards to California whence he transmitted a great variety of seeds of valuable trees and flowering plants adaptable to the climate of Great Britain, who, after devoting ten years of the prime of his life in adding to the arbor and flora of Europe suffered an accidental and lamented death in one of the Sandwich Isles on July 12th, 1834 in the 35th year of his age.'

His plant and tree introductions were legion and 'there is hardly a spot deserving of the name of garden either in Europe or the United States in which some of the discoveries of Douglas do not form the chief attraction'. Dr Charles Sprague Sargent, one of the most notable of American botanists, said of him that no other collector reaped such a harvest in America or associated his name with so many useful plants.

And what a magnificent array they made—the flowering currants, no fewer than fourteen, potentillas, antirrhinums, *Clarkia elegans*, penstemons (fourteen), the Californian poppy (eschscholtzia), *Garrya elliptica*, *Camassia esculenta*, *Limnanthes douglasii*, *Mahonia aquifolium*, musk (*Mimulus moschatus* and four others), godetias (three), *Nemophila insignis*, the snowberry (*Symphoricarpos racemosus*), *Lupinus rivularis*, *L. nanus*, *L. densiflorus*. *L. polyphyllus* (one of the parents of the modern lupin) and nineteen more, *Gilia capitata*, *Iris douglasii*, *Clematis douglasii*, many berberis, coreopsis, phacelia, *Gaillardia aristata*, gesnerias, loniceras, heucheras, oenotheras, meconopsis, *Sidalcea malvaeflora*, *Erigeron speciosa*, vacciniums, *Rubus spectabilis*, *Gaultheria shallon*, linums, *Clintonia elegans*, collinsia, *Ipomopsis elegans*, *I. douglasii* and *I. nivalis*, chelones, platystemons, leptosiphons, eutoca (three), lathyrus, spiraea (three).

Among the deciduous trees he introduced were red oaks, the maples *Acer circinnatum* and *A. macrophyllum*, *Amelanchier florida*, *Arbutus menziesii* and *Craetaegus douglasii*.

His collection of conifers was to alter the very landscape of this country as specimen trees, shelter belts and copses of his graceful, dignified pyramidal Pacific-coast giants sprang up on the great estates and on the lawns of the great houses throughout Great Britain.

Among them was the one he named for himself and which is still his finest monument, the Douglas fir (*Pseudotsuga douglasii*—now *P. menziesii*), the dense and prickly sitka spruce (*Picea sitchensis*) and the grand collection of towering pines—*Pinus lambertiana, ponderosa, sabiniana, coulteri, monticola, radiata* and *contorta*; then there were the beautifully decorative silver firs, the Abies—*A. grandis, A. nobilis, A. magnifica, A. menziesii, A. douglasii, A. amabilis* and *A. bracteata*.

It is obvious that had he lived Douglas would from his journals have written one of the finest adventure stories of all times which, coupled with his success story as a plant hunter, would have been one of the most fascinating books to have come out of botanical travel. There is no doubt that his early death robbed the world of an autobiography which would have been a travel classic.

8. Revolutionary Methods

WHILE Douglas had been plunging his way through the gloom of the giant redwood forests, or seeking natural treasure amidst the everlasting snows of the Rocky Mountains, the gardeners of England had advanced in their techniques of propagation, in the structure of their propagating houses and covered gardens generally, so that it could be truthfully said they could grow almost anything from anywhere—once they had received it in a viable state.

As has been said previously, Douglas's finds were hardy, and his principal method of introduction was by seed. His plants and his trees furnished the borders and the parklands of the great country houses and the gardens of the villagers' cottages as they had never been furnished before.

Yet the owners of the big houses and their extraordinarily skilful gardeners (of whom Joseph Paxton, at Chiswick first, and by 1830 well established at Chatsworth for the Duke of Devonshire, was an outstanding one) still hankered after the exotic, the rare, the flamboyant and the novel in nature with which to grace the magnificent 'crystal palaces' now surrounding and, in many cases, actually adjoining their homes as vast, high-ranging conservatories—the jungles on the doorstep!

There still remained for these wealthy owners of vast estates and opulent stately homes the problem of transporting beautiful plants from a tropic or subtropic shore in full vigour to the imitative temperatures and surroundings of the glasshouses. So often in rain forest conditions or those of tropic humidity seed was difficult to come by, difficult to dry successfully and almost impossible to germinate under artificial conditions.

As has been seen, the old plant cabins, rough wooden boxes lidded with rough glass and accompanied by a welter of instructions for opening, shutting, the airing and watering of their precious content over thousand of miles of land and sea, were very much hit and miss affairs. Good luck played as much a part in the success of the operation as any gardening skill or pseudo-scientific technique. In the 1830's, however, members of the Horticultural Society had given close and reasoned thought to the problem. Some of the scientific facts surrounding plant transportation had been deduced and scientifically analysed so that it was possible to say that plants could exist and did exist under amazingly varied conditions of light and heat—from 30 to 40 degrees Fahrenheit below zero to 170 or 180 degrees; in half candlelight or the fierce noonday glare of a tropic sun.

It was an amateur naturalist who actually hit upon the secret of plant transportation at the same time as Douglas was feeding his eyes on orchids at Rio. He was Dr Nathaniel Bagshaw Ward, a general practitioner in the dockland of East London. He was examining, in the summer of 1829, a wide-mouthed bottle covered with a lid in which he had buried the chrysalis of a Sphinx butterfly in moist mould. Within a week or two there arose from the mould a seedling fern and grass. The doctor, speculating on this growth, noticed that the mould had kept moist because during the heat of the day moisture had risen from the mould, had condensed on the side of the bottle and run back again keeping up a similar degree of humidity all the time.

The fern and the grass lived for four years in the same bottle until the lid rusted and rain water got in when the doctor was on holiday. Being of a scientific nature and calling he thought about the phenomenon and decided that the plants had lived so long without any man-given aid or attention because of 'a moist atmosphere free from soot or other extraneous particles; light, heat, moisture and periods of rest and change of air'.

Dr Ward was known to Anderson of the Chelsea Botanic Garden, Sir W. J. Hooker at Kew, and Dr Lindley of the Horticultural Society, and he knew of their difficulties in transporting plants and seeds, and had in fact talked personally to Menzies, who had told him the sad story that on his voyage round the world with Vancouver he had lost all his living plants. So with the bottle as a beginning, in 1833 Dr Ward decided to go on from there and had two cases modelled on the principle of the bottle, but shaped like the old plant cabins, with all glass sides and tops, suitably strengthened at the corners and edges, and as hermetically sealed as the manufacturers could make them—in the other words a miniature, nearly air-sealed greenhouse!

He filled the two cases with other ferns and grasses and sent them to Sydney, where they arrived in perfect condition. The return journey of the Wardian cases was the real test, however, for in February 1834 the cases were filled with plants which included *Gleichenia microphylla* and *Callicoma serratifolia*. They travelled by ship through a temperature range of 90 to 100 degrees in Sydney, down to 20 degrees at Cape Horn with the decks covered with frost and snow, rising to 100 degrees at Rio, up to 120 degrees crossing the line, and arrived eight months later in the English Channel at a temperature of 40 degrees. The plants, which had been placed on deck and never watered, were found to be healthy and vigorous. For the first time a gleichenia had been brought to this country alive.

Now the way was open to an absolutely new and glorious world of floral gold, of exotic botanical treasure only before heard of in travellers' tales or dimly glimpsed in dry-as-dust, colourless herbarium specimens.

Naturally the great nurserymen of the period, Conrad Loddiges & Sons, of Hackney, London, the specialists in exotic plants at the time, tried out the new wonder and recorded its efficacy and practicability. The news was exciting, the prospects held out almost beyond imagination, and, down in the heart of the Peak District of Derbyshire at Chatsworth, the sixth Duke of Devonshire and his gardener, Joseph Paxton, saw an opportunity to fill their new glasshouses being built at the time—1835—with a flora worthy of a duke's collection of rarities and of a Paxton's overwhelming keenness and enthusiasm to make his master's plant collection second to none in the land.

They came to a decision, spurred on by the wondrous tales they had heard of a fabulous tree of Ind—*Amherstia nobilis*—described by Dr Nathaniel Wallich, a Danish surgeon, Superintendent of the East India Company's botanical garden at Calcutta, as being one of the superlative wonders of the flowering tree world. It had first been found, it was rumoured, covered with its stabbing, startling blood-red flowers, in a Burmese monastery garden where the devout devotees of the Buddha offered them as floral sacrifice to the graven images of their Lord and Master.

No one in England had such a tree, no one in England had much hope of getting such a tree—the expense, the hardships, the extreme difficulty of transporting this Far Eastern treasure to these inclement shores were all against it; but that was the challenge the duke and Paxton wanted.

Money was no object—only a short time before this the duke, in Russia on the king's business, had spent some £80,000 of his own money. The gardens at Chatsworth were costing him over £9,000 a year. Yes, they would send to India for Amherstia and as many rare orchids and strange exotic plants as could be found and brought back alive to their glass temples. Between them they looked over with quizzical eyes the young, keen under-gardeners Paxton had gathered round him. Their choice fell on an unmarried man, John Gibson, who was about twenty-four at the time. He had been at Chatsworth but two years and before that, according to the embossed notepaper he was still using, he had worked at the nearby nursery of John Smith at Darley Dale.

From the extreme insularity of the Derbyshire countryside of the early 1800's this young man, who had probably never travelled farther than Matlock or Chesterfield, and who was almost certainly the product of a small village school in which the three R's would be the only subjects, was the one chosen to be sent to the far ends of the earth, to a strange land where every single aspect was ineffably alien to his upbringing and background.

That was John Gibson's lot, and how well he carried out his mission subsequent events showed in the highest degree. Either the duke and Paxton were infallible judges of character or they made men of sterner stuff in those days!

From the very day he left Chatsworth—20th April 1835—John Gibson proved himself the right man for the job, and long before he left the country his letters to Paxton are packed with solid common sense stemming from what was obviously a more than normal keenness of observation and an almost fanatical sense of duty.

But first let us see what was expected of this journeyman gardener catapulted from a Chatsworth anonymity to hobnobbing with a governor-general of India. The memorandum he carried from the duke showed very well indeed what his master expected—supreme resource and diligence on the part of his servant.

These terms of reference copied out by Gibson told him he was to proceed to Calcutta and present a signed letter from the duke to Dr Nathaniel Wallich, already, as we have seen, a name to conjure with in the learned botanical world for his book on Asiatic plants. But if Dr Wallich wasn't there, or didn't think the time propitious for plant hunting, then 'Gibson will have to decide, assisted by Dr Wallich, whether to remain in Calcutta or proceed on board *Jupiter* to Ceylon. At Ceylon he will have the same sort of decision to make. If Sir Robert Wilmot Horton should have left Ceylon Gibson must seek the principal person at the head of the Government and request him on the part of the Duke of Devonshire to open the letter to Sir Robert and have the goodness to consider it addressed to him. Gibson may find it desirable to make a journey into the interior of Ceylon to collect plants, in which case he must inquire what chance there would be of any opportunity of returning to England and of sending plants of his finding.'

Yes, Gibson was certainly on his own, cap in hand to lords, governors and government servants, generally deferential to learned botanists, and as easy as might be with a posse of near head-hunting, betel-chewing natives. One wonders what a Derbyshire gardener thought of seeking out 'the principal person at the head of the Government'.

Not that Gibson's outgoing from these shores was an easy process. Not a bit of it. He went up to London by coach on a journey that was probably his easiest for the next two years, to find out details of his 169-days' journey under sail from Woolwich to Calcutta in one of His Majesty's ships. He wrote back to Chatsworth joyously that all was well; he had fixed up ship and berth and was to travel in H.M.S. *Jupiter*.

He had seen the captain and was to travel as part of the staff of the new Governor-General of India, Lord Heytesbury. Already his vigorous mind was away; plans crowded in thick and fast. They were to call at Madeira a month—he would collect there; they were to stay at Rio a month where he would travel into the interior and 'I hope I shall reap a good harvest . . . I hope to fill my expectations with satisfaction on the island [Madeira] that so much abounds with plants. . . . If you know of any island where I should be likely to find anything I should be glad if you would inform me'.

John Lindley, secretary of the Horticultural Society, and orchid specialist, went down with John to the ship lying at Woolwich to see the boatswain about his berth. 'I like it very much,' Gibson wrote to Chatsworth. 'It will be very comfortable. The boatswain seems to be a quiet and intelligent civil man. I shall be quite retired from the rest of the crew.'

A little snag arose, however; after all, his master would never have had to see to such things and Paxton had never travelled so far; Gibson found he had to provide all his own bedding, towels, soap and several more personal items. He went out and bought them and sent along the itemized account to Paxton. Now there was a bigger snag. Sir Robert Peel's government had fallen and with it Lord Heytesbury's Governor-Generalship as well as Gibson's sailing arrangements. The duke fortunately had a foot in both camps and, when Lord Melbourne appointed Lord Auckland, Gibson found himself on the new Governor-General's staff. But of course this took time, and in the meanwhile his baggage so neatly stowed aboard *Jupiter* had been unshipped.

That did not stop this indefatigable man from improving the shining hour. He went along to see Mr Low, of Hugh Low & Co.'s nurseries at Clapham, where he had secured dry moss for plant packing and gave a hand to Mr Bailey, the duke's head gardener at Chiswick.

September came along—he had left Chatsworth in April—and John was still kicking his heels at Chiswick Garden. Did ever a treasure hunt start so dismally?

But things were stirring, and on 12th September Gibson was able to report that Lord Auckland had been named Governor-General, the *Jupiter* had been recommissioned and a great store of medical and ornamental plants as well as fruit bushes and trees had to be got to the ship from Mr Anderson of the Chelsea Physic Garden, and Chatsworth too, and be most carefully packed and stored on shipboard by the young gardener.

Seeds for Calcutta were also in his charge from the Horticultural Society. Now he was hurrying about here and there. The day before his letter to Paxton he had been along to the Admiralty, where Lord Auckland was just handing over the reins of First Lord to his successor, to see if he wanted any particular plants to take to India with him from the Chatsworth gardens. How did he gain access to his elevated presence? Gardeners must have had charm in those days. He had been down to the docks again, and his friend the boatswain had told him he would be boarding with his lordship and that his messing had been agreed at four shillings per day.

Seeing that orchids were, after amherstia, one of the main objects of his journey, Gibson lost no time in looking at the latest arrivals from all parts of the world that were starting to brighten the scene and excite the eye in the great London nurseries of the early nineteenth century. He went along to Conrad Loddiges at Hackney, there seeing several kinds of orchids in flower—*Angraecum caudatum, peristeria* 'and 20 other common kinds', for Gibson was critical and his standards were high. At Joseph Knight's, the Exotic Nurseries in the King's Road, Chelsea, he reported a 'beautiful new eulophia in colour most splendid and is a fine foliage plant. I do not see much else that is very good'.

Packing his most valuable cargo of plants for India was now his most urgent and difficult problem. Dr Lindley, it seems, had recommended to the duke the new-fangled packing-case advocated by Dr Ward, and Gibson was to be one of the first of the gardener guinea-pigs to try it out. While at Loddiges' he took the opportunity of talking to Conrad, who was the first man to have used the case to bring back an orchid

alive. He wrote also to the practical Paxton to see what he had to say about this novel
idea, although of course both knew the duke was determined to try out the cases whatever the cost. 'This kind of packing-case', Gibson wrote, 'has been sent from the
tropics with the greatest of success, the plants having arrived in the finest order and
have again been sent from England to other parts of the tropics with equal success
according to the statement of Mr Loddiges who is the person who received and sent
them back and is now making use of the same kind of case universally. The description
of the case is that in the first place they are styled airtight boxes, the tops are screwed on
and the plants never allowed to get any water or air after being well watered when first
put in the case. As the water evaporates without escaping from the box and condenses
it is said that it is found to be a sufficient supply during the voyage. It is the same form
as the common Indian case but there is a slide at the end and when open it has the
appearance of a dog kennel. This is to admit the plants as the tops are to be screwed on.
But in large cases the plants are put in before the tops are fixed. The top is to be glazed
with fragments of plate glass and made airtight.'

Ever careful and diligent, John paused to say he had noticed that Mr Loddiges,
because of the high price of plate glass, even short bits, had covered his case with
ordinary glass and used a wire cover, a much cheaper job and just as effective.

At last *Jupiter* set sail and on 1st October from Spithead Gibson gave Paxton a full
account of the last hectic days before they took to the high seas; winds and rough seas
had laid many of the crew, but not Gibson, in the scuppers.

At Spithead Lord Auckland and his suite came aboard, accompanied by his two
sisters the Misses Eden, Miss Emily and Miss Fanny. Once they were settled in, *Jupiter*
weighed anchor on 3rd October. In his letter Gibson took occasion to thank Paxton for
the signal honour he had done him in selecting him for this exciting trip. 'I cannot but
reflect', he told the great gardener, 'and say that I shall never be able to repay you for
your unbounded kindness to me except by acting up to your desires and wishes as far as
lays in my power.'

He mentioned with pride how he had been able to get his plant boxes placed on the
poop, railed off to keep the curious sailor away from them, for the poop was the known
place for plants on board ship from a gardener's point of view, but what captains and
officers thought and said about the practice would probably add a most lurid page to
naval and mercantile history! He was not at all pleased, at this stage, with the looks of
the plants in the new cases, but he reported that his plants in open cases looked very
well indeed. 'I do not like the appearance of the plants in the so much famed air-tight
cases, they do not look so well as those in the common cases. I can perceive a difference
in them already, but the weather has been so dreadfully cold since they were shipped
that if I can keep them safe another fortnight then there will be no danger afterwards.'
But his charges in the open cases were a lot more trouble to Gibson, for when it was hot
they had to be opened out and watered and when the storms came they had to be
tarpaulin-covered and roped down to keep out any salt spray, a sure plant killer.

A rough list of plants he was taking out for Dr Wallich showed he had under his care figs, peaches, nectarines, plums, apples, pears, vines and a case full of greenhouse plants from the Horticultural Society, two very rich cases from Kew, one of them containing *Aracauria excelsa* (the Norfolk Island Pine), *A. cunninghamii* and *A. imbricata* (the Monkey Puzzle tree). To fill a particular request of Dr Wallich he had packed also three fine plants of a glycine species, a plant for the stove introduced from Guinea only some fifteen years before, which, he said, the doctor thought as much of as he did of amherstia. Also in the cargo from Lee's Nursery was *Ornus rotundifolia* (fraxinus), styrax (a small flowering tree from China) and pistacia (the mastic tree).

Sixteen days later the postmark on his letter was Madeira. *Jupiter* had made a record run of ten days, on three of them covering 240 miles in the day; not without discomfort, though, for Miss Eden said, and it was agreed by the crew, that she was the noisiest craft afloat, such a 'rolling, creaking article' that it was literally true that two persons could not make themselves heard in a cabin, such was the noise of the timbers and spars.

Straight away John Gibson was ashore thirsting for first plant blood. 'I have visited all the gardens in the Island which are of any note but without success of finding anything new.'

He was pleased, however, to see the different kinds of plants growing 'spontaneous'. After all, hours and hours of art and artifice, with no expense spared, had to be lavished on similar plants he had only ever seen under glass at home. Here they were just growing wild—oranges, lemons, grapes, bananas and guavas. 'I did not expect to see *Dacrydium elatum* which is very plentiful here, likewise also the finest species of salvia; the natives make hedges of the myrtle and fuchsias and mix the different species of fuchsias according to colour and at regular distances which is very beautiful. I am surprised at finding such fine species of *Erythrina crista-galli* [the coral tree] and not less surprised with the bigotry and disdain with which the natives treat this beautiful plant on account of the form of its flowers which they say is the imitation of the most secret organs of the feminine gender, the females are supposed to pass this plant without ever elevating their eyes when in its finest dress. But His Lordship when seeing the plant (as large as an oak tree) in full flower could not pass without a branch of it to acknowledge his gratification.'

Gibson noted very many common cacti and an abundance of *Passiflora quadrangularis*, and a plant indigenous to the island which the natives called the English tomato and which, he said, was the most beautiful preserve he had ever tasted and was also good in tarts. He had tasted it at a private house and found out that it was *Physalis peruviana* (the Cape gooseberry) and that it could be grown in England very easily. An oxalis was noted and there was a short dissertation on Madeira: 'The natives are a curious race of people imbibing much bigotry but very civil. The island is very mountainous and very pleasant.' His plants were looking very well, and now for Rio.

Madeira was left behind on the 18th and a fine, quick passage saw *Jupiter* tying up in Rio harbour on 16th November. Four days later another epistle went off to Chatsworth. The season was wrong for collecting in Rio, but they had crossed the line and he along with 108 others had been put through the traditional ceremonies at the Court of

Neptune. All 109 had been shaved and ducked in a giant sailcloth filled with water and rigged up on deck. What with pitch for lather and broken-down old razors as well as the extremely rough handling, many came out of the ordeal much the worse for wear, but Gibson wrote blithely of his part and boasted, 'I was not exempt'.

The weather not being propitious for collecting did not stop Gibson seeing what there was to see of the flora, and his eagle eye noticed twenty species of orchids in flower, principally epidendrums and vanda, as well as common kinds he did not think worth mentioning by name. He painted an exotic picture for Paxton and the duke, writing of the abounding beauties of billbergias, and tillandsias mixed with rhipsalis (mistletoe cactus) and musa forming a most curious scene; there was too such an abundance of tropical fruits of all kinds: ananas, breadfruit, bananas, jacquinias and numerous others which were hardly noticed by the natives. He had seen the barringtonia in flower and fruit, but the finest plant he had seen was *Poinciana pulcherrima* which shone above everything else in company with it. Creepers were numerous, and among them he had found the same species he had seen in the greenhouses at home.

He had travelled seven miles inland to see the Botanic Garden, laid out, he reported, in masterly style, but not kept up very well, although a hedge of *Gardenia radicans* delighted him not only for its beauty but for its fragrance. As a last piece of profitable time-filling he had arranged with an English gardener of a Rio resident to send plants to the duke listed by him (Gibson) which he thought would do well and look well at Chatsworth.

After a voyage which brought gales, a spell in the doldrums, short rations of both meat and water, and a hectic night when two sails, several booms and part of the rigging were carried away, next stop was the Cape of Good Hope where *Jupiter* arrived on 14th December. Here the Dutch had gardened for years and from hundreds of miles inland had brought the Cape Province botanical harvest to a well-maintained botanical garden. There Gibson had a royal time. He made what he called a most extensive collection of Cape plants for the Calcutta Gardens, including four species of zamia, six plants of *Tamus elephantipes* (*Testudinaria dioscorea*), *Banksia serrata*, twelve eucalyptus, seven acacia species, a fine collection of Cape bulbs and about two hundred species of flower seeds as well as fruits of the Cape.

He had been fortunate, he told them at Chatsworth, to meet Baron Ludwig, the famed German botanist employed at the Cape by the Dutch, and had found him both genial and generous, for not only had Gibson been shown the particularly fine garden but from the same source he had been provided with the Calcutta selection as well as means for his first practical test as a collector—a light wagon and six horses for a journey upcountry. His companion, introduced by the baron, was James Bowie, an experienced Kew collector, former companion to Francis Masson, as instructor and guide.

On their first day out in the veldt they travelled twenty miles, Gibson reporting a collection of no less than two hundred species of plants. He saw the weird heads of the protea, the abundant heaths and leguminous plants and, naturally, a fine array of Cape bulbs blooming in their natural haunts not, as at home, in the cold house after infinite care. But John was not yet carried away, for while he admitted that many of the plants he had seen would be new to Chatsworth, and that was an admission coming from him, he found them neither very new nor very valuable, and said so. One thing he proved to his own satisfaction, and he told the botanically minded genius at Chatsworth of his discovery, was that there were epiphytic orchids at the Cape. Contrary to the general opinion, he reported they were there and he had seen one brought by Mr Bowie from a spot four hundred miles from Cape Town. Once again he pursued his master's interests with avidity, and although his stay was not long at the Cape, he pressed Paxton for the duke to write to Baron Ludwig so that Chatsworth would have access to the Cape plants he had seen, as he knew the baron would oblige. It is almost certain Gibson asked him to do so, for Paxton related that next year, 1837, the botanical baron stripped his garden at the Cape of the rarest produce of Africa because of what he had been told about the new conservatory.

Another toilsome journey was in front of Gibson and *Jupiter* as they left the Cape and voyaged into hotter and hotter climates. For seventy-two days they were out of sight of land altogether, and not until 2nd March did they sail off Saugar with a jungle landscape in the offing. Two days later they were looking forward to a successful landing at Calcutta staithe, but when in tow the ship was caught in an eddy and driven aground so that the whole party transferred to a steamer for the last few miles upriver.

The first news of Gibson's arrival at his journey's end was to Paxton from J. W. Masters, the English head gardener at the Botanic Gardens with whom Gibson was lodged since Dr Wallich, the curator, was in Assam. He gave a delightful picture of the young under-gardener receiving his first view of amherstia, which for the first time since planting in the gardens had lit its blood-red blooms. 'Mr Gibson appears fully alive to the work that is given him,' wrote Masters, 'and when he sees the *Amherstia nobilis* or a new orchid he runs round it clapping his hands like a boy who has got three runs in a cricket match.'

'Gibson's splendid collection of plants, embracing a great many which we had not in the garden,' had arrived and, glory be, the duke's experiment with the Wardian cases had succeeded, for those plants packed in them were in the best order. The gardens as a whole must have made a striking impression on the Derbyshire gardener, for at that time it was famed throughout the botanical world as the most beautiful tropical garden in existence, with its great Cycas palm avenue, its groves of teak, mahogany and cinnamon, and its great banyan tree which some years later was measured at 80 feet high and 300 feet through.

After what had obviously been a most joyous landing and initiatory survey of the garden with such evident enthusiasm Gibson sat down on 2nd April 1836 to write to Paxton himself about his adventures. First of all he had seen to the return by *Jupiter* to Chatsworth of a case of orchids and seeds from the garden. Many of them had been on his request list made out before he left. He had used the Wardian cases for this since, he reported, the plants he had brought by that method had done well, and only the fact

Above: An example of the magnificent and ornate conservatories being built during the nineteenth century to house the wealth of tropical and subtropical plants being sent home by the plant hunters. *Below:* It was to the Great Conservatory at Chatsworth House that all Gibson's treasures were consigned.

A near contemporary view of the Calcutta Botanic Gardens set up by the East India Company and the base for Gibson's Upper Bengal plant hunting.

The kind of craft and scenery on the *jheels*, the flooded waterways of Bengal, through which Gibson passed from Calcutta, by water, to the foot of the Khasi hills.

The Cherrapunji plateau from which Gibson worked the Assam hills.

The Mamloo Cas
cades seen by
Gibson on his wa
from Pandua to t
foot of the Khasi
Hills.

The wild jungle scenery, with a bridge made of aerial roots, which Gibson found he had exchanged for the urbanities of the Derbyshire countryside.

that they had no special greenhouse in which to unpack them, as they had at Chatsworth, had meant the death of many in the scorching atmosphere of Calcutta.

This did not suit Gibson, so carefully trained to look upon plants as delicate children in need of every care and attention from seedling stage to flowering glory. He told Paxton he could not stand to see valuable orchids brought from far Tibet or Assam 'stuck up to an old shady mango tree and left to themselves to live or die. I think I shall be able to introduce a system of growing them in pots which will be a great improvement in this place. Some few which I have potted in the Cooperian [James Cooper, famed orchid grower for Earl Fitzwilliam at Wentworth Woodhouse in Yorkshire] system in small pots are growing well which gives me great encouragement. The most beautiful of all the plants amherstia is still in flower and will apparently keep on for some time. There is not a hope of getting seeds from it this season.'

In the meantime he had been busy at Barrackpore higher up the Hoogli at the Governor-General's country home, where he had laid out a new garden for the ladies; 'there is a fairy flower garden directly opposite the house', wrote Miss Eden. He had also spent some time 'in arranging and correcting the place'.

By now Gibson had taken stock, he had seen the climate, had experienced the practice of bringing plants alive to India from England, he had seen, in miniature, what sort of plants grew where and now he had formulated his plans for the future exchange of horticultural treasure.

On 4th April, therefore, he wrote Paxton (the letter got to Portsmouth on 4th September): 'I am induced to write a few lines on the subject of importing plants to India from England which will not only benefit this country and enrich the collection of the Botanical Garden of Calcutta but will continue the anxious communication of sending plants from India to England which will doubly repay for any trouble which may be incurred, particularly as the Duke of Devonshire is so anxious to extend his collection, the interest of receiving Indian plants a year hence will be the same as at the present time. And as European plants are equally desirable in India it will likewise be as interesting to introduce them into this country. I have drawn up a list of different kinds of fruit trees, shrubs, seeds which are particularly desirable as there are no such things in the country which is the following: grapes, peaches, nectarines, pines, plums, apples, pears, gooseberries, currants, strawberries and any other fruit trees, all the European forest trees particularly oaks, ash, pines, beeches; shrubs—hawthorn, holly, laurel, box or any other shrubs. Flower seeds—heartsease, ten-week stocks, Grecian stocks and any other kind of flower seeds however common. The coreopsis, hollyhock and larkspur are here, but no other common European flower so any of the above will be thought rarities. The time of sending the different seeds will be noticed as no other month is as desirable for their arrival as September or October. If they arrive long before or long after this time they cannot be sown in consequence of which they soon perish and are lost. The time allowed for the passage is generally 14 weeks. There is not so much difficulty as to the season of arrival of plants but the above mentioned time is preferable. All boxes sent to this garden are refilled and returned. I did not say anything about *Musa superba* which I have sent but I will now say that it is one of the most showy plants in this garden, the stem grows to an immense circumference, as much as 1½ feet in diameter with beautiful fine foliage. It is only propagated by seed, it does not throw up any succors.'

Other plans were being formulated too. Dr Wallich had returned from Assam where he had been searching for a rare tea plant, and letters and memoranda had passed to and fro between his garden on one side of the Hoogli River to Lord Auckland in Government House three miles farther upstream on the other.

With much botanical travelling experience behind him Dr Wallich had drawn up Gibson's plan of campaign, which had received the Governor-General's seal of approval. This had rather a damp start, for it laid down that Gibson should not set off on his journey upcountry until the rains began in June. Then the duke's gardener was to proceed by water to Chhatak in East Bengal, near the town of Sylhet in Assam, down the Surma River, proceeding from there to Cherrapunji in the Khasi range, a month's journey.

As a prelude to glories to come, with Lord Auckland's approval in hand Dr Wallich sat down on 15th May and wrote directly to the Duke of Devonshire assuring him of floral treasure unbounded, of orchidaceous wealth at which the imagination boggled; such a glittering prospect indeed that both the duke and Paxton must have gone into transports of joy as they already filled, in imagination, their tremendous new glasshouses with these jungle flowers of the east.

The plan he had in mind, Dr Wallich told the duke, would provide, besides amherstia, orchids and 'such a consignment of them I pledge myself has never been seen in England or anywhere in Europe. The plan will be forthwith put into execution by your gardener Gibson than whom I am sure a more trustworthy man could not have been selected for the interesting object Your Grace had in view, who is incessantly exerting himself to fulfil those objects and is wrapped up in delight at what he sees in the flora of this country, being from dawn of day until late in the evening out in the garden preparing a great variety of plants for future despatch. As soon as possible after the rainy season (the real summer here) has come next month, he will proceed to the Khoseea [Khasi] range of hills to a place called Chirrapoonje where he is to remain at least two months making excursions in all directions collecting and forwarding successively Your Grace's property of which good care shall be taken in this garden and, on his return, bringing whole boat loads with him.

'I have been on that range very lately in October and November last on my way across that part of the country to Assam, and I can declare with truth that the imagination cannot depict to itself a richer country in botanical rarities—above all orchidaceous plants.

'Amongst a vast variety of beauties of that sort I have seen almost whole trees covered with that most lovely epiphyte *Coelogyne wallichiana* and *C. candida*, especially the former. Almost all the plants noticed in the catalogue of the Linnean Society's East India herbarium presented to them by the munificence of the Court of Directors [of the

East India Company] as coming from Pandua, Sylhet, Cachar and Khoseea have been derived from the Chirrapoonje and its neighbouring eminences, this is also the case with regard to the species recorded by Dr Lindley in his valuable memoirs on the orchidea. I mention all this as a guarantee for the successful issue of Gibson's visit to this most interesting country.

'On his return he is to visit the coast of Martaban, another very rich field where, among others, he will procure plants, and, if possible, seeds of the Amherstia which Your Grace will be glad to learn has bloomed beautifully in March last in this garden—though I grieve to say before my return from my tea tour in Assam.'

To dot the i's and cross the t's of Dr Wallich, Gibson wrote to Paxton on 21st May telling him of his destination. 'It is famous for dendroba, coelogyne and aeridia—the splendid *Dendrobium teres*, lately figured is found there, there is likewise a species of peristeria found at Silhet which perhaps is entirely new, and besides there are many other fine species known to exist there and, indeed, from the strain of Dr Wallich's description of the orchids of Silhet, I hope to do something worth notice—there are two places of the name of Silhet, one is a town, the other is a district both in the province of Bengal. The district of Silhet is the appointed place for my harvest. To accomplish this in a proper manner it will take from three to four months, and the appointed time for me to start is about the 20th of next month [June] which time is the commencement of the rains. The next thing Dr Wallich proposes is a visit to the coast of Martaban and to Mulmain [Moulmein in Lower Burma], this last place is where the Amherstia grows and its native place and, as Dr Wallich cannot furnish me with a plant of the Amherstia from the Botanic Gardens, it is quite indisputable that it should be procured by some means or other, which, by acting according to the last proposal, it appears there will be no difficulty in attaining this grand object, and to render it his assistance Lord Auckland will write to his Agent in the Birmese [Burma] country to inform him of my coming, at the same time wishing him to give me all the assistance possible in getting Amherstia.

'This, I think, will be a most interesting track for me,' added Gibson, and went on to mention that Ceylon was out this season as the botanical doctor thought he could do better by not squandering his resources and strength and applying his zeal to the Khasi Hills flora. Gibson himself agreed, with a characteristic line to Paxton, 'for we must not attempt at too much, for what is done must be done well to ensure success'. Mind you, he took the precaution of saying that if success did not come his way on this first trip then he would stay another season and explore Ceylon. However, ignoring any question of failure the arrangements were, he told Paxton, that he should leave Calcutta about the middle of February next year (1837) which would allow him time to arrive in England about June. In the meantime the collection to be made for Chatsworth from the Botanic Garden had been arranged for according to Gibson's plans. As soon as the rains came work would start on what he thought would be a most valuable collection. They would all have been potted by June and, as plants grew quickly in the humid atmosphere, they would be well established for travelling in good time.

At the time of writing, however, things were vastly different from the rainy season.

'I cannot relate the miserable state in which every thing is now existing,' he explained; 'in consequence of the very dry weather and hot winds which prevail, everything is literally parched up. The thermometer ranges one day with another from 90 to 95 degrees in the shade and during the night about 80 degrees.'

He appreciated very highly the kindness shown to him by Lord Auckland and his sisters, the two Misses Eden, and told Paxton: 'I never saw, nor could I suppose that a man of such high appointments as Lord Auckland and of such high abilities would ever look upon a humble subject like myself with so much kindness.' But he had tried to repay it. 'I have done as you wished me with regard to Lord Auckland in doing anything he wishes. When Dr Wallich was absent I spent a good deal of time in the Barracpore garden [Lord Auckland's country seat].'

He had not as yet heard a word from Chatsworth, although it was almost twelve months since he left there and already it was July. The rains were later than usual and Gibson was still waiting impatiently to get off, but on the 3rd he told Chatsworth there was every sign of his immediate departure. 'The particular time has come when duty calls upon me, when I must exert myself to the utmost extent, as I have not in consequence of unfavourable seasons, as yet been engaged in that close and interesting pursuit [collecting], but now I am glad to inform you I am preparing to embrace the first part of my mission to Silhet in the course of three or four days when the present gale has ceased to blow. The rains are much later this season than they have been for some time but they are now come with a vengeance. My boat and everything is prepared and as soon as the weather is considered safe I shall start. Boats on this river are upset, go down in numbers, and are never afterwards heard of. The wind is so strong and so instantaneous that they have not time to get ashore before they are sunk.'

He was now in a position to persuade Dr Wallich that to dispatch plants to England then was the wrong time, as they would arrive in October, November or December just in time to be killed in the cold of the north Atlantic. He persuaded the doctor and Masters that January was the time for dispatch so that Chatsworth could look out for successive plant parcels from May to July after they had rounded the Cape in the summer season. Plants were at that time being prepared for that long voyage by being reduced in bulk and being potted into smaller pots. There were such plants as '*Careya herbacea* (stove shrub), *Jonesia asoca* (*Saraca indica*), *Liriodendron grandiflora* (tulip tree), *Bignonia amana*, *Aralia lusida*, *Hutchinsia glauca*, *Roxburghia viridiflora*, *Musa rubra*, *M. glauca* and *textilis* as well as any other plants which would be rare and valuable in England'.

He was able to report that his terrestrial orchids were flowering in the garden and, wonder of wonders, amherstia was showing new green again, putting on its fine velvet-like foliage for the third time since his arrival, as well as having flowered once. That seemed to show it was a fast-growing tree, and indeed Mr Masters had been fortunate to raise two young plants of the wonder tree by shoots on the Chinese method of propagating fruits.

He wondered very much about the chest of plants sent home from Calcutta by the

Jupiter; as yet he had not had a word from either Chatsworth or anywhere else in the homeland. He told how the *Jupiter* had taken the long way home, and after leaving Calcutta Garden Reach on 4th April had not arrived in Ceylon until 28th May, and did not sail again until 4th June. She was to touch at both the Cape and St Helena, taking five months to get home.

But that really was not a matter of great concern to Gibson just at that time, for he was already in imagination collecting in Assam and he anticipated his plans for the great harvest he never seemed to doubt he would gather. 'During my stay in Silhet I shall send to the botanic gardens two or three small packages of seed and plants every week by post and, as convenience may allow, despatch boats loaded with orchideae; the plants will then be prepared at the garden for packing and seed, at intervals, will be sent home.' He was well, he told his fellow gardeners at Chatsworth, 'with the exception of being dreadfully miserable in consequence of the dreadful heat of the climate, the thermometer is seldom lower than 80, but often as high as 98 or 99 degrees and with this not the least breath of air'.

A fortnight later the rains came at last and, after giving time for the headwaters of the Hoogli, the maze of deltaic rivers and channels in their way to raise their trickles to streams, the nullahs to fill and their intermittent pools to flow, on 6th July Gibson at last started out on the greatest adventure of his life. He was frightened to death of the natives and was worried about his health, as letters home from the Misses Eden showed, but he found time to write two last letters. One of the many by which he kept Paxton acquainted with his every move, and his first to the Duke of Devonshire personally. Here was no cap in hand, tongue-tied labourer writing: 'I am glad to inform Your Grace that the memorandum Your Grace was pleased to draw up with regard to my mission to India has hitherto been strictly attended to, and, embracing the kind information and directions of Dr Wallich, I have no doubt of giving Your Grace satisfaction when I return to England.'

He told his ducal master of the many orchids he expected to find and of 'an entirely new and beautiful didynanimous plant bearing fine scarlet flowers in bunches like *Bignonia grandiflora* in size equal to that of digitalis. It is a truly parasitical plant with the habit of the hoya from which it is scarcely distinguishable only by the flowers; it is not yet named'.

On 6th July, in a small boat manned by himself and two native gardeners as collectors from the garden staff, Gibson was waved off from Garden Reach pier by Dr Wallich and Masters with many words of good cheer and advice from both. Here he was now on the broad stream of the Hoogli River, really on his own. Success or failure depended entirely on his own resources, his physical stamina, his ability (or luck) to dodge cholera, smallpox, malaria, ague, dysentery as well as the test of himself against sheer physical exhaustion in the course of his work all upriver ahead of him. He had seen Dr Wallich return from the same territory a physical wreck, taking weeks to come round to something like his old self. There were dangers from animals, too, in the jungles in which he was to be spending so much time searching for his rare plants—

elephants, tigers, rhino, buffalo and snakes could be awkward and they could certainly be frightening to a young gardener from Derbyshire who had seen them in pictures only.

So here he was, away from the comparative luxury and shelter of Masters's anglicized home in the Botanic Garden, beginning a 250-mile journey into completely unknown country. His craft was a type of junk with sails set athwart the boat and with little or no living accommodation, as the practice was to tie up at night and pitch camp. It was a strange scene for the insular countryman as they paddled slowly up the muddy swirling waters, with strange scents of sandalwood, the incense of Hindu temples, the acrid smoke of dung fires from the mud-hutted and palm-thatched villages by the banks, the curious timbre of sound as conch shells called the natives to Siva service in the much-carved temples they passed by the water's edge. They forced their way up to the head-waters of the Hoogli to cross the great Ganges delta, taking one of the three headwaters, the Matabhanga, towards the confluence of that other great river the Brahmaputra, then across the jheels, those long, bleak stretches of plain cut into weird shapes by canals, rivers and lagoons. From Calcutta up the Hoogli the journey was relatively easy and comfortable, but yet with danger always lurking from sudden high winds or the Hoogli bore, which took hold of native rigged boats and turned them over to sink without trace. At the head of the Hoogli, some sixty-four miles above Garden Reach, their boat took them up the narrow, tortuous Matabhanga to meet the Ganges, then to Dacca and to the Meghna River in the Brahmaputra delta, and then to the Surma to make for Chhatak. Soon after the main headwaters of the Hoogli had been left behind, a matter of at least three or four days' journey, another twenty or more days' arduous adventure lay before Gibson and his two native helpers. They were using a small boat now, his own two men paddling at bow and stern and, amidships, under a primitive type of arched plaited bamboo shelter, Gibson had a space just big enough for him to lie down, no room to sit and no opportunity either to see or to prepare for the dangers of shoals, bore or floating debris, for with the rains huge floating islands of vegetation threatened all craft afloat. Across the jheels, up the canals they paddled, no maps, no compass, only native memory for landmarks and features to guide them, so that it was easy to get some miles up a creek only to find it was the wrong one, or turned round on itself or came to a dismal bleak end. But at least Gibson was seeing something of the flora and the constantly changing scenes of this strange unknown country which served to whet his floral appetite.

Along the natural channels long tropical grasses, ten feet high, and in bewildering variety, made tunnels for their craft, while roses, rattans, figs and laurels and the beautiful convolvulus lined the banks. The waters were steadily rising under the influence of the monsoons, and rain dripped incessantly through the bamboo roof of Gibson's shelter. As they tied up at night and clambered up the high banks to camp near some native village he could see, still higher, on curious knolls above the surrounding plain, other villages on the teelas, those strange geographical features on whose tips were almost invariably huge trees in whose shade and shelter the native villages perched.

Around these knolls Gibson could see the beginnings of what soon would be an inland sea as the Brahmaputra and rivers and streams of the Khasi Hills spilled their turbulent waters into the plains. There were even pelicans sheltering in the trees and soon, very soon, it seemed to Gibson as if the whole of Bengal had taken to the water, as indeed they must, for all communication during the rainy season was only possible by boat. The waters lapped to within an inch or two of the thresholds of the grass-thatched huts of the villages on their island sites. The ten-day journey to Chhatak from Dacca was tiring and, as an additional irritant, there was the unpleasantness of malarial insects and leeches from the swamps surrounding them. As they came nearer to Chhatak the 15-foot-high banks of the Surma, itself here a quarter of a mile wide, were covered in a jungle of coconut palms, betel nut, figs and banyan trees. Natives peeped at them curiously from mango groves and swathes of bending bamboos.

Chhatak at last, and the goal still twelve miles away, but there rising magnificently from the jheels, like a Rajput castle above the desert, could clearly be seen the Khasi range. Knee deep in dense green jungle their sheer rock tops cut the horizon, and over those sheer cliffs could be seen the quiet silver fingers of giant waterfalls precipitating from the craggy heights to the jungle below.

At Chhatak, always excessively damp and hot, set amidst interminable swamps, it was a change-over of boats again to a smaller but similar one; they were leaving for the fourteen-hour journey to Pandua up the narrow river which led to the very foot of the mountains themselves.

Pandua, which sixteen years later was castigated by Dr Hooker 'as a more pestilential hole cannot be imagined', was the end of their journey on water, or should have been, for mules had been sent down from Cherra to help him climb up the 4,000 feet to the tableland where he was to live for the next two or three months.

But Gibson's luck was not in and he wrote telling of his experiences: 'We had great difficulty to get from Pandua to Tharia-ghat, the stream being so powerful at the foot of the hills and in several places, a short distance from Tharia-ghat, we were obliged to take to the water. The mule which Mr Inglis sent to convey me up the hills I found very useful.' He obviously was an amphibious one, for he had to be pulled through the swollen watercourses before he could be of use again.

This was as nothing now Gibson was almost at his world's end—his Mecca was in sight sheer above him. Already he knew this was the floral storehouse of which Dr Wallich had told him so much, for all around him was luxuriant jungle, tropical vegetation beautiful in its vivid greens and wonderful in its profuse diversity. Huge, brilliantly coloured moths and butterflies visited the lush balsams and euphorbias abounding under the jungle cover. Above all was the roar of the giant waterfalls which plunged headlong into the midst of the steaming greenery, drowning the strident cries of birds and beasts. At the foot of these hills no natives, and certainly no European, dare stay at nights, for death came slowly but painfully from the agues, malaria or dysentery induced by this humid heat. But the beauty of it all! 'The whole of the vegetation is now in flower which forms one complete mass of flowers all over the plain

and jungle.' So wrote Gibson from Cherra on 2nd August after he had settled in at the
little bungalow which was costing him 30 rupees a month. He had arrived there on 31st
July and was happy on this mountain plateau, although not a single bush or blade of
grass was to be seen immediately about him. Cherra stuck out its bald head over a
luxuriant ruff of jungle greenery which ringed it. It was a strange haven Gibson now
had to make his home for the next few months—a few European-style bungalows, a
mile apart, dotted the bare plateau of mingled red and grey rock through which the
waters ran in deep fissures to dash their dazzling whiteness over the stark edge of the
mountainside. So frequent were the short, heavy deluges from the copper-dark clouds
crowning the mountain top that the whole plateau became flooded. Fortunately for the
few European and native inhabitants the porous limestone and sandstone cap made
short work of the inundations, which raised the many rivulets and streams as much as
fourteen feet in as many hours. Now he was seeing face to face, nay torso to torso, some
of the native tribes, gory tales of whom he had learned from the old sahibs. He had only
to set off across the plateau, to climb higher and higher into the range behind him to
pass Poonji, the populous native village where the Khasians haggled and gaggled in the
great market square. To a Derbyshire Peak man they were a queer folk, with their top-
knotted hair, their filthy bodies half naked and half covered in gaudy red and blue
shirt-like costumes drawn in at the waist. Did Dr Wallich warn him of the dangers of
living among these people? For there was no doubt he was apprehensive of what might
happen to him, as chance remarks in his letters show, and the Khasians were noted for
murdering for the most trifling offence against them.

His intelligence and great love of plants surmounted his fears, however, as his letter
to Paxton of 2nd August shows. 'I never saw', he wrote, 'nor could I believe that there
was such a fertile plain under the heavens had I not the inexpressible pleasure of seeing
it and I think the whole of the plants are entirely new to European collections.'

Now his energies were unbounded, his days long and his collections approaching the
incredible. As he sat on the veranda of his bungalow a short time before turning in at
night, surrounded by drying plants and seeds, he might well have thought he was
dwelling on some Asiatic Olympus. There he was on the bare Cherra plateau and 4,000
feet below lay bay-like valleys carpeted in lush green velvet from which grew tall
curvaceous palms, tree ferns with many spreading crowns and rattan shooting streamers
above the great trees like huge ostrich plumes, and as a tiara the brilliant jungle greens
were rainbow hued from the eternal waters falling from the ragged heights above.

Beyond, the jheels spread like a broad shallow sea. He complained of the rains.
Probably the hard-bitten, time-serving officials like Dr Wallich, in order not to dampen
the ardour of so enthusiastic a young man, had refrained from telling Gibson the blunt,
dismal fact that the Khasi range was noted for the world's highest rainfall, with an
average of 500 inches a year, in some years reaching 600. He later found that the
Khasians did not even bury their dead in the rainy season and was astonished to find the
corpses embalmed in honey. Indeed Dr Hooker, only five years later, on the same hills
recorded 27 feet of rain in one month, on one night he recorded 30 inches and altogether

500 inches in the seven months he was in the district. That was rain and Gibson did not like it; it made him miserable and he said so, but it also made the tropical rain forests from which he was filching his floral gold!

He told Dr Wallich that 'incessant rains' prevented him from collecting seeds but made the conditions perfect for orchid collecting. By the 15th of the month he had become acclimatized and had sallied forth with his servants, had taken his mule down the narrow mountain paths and had penetrated deep into the jungle. Deep in the dappled, humid shade with a lush, luxuriant vegetation, whether he knew it or not at that time, there were more than 520 different kinds of orchids, terrestrial and parasitical and ephiphytal, growing in great masses on trees and rocks or in deep mossy clefts. The brilliantly glossy-leaved trees undergrown with abounding, striving, climbing parasitical plants, shrubs and grasses must have seemed like one great stove conservatory as Gibson picked his way with his native collectors between thickets of euphorbias and figs whose elongated roots twisted everywhere and made living bridges over the rushing streams. There were red oaks, oranges, jacks, bananas, vines, peppers, scores of impenetrable bamboos in bewildering variety, screw pines, the date plum and above all the graceful swaying heads of palms and tree ferns around him as he laboured. Great hanging leaves of the wine palm threatened to cut their faces as they harvested, and ever present the rainbow mist and waters' roar. He must have come across the natives whose life so centred on Cherra market that they knew no week but one of four days separating the market days. He must have seen and used the ladders these strange people used to scale the vertical mountainside to get to market.

What a harvest he garnered here! 'I am now happy to inform you, he wrote Dr Wallich, 'of our very successful and interesting operation. I must say they surpass all my expectations in every form. You will be surprised to hear that we have already made an extensive collection of plants consisting principally of orchideae, and of these we have collected no less than 50 species some of which are beautiful beyond description or comparison. Of the most beautiful tribe you call Aeschynanthus [a climbing stove plant with fragrant and richly coloured flowers] I have found four species one of which has a yellow flower. I have them all in flower on my verandah packed up in moss—it is impossible for me to describe the beauty or elegance, but this you are perfectly acquainted with. I know of no place so suitable to their habit as the stove at Chatsworth, that's the place.

'The shrubs and trees are of a very interesting nature, some of them as well as curious are particularly interesting and beautiful and will be valuable in any form in England. There are several curious shrubs which grow upon trees and rocks; they form a sort of calosity or substance at the roots, this is strange to me. The flowers of one of them are exquisitely beautiful of which I send a small specimen in flower [Dr Wallich's note, *ceratostema*]. I shall make a large collection of all the shrubs. The herbaceous plants and annuals are very fine, they are now all in flower, the harvest of these I expect to reap in about a month, indeed several are now in seed but the weather is so incessantly wet there is little chance until a change takes place, even for a few days.'

Oh the bubbling-over love of plants of the man and how he went on about them! It must have rekindled the spirit in poor, jaded Wallich as he read on, 'I am delighted beyond anything to see such a grand display of the vegetable kingdom. I find something new every day which not only affords me pleasure and encouragement now, but to look forward to the time when I get the satisfaction of having these rarities in England, to arrive which will give my employer so much pleasure and satisfaction. This is the point I am so anxious to accomplish. [Dr Wallich, spurred on by the young man's enthusiasm, notes in the margin: 'We must try and do our best.']

'Would it be possible', Gibson asked, 'to send to England in a living state the most superb tree fern which is so common here and so fine. I think if they were taken up when in their torpid state and packed in wooden boxes and immediately shipped to England they would arrive in a living state. To see one of these large specimens in a stove in England exhibiting its fine foliage of such extraordinary magnitude would be a real enchantment, particularly to the Duke of Devonshire.'

He was having trouble drying his plants, for the temperature of some 80 degrees every day and incessant rain made only for high humidity. But he soon found, as collectors did who came after, that good, hot coal was plentiful in the outcrops on the range and could be had for as little as 6s. for a week's supply. Big fires all day and all night did the trick and he was happy again. He must, even by now, a fortnight after his arrival, have realized he was living in a botanical paradise which later, when systematically surveyed, showed the Khasi range flora to be the richest in Asia. Within ten miles of Cherra station it was found possible by Dr Hooker to collect upwards of two thousand different species of flowering plants, there were at least fifty different orchideae, a hundred and fifty different ferns, twenty or more different bamboos and a bewildering profusion of mosses, lichen and fungi.

Gibson was making a collection for the duke of these ferns and mosses, a job he had taken over from his men, for it was a task he found absorbing. He had dried about eight specimens of each different variety and wondered whether he ought not to be drying more, for he recalled when he left a year ago the duke was busily forming a herbarium of British and exotic plants.

He had worked out a method, he told Dr Wallich, for getting the precious orchids down to Calcutta. 'I tie a little moss round each of their roots and am getting shallow baskets made to plunge them in and each basket will hold from 40 to 50 plants and will be easily carried down the hills by our men. I shall plunge them in moss level with the rim of the basket and support them with sticks so that they may be turned about in any way without being broken. This is the same method as practised in England by the nurserymen. The plants will grow and will be in beautiful order when they arrive in Calcutta. These baskets can only be sent by boat.'

For a description made in 'a rough way', as Gibson called it, he went into enthusiastic detail about a plant neither he nor the doctor was sure of. Gibson called it 'Orobanche acaulis' (Wallich amended this to aeginetia) and wrote of its 'Cal. spathulate opening lengthwise beneath, as long as the tube of the flower. Flowers campanulate, unequal, upper lip bifid reflexed, inside of the flower of a beautiful delicate yellow, this yellow is bordered by dark velvet in the mouth of the flower and blended into the dark purple lips. On the lower lip is a large yellow spot. Flower stem rising from the root about one foot high and each having from 10 to 12 flowers and destitute of leaves when in flower'. That was the theoretical botanist and enthusiastic flower-lover Gibson was.

On 18th August part of his collection was already on its long journey back to Garden Reach, and Dr Wallich was asked to look out for a packet of seeds sent by Dawk (a system of post worked by native runners in relays) on the 16th and a small basket of orchids by Bhangy (parcel post often carried on a yoke round the neck of a native) on the 17th; a similarly filled basket had gone off on the 18th. He hoped his method of packing had stood up to the climate, the distance and to native handling, and had the grace to admit that while he knew the English method he had used was successful there he had no idea what would happen here.

Back to his expeditions in the surrounding jungle treasure house like a diver bringing back his pearls from the seabed he showed in enthusiastic letters his latest finds: 'I was surprised a few days ago with finding *Wallichia caryotoides* [a small tufted stove palm]; I loaded one of my khusiers [hurkarus, postal runner] with plants of it. The seeds of it will be ripe in the course of a fortnight. I saw yesterday roxburghia in a wild state and also the species of aesculus [horse chestnut] of which you have at the Botanic Gardens. I found a most noble dendrobium which I think is new, it is not in flower, but the plant takes my attention very much. It is in the way of *D. densiflorum*, but a much finer species in appearance. It has flat or compressed stems from one to one and a half feet long and from four to six dark green leaves on each stem—there are seed vessels on the plants which come from the axils of the leaves, and from the same place another dendrobium-like species with pubescent leaves. Dendrobiums are very numerous here and very fine; was you aware that *D. densiflorum* grew at Cherra? I am much pleased to find the Hoya tribes so numerous. I brought home yesterday three kinds which I cannot recognize—one has smaller round dark green leaves—I have not seen the flower of this specimen—one of the others has leaves as large as *H. carnosa*, the same form and size only not so thick, the young leaves are pubescent on both sides, flowers white and very fragrant—I can enumerate five or six species of hoya which I have not seen before. Has the genus cattleya ever been found in the East? I believe I can boast of having one [a side note by Dr Wallich states: 'No C. in N.E. India'].

'*Acanthophipium bicolor* which is found at Ceylon—is the noble plant found anywhere on the hills? The Duke is very anxious to get it, there is not much more than four plants of it in England. *Phajus* [*Phaius*] *maculatus* is common in every jungle, at least I think that is the plant. I am making such work among the cyrtandraceae [gesneriae] you may expect a good stock by Mr Inglis's boat which leaves here on the 1st September. Did you taste the pineapples of the hills, they are really excellent. There are two kinds here which equal the English grown ones, are they of the hills or have they been introduced? ['Introduced, of course,' writes Dr Wallich, 'but may be said to grow

wild in the Khosea hills as the pineapple does in many other parts of the East Indies.']—
They are numerous enough to be called natives.'

Dr Wallich, who wrote to the duke on the 26th, could think of no better way of acquainting his grace about the successes of his mission than by forwarding four of Gibson's recent letters. Then, as if to dot the i's and cross the t's of Gibson's complaints about the weather he was battling against Dr Wallich told the duke: 'I do not wonder at the difficulties he meets with in drying out specimens, etc. The present time of the year is the rainy season in the Khosea hills, the rains are remarkably long continued and heavy, when everything, living or dead, is saturated with moisture and when even the letter mail, much more so the packet mail, is frequently drenched through and through before reaching Calcutta, on which occasion anything in the shape of seeds or roots or orchidea must possess a very strong degree of vitality to resist putrefaction during the eight or ten days of heat, damp and confinement which the Chirra post usually takes to reach Calcutta.'

A delightful sidelight on Gibson's labours came from the pen of Miss Emily Eden in a letter to the duke. She had been waiting, she told him, for a letter to her personal maid from 'the Duke's gardener', an inspired author who wrote of high adventure in a most illuminating, unforced natural style because he knew no other. Miss Emily added that she had even got into the habit, as had those at the gardens, of expecting almost daily, another huge cargo of plants from Cherra, but the Dawk must have been late this time; however, she still had plenty to tell the duke.

'Gibson', she told him, 'wrote a letter to my maid—a lady of very respectable age, so if there is a Mrs Gibson she need not be alarmed.' He had been in a horrid fright about his personal safety before he set off but found that was a mistake. He mentioned the thermometer being at 60, air delightful, butterflies innumerable, 150 new parasitic plants already secured 'and in a word, when I tell you Mrs Wright I am in my glory you will excuse me entering into further details'. There was something rather sublime, quipped Miss Eden, in the idea of Gibson in his glory:

'Scene—A tent at Chirrapunji with a foreground of palanquins and bearers, and Gibson in the midst crowned with an orchideous wreath and holding a large Purple Emperor by one wing. George [Lord Auckland] gave him a travelling case containing a silver bottle, goblet, knife, fork and with an inscription on the bottle stating that it was the gift of the Governor-General as a mark of his regard for Mr Gibson's character —or words to that effect—and it charmed the aforesaid Mr Gibson but as he felt sure the Indian savages would kill him for the sake of his goblet and then eat him with his own knife and fork he left the casket in my care and I feel the responsibility deeply.'

Gibson, it will be remembered, spent most of his waiting time at Calcutta reordering the Barrackpore garden for Miss Eden, and it is of interest to read her description of it to the duke: 'I wish you could see it, in eight months it has become an overstocked garden full of ixias and ipomaeas, balsams the size of gooseberry bushes and Cape Jasmine like large trees. I dare say you have a few plants of *Gloriosa superba*, which well deserves its fine sounding name, in your hothouse—and you probably think much of them—that is my weed and I shall be obliged to have thinned for fear of a *Gloriosa superba* jungle fever. My only plant of heartsease died of the climate and I would give all the other fine plants for a bunch of lilies or vulgar looking wallflowers such as the common people carry on Sunday evening when they come trailing back to town. I think I hear their feet scraping tiredly along the pavement and see the nosegays I want. A common white daisy, I think I told you, is not to be had at any price. Now we import much American ice I do not see why some of the rich baboos [native merchants] do not set up cold houses in rivalry of the English hot houses. Who knows whether by a proper process of refrigeration they might not bring the snowdrop to perfection?'

That of course was the exile's proper nostalgia for the things of home, but Gibson had no time for that, what with his most regular correspondence, his daily skirmishes in the orchid war and his nightly drying out and packaging sessions. Probably by the same ship's mail as Miss Eden's pleasantries went Gibson's first letter from the Khasi range to the duke. 'Your Grace', he wrote, 'will be pleased to hear that the field for my researches are almost unbounded, the variety and beauty of the plants are beyond description and the orchids abound in the greatest quantities—both terrestrial and epyphytous, of the latter I can enumerate 50 species which will be new to Your Grace's most extensive collection at Chatsworth, and to this number I can with safety add 50 other species which may be in England, but in very few collections. The epiphytes consist principally of dendrobae, vandae and coelogyne, the former of these being of a most resplendent character. There are two species with flowers as beautiful as *D. calceolaria*, one of them bears its flowers at almost every joint of the stem from two to four at each joint and as many as 30 flowers on one stem—the other has its flowers in terminal racemes—there are several other sp. equally beautiful.

'The vandae consist of sarcanthus, aerides and saccolabium, there are but few of these now in flower but the plants themselves are fine and of the last, *Coelogyne wallichiana* is one of the commonest plants—it grows upon banks and trees in abundance— *C. interrupta* and another species resembling *C. fimbriata* in habit but much larger in every form and more beautiful are equally common, also several species of this genus.

'Another tribe of plants which abound here I think Your Grace will find as interesting and as beautiful as the orchidaeous plants namely the cyrtandraceae [gesnerias], the tribe Dr Wallich calls aeschynanthus, and who says himself that they do not yield in beauty and splendour to any other production. I enclose a flower of one of the species. This is the plant I attempted to describe in my last letter to you as being so truly beautiful and as being discovered and figured by Dr Wallich during his tour of 1835 in this range of hills.

'The tribe here is so numerous that I have already found five species. They grow upon rocks and trees in airy sites in woods and their habit is such that I think there is no doubt of plants being carried home in a living state. They will bear a considerable degree of cold as the mean temperature here is about 65 degrees.'

He knew, he told the duke, that at last the magnificent hothouses at Chatsworth were ready and waiting for his treasures to fill, as Miss Eden had told him, and those same treasures were, he knew, finding their way safely to Calcutta by both Dawk and Bhangy post. 'I only hope', he sighed, 'that my collection will be worthy of a very conspicuous place in one of the new hot houses and will give Your Grace every satisfaction.'

In a few days from the date of this last letter he tried new pastures and sought a different subject altogether—rhododendrons. In the extensive pine woods of Mysung, about two days' journey on the hills from Cherra, he had been told there were rhododendrons in plenty as well as more orchids. In the meantime he sent a specimen of a new shrub to the duke. He had found it growing upon rocks and upon trees. He did not know a single collector of exotics at home who would have a single plant of it and he called it *Ceratostema variegata* of Roxb. While Gibson was toiling away in the hills his success, as evidenced by the boatloads of jungle spoil reaching the gardens, was materially to alter his plans. Dr Wallich, who told Lord Auckland in a note dated October of this magnificent cargo, asked if Gibson could stay in the Khasi Hills rather than go to the Martaban coast, where amherstia was to have been the principal trophy. The doctor now found he would be able to supply a plant or two of this rarity for Chatsworth from the Calcutta Gardens.

Lord Auckland agreed to this change of plan, and dropped a line to the duke to tell him so, also letting him know that on the *Orient*, sailing in November, would go a wealth of plants.

During this time Gibson and both his native helpers had been down with a heat affliction, but he was soon up again and, writing on 11th October, told Dr Wallich of some of the beautiful flowers now blooming around him.

There were '*Dendrobium dencidous*, beautiful in flower, and two lovely species of coelogyne, perhaps *wallichiana* and *maculata*', and of the latter he sent back a basket in full flower by the parcel post and followed it up next day with another. Not only Gibson and his helpers suffered from the heat; he spoke of the different kinds of plants suffering, particularly the epiphytous plants. Then the train of thought took him back to Chatsworth where every possible allowance was made for the demands of all plants from whatever clime and situation they might have been wrested. 'I wish they knew at Chatsworth', he told Calcutta, 'what valuable treasures are now ready at the Botanic Gardens awaiting a favourable season and opportunity to be despatched for that magnificent place. They would jump for joy—God grant they may arrive in a good state.'

A previous note from Calcutta had told him of the changed plans, but because two letters had crossed, he was preparing to leave Cherra and work his way down the Brahmaputra to the Martaban coast, the completion of his pilgrimage to find and take possession of the Holy Grail—*Amherstia nobilis*. He now found he was not to go; he was to carry on collecting the treasures of the Khasi range. The dutiful servant, the true master's man in Gibson, was expressed in his reply, which gave no indication of surprise or disappointment. 'I would answer that it is the particular wish of his Grace the Duke of Devonshire which I have in his own handwriting, that I be guided entirely by the directions of Dr. Wallich and this I anxiously will do. Whatever Dr. Wallich wishes and recommends to the fulfilment of the mission this I will gladly agree to and use every means in performing it in the most successful manner possible.'

Seeing that the die was cast and Gibson could look forward to several more months' plant hunting at his present station his active mind was already probing and planning the future. 'Undoubtedly there still remains on the Khosea hill a most extensive field for my researches and particularly about Chirra—and in three months yet to come I could strip off a share of the greater part of the fine plants which abound in every wood —it is impossible at one visit to a wood to discover all the plants contained in it, particularly the orchids and the epiphytous plants—these are so numerous and so curious in their locality that a person may go to some of the woods and reap a most splendid harvest, yet leave behind some of the most lovely of plants—another person shall go there next day to the same woods and bring back with him also valuable treasures which the former person could not find nor believe they came from the same wood. I had looked for half an hour at some of the large trees which have been covered with them trunk and branch but could not see anything new and have afterwards sent a man up the tree when he, to my great surprise, threw down new and valuable plants. Not only are they so curious in locality, but so near alike in appearance from a distance.'

He concluded his letter by agreeing again to the wisdom of cancelling his Martaban expedition, as he did not think the three months remaining would have enabled him to do the thorough job at Martaban he was doing and determined to do at Cherra. On 2nd November the first fruits of the harvest were at last on their way to their Chatsworth garnery, the first trickle of a gargantuan flood. Dr Wallich himself had the honour and the glory of arranging and dispatching this aperitif of the floral feast to follow. He wrote to Chatsworth from the captain's cabin on the *Orient* on her way out of the Hoogli. Two closed chests were on board addressed to the duke, and 'Captain White, a dear friend of mine, who has taken more plants, larger collections and greater pains than anyone I know of, will be good enough to present this letter and the two chests'.

In the chests were 'species of phaias, one probably *P. maculata, Eria paniculata,* two dendrobiums' (probably, he thought, *densiflorum* and *clavatum*) 'and two species of coelogyne, namely *C. maculata* and *C. prolifera* Lindl. The *maculata* is lovely beyond all I can express. The plants are now in the highest state of perfection and they are all derived from Your Grace's gardener, Gibson, of whom I cannot speak in sufficient highness of praise'.

The letters from Gibson to the doctor were sent along to the duke with the plants to show how willingly his gardener had accepted the change of plans, and again the doctor could not forbear to mention how 'absolutely indefatigable in his researches' Gibson was. 'He has sent the most magnificent collection of orchidae, cyrtandracae, etc. down to me, a still greater collection is at the moment under way and I left a host at the Gardens in readiness to be despatched for a third assignment.

'In short, there never was anything equal to this seen in India. I had almost said any-where else—this being the least favourable season for sending plants home. With reference to the period of arrival at home I have confined myself on this account to forwarding only two chests, if these arrive in a quarter of the state of beauty they are now in I should truly rejoice.'

And now we are let into a secret, the way to keep a man on his toes; no wonder poor Gibson had little time to reflect on either his tired bones or his divorcement in a strange land from his family and familiar surroundings. From Calcutta, it seemed, the doctor (or so he told the duke) encouraged Gibson to write every four or five days and the doctor replied, 'to keep him active in that way, knowing the great effect a brisk correspondence has' and the results admirable in every way, for the Duke could be told of his gardener, fifteen thousand miles away, that 'he seems to be in a continued trance of rapture and admiration and I can readily enter into his feelings when he says it is with pain that he is forced to leave some few orchideae, etc. behind. He would be glad to send their forests and all if he could. In short he is in every possible way the best man Your Grace could have sent out on the business in which he is engaged.'

Captain White, besides taking the letters, carried six open chests full of plants from the Calcutta Gardens, gifts from its curator. On 8th November, in a bungalow full of floral rarities, Gibson sat down to write his first letter from Cherra to Paxton, a letter brimful of high spirits and enthusiasm. 'I must say that I never addressed you with so much pleasure and satisfaction on my own part as on the present occasion and hope that it may equally meet with your satisfaction and approbation.'

His last letter to Paxton had been date-lined Calcutta, 2nd July, so there was plenty to tell and, my word, Gibson was the man to tell it! 'My operations on these hills have been crowned with the greatest possible success and have far exceeded Dr. Wallich's expectation which he says himself was not very limited and I do assure you that such is the extent and splendour of my collection as to make it one of the richest collections that has ever crossed the Atlantic. It is impossible for me to describe or enumerate the number of valuable plants of which it is composed. I am just returned from a tour into the interior of these hills which has occupied five weeks and I am happy to say that splendid indeed are its results. I should have written you sooner but as I was anxious to acquaint you with the result of my tour I have deferred it until the present moment and now I am happy to say every step that I have taken has been attended with the greatest success.

'The Khosea hills cannot otherwise be styled than one of the richest floras of the world. The orchideae are splendid indeed and I do not hesitate in saying that I shall supply from 80 to 90 new species which are not in England. However this will depend upon the success I may have in transporting them to that place of all places in a living state. God grant that I may be lucky in performing this hazardous task as I have been in the former part of collecting. I have directed my attention principally to the orchids considering the great injunction under which you placed me (do not return home without a valuable cargo of orchideae) and the great taste of His Grace the Duke of Devonshire for this tribe of plants which abound here in the greatest variety, some of which are truly magnificent.

'I will refer to a few kinds which I have no doubt will be highly prized when they arrive at Chatsworth—*Acanthophippium bicolor, Coelogyne maculata, C. interrupta, C. wallichiana, C. elata* (Lindl.), *C. prolifera* and several others of the genus; *Dendrobium longicornu, D. densiflorum, D. chrysanthum,* and numerous other lovely species of dendrobiums, most of which are new species; *Eria pusilla, E. paniculata, E. exorticate, E. lonifus, E. densiflora* (Wall.); *Vanda terres, Saccolabium guttatum* and several other new species; *Phaius albus,* renanthera, sarcanthus many species; *Trias racemosa* (Wall.), *Oberonia iridifolia,* phyllostachys, also three or four other species and besides the above a great number of lovely and interesting orchids for which I have not received any name at present from Dr. Wallich which leads me to suppose that the greater part of them are new to him. I return his list of the plants which I sent down from hence to him he has merely made observations on their habit which also leads me to suppose the greater part of them are new to him.

'I must not omit in this place, after noticing the fine orchids, to notice the cyrtandracious plants which I think surpass anything that I have ever seen. I made an observation on one of these plants—*Aeschynanthus parasitica*—the fine didynanimous plant with large scarlet or vermillion coloured flowers in my last letter to you—this is a real beauty; there are several other species of this genus equally beautiful also genera containing beautiful plants, greater part of them grow upon trunks of trees and upon rocks, they form most extensive substances at their roots which contain the necessary support for the plants; none of them grow in soil.'

He spoke of amherstia and the plans for getting it from Calcutta now instead of Martaban and added: 'I know of no place so well adapted for its successful growth as the large house at Chatsworth where I have every hope of seeing its fine velvet like foliage and unequalled racemes of vermillion coloured flowers displayed.'

He knew well all the Calcutta news and could tell Paxton that already two glazed cases full of orchids were on their way to Derbyshire on board the *Orient*. Unfortunate, he thought, was the timing, for they would arrive in an English winter climate and might get there before this warning letter. He was certainly worried about this shipment of Khasi orchids of 2nd November, which he thought two months too soon to allow of a propitious estimated arrival time.

Gibson was now eagerly looking forward to his own departure and wrote that in two months, and certainly by early January, he would be leaving Cherra and the mountains to prepare for the final journey to England the following month with his triumphant collection. Many chests were already filled with plants where Masters and Dr Wallich had been busy at Calcutta, and with a last wish that all was well at Chatsworth and a note that he and his two native collectors had been down with an indisposition due to the heat and the 'vile climate', he signed off.

By 30th December three more chests had been dispatched in charge of Captain Pryce, R.N., on board H.M.S. *Repulse,* and in a note accompanying them from Dr Wallich to the duke, who now saw what 'a keen, enthusiastic, dedicated intelligent gardener' like Gibson could do when let loose among the Indian flora, he appealed to his grace to send

THE GOLDEN AGE OF PLANT HUNTERS

back either Gibson, or someone, or two gardeners like him, to collect in the untouched botanic paradises of Nepal or 'Kanivarr', or at any other place for that matter, where he could be assured of making splendid collections. He realized, he said, it would be extremely difficult to get anyone to equal Gibson's steady, zealous and indefatigable work in the service of his master, to send to India. A note to Dr Lindley, on the side as it were, which somehow reached Chatsworth ultimately, told Dr Lindley to watch out for the Duke of Devonshire's getting a tremendous collection of orchids. 'We have a very excellent gardener in the Khasia Hills sent out by the munificence of the Duke of Devonshire. He has sent enormous collections of plants, principally orchids; one fiftieth part of the quantities sent would be enough to stock Chatsworth and your garden too.' Was this a hint to wait for the crumbs to fall from the gentleman's table?

On the last day of 1836 Dr Wallich wrote again to the duke of more cases on the way, this time with Captain Brown in the Duke of Bedford. Gibson's boat, added the doctor, had arrived at Garden Reach on the 27th, 'and nothing could surpass the beauty of this cargo. Gibson has surpassed himself again. The collection was superb'. Already fourteen cases had been filled and glazed, all waiting to be sent Chatsworth-ward. He was able to announce that Gibson had left his mountain top and was at the foot of the range, not anxiously waiting his boat back; oh no, he was finishing off his collection by foraging at the foot of the mountain for a time in the heavy jungle which cut into the deep dark ravines of the range.

From Gibson the next letter home was on 9th January 1837, from Pandua to Paxton, in jubilation: 'I have the great pleasure to inform you I have now completed my labours in the Khosean range and I am able to proceed this day to Calcutta in company with my most valuable collection, where I shall arrive about the first of February.'

There were yet twenty-one days of anxiety about his charges in the small boats and at the porterages where they would be in the hands of natives to whom orchids were not worth a farthing, but old England was in his sights as he wrote on: 'You will be delighted to hear that I have reaped so rich an harvest and when you see all the treasures of which it is composed you will decide on my satisfactory labours and, indeed, when you receive this letter I hope you will have seen some part of my fine orchideae and see them in good order.'

He found it impossible to list by name just all the fine new things he and nature had produced, as he put it, because for one thing so few of them had names at that juncture; that was a pleasure to come. He did know that one orchid with sky-blue flowers at that very moment blossoming at Calcutta was called by the learned doctor Dendrobium coerulescens. He had not seen it himself but he knew by its colour alone it would rank as among the most valuable of the tribe.

Then with Chatsworth vividly in mind, he added: 'What a noble collection we shall have if I am favoured with success in crossing the little fish pond that now parts us and, at the season I shall leave Bengal, there is every reason for success.'

Speaking of his intention to write from Calcutta before he set sail, the first show of any personal feeling crept through. England, Chatsworth and home were looming so near after some two years, during which time he had not heard once from the homeland. Communication was so slow that for all his unflagging work, his dispatches of regular cargoes and his regular letters home nothing had come across the sea to tell him what was thought of his work, of his many parcels and chests of plants and seed and how they had fared. For all he knew Paxton could have been dead as well as his noble master.

Something of all this welled up in his letter. 'I am almost lost', he complained, 'with being away in the woods and jungle and indeed almost gone wild with having no personal commerce with my countrymen, nothing but blackmen from day to day. But all this adds to my expected satisfaction when I arrive on the little spot where little else but my native tongue is universally spoken.'

Even his fears, only once broached before to the gentle, comforting, confiding Wright, the maid at Government House, were coming to the fore. Now the task was nearly over he could afford to show his true face to the world. He did not know when he set off for Cherrapunji nearly a year previously that he was going to spend those months within reach of probably the most savage tribes in India—cannibals and thugs. But now he knew and told Paxton of the Khasians 'who were far from civilized' and there were other tribes too, 'varieties of the human race who were even less civilized'.

Back in Calcutta Dr Wallich was beginning to realize that ship freight charges of Gibson's successful harvest were mounting up as he notified Chatsworth of another four enclosed cases of orchids on the *Roxburgh Castle*. He mentioned that the charge had been fifteen pounds. He mentioned also the enormous supply waiting for dispatch and, with a third boat coming down the Hoogli with Gibson, he wondered whether he was not spending too much of the duke's money. Yet he thought he was following the correct procedure and acting up to the duke's wishes by sending plants with every available ship as they became ready for dispatch.

At first Captain Lumb had asked ten pounds for two cases, but he (Dr Wallich) had agreed with Captain Cumberland of the *Roxburgh* to fifteen pounds for four. Even this he thought a bit high, but he had taken counsel with Lord Auckland and as some explanation of the high cost Dr Wallich pointed out that 'the shipping interest is at the present moment so flourishing and consequently freight so high some of the Commanders have actually preferred filling their cabins with light goods instead of passengers'.

Hitherto, he reminded the duke, plant cases had been free, and added he was happy to report that Gibson was in excellent health at Pandua. 'I half envy Gibson,' he concluded; 'he goes home with gladness in his heart and I dare say satiated with India. I who have lived and languished here 30 years nearly, must still drag on several years longer. I may then perhaps be able to go home provided I have not been sent to the endless home beforehand and really in this existence of desolation and sadness (for that is my portion) I very much question whether the latter is not preferable to the former contingency, my patience is well nigh extinct.'

Then he asked forgiveness for the outburst; it was due to his recent parting for the second or third time with all he cared for on earth—his family, who had had to return to Europe ill as a result of the climate and the conditions.

In a postscript he gives the plan for the subsequent numbering of all plant cases bound for Chatsworth, asking the duke to take the first two cases forwarded on the *Orient* as '1' and '2', pointing out that nine cases had now been sent, all with the exception of two, which would be filled at the gardens, as a result of Gibson's endeavours.

The ever open market for plant freight was becoming well known on the Hoogli now, for Dr Wallich reported on 21st January that a Captain Pollock, who was dropping down the river past the gardens, tied up in midstream for a short time and called offering portage to England on his ship the *Lady Raffles*. He took on board No. 10 filled with fifteen items. The 5th of February saw cases 11 and 12 on board the *Duke of Buccleuch* in charge of Captain Martin.

Now at last, Dr Wallich reported to Chatsworth, Gibson was at Calcutta, having arrived on 1st February with a magnificent boatload of plants, chiefly orchideae. Never was anything more splendid seen anywhere. 'He will proceed to England towards the end of the present month with as large a collection as we can embark on one ship and, in the meantime, ten cases are in readiness to proceed on the *Bruxburneberry* (Capt. Chapman) with another six cases to go via the *Duke of Northumberland* (Capt. Pope) to sail on the 10th.'

Along with the cases on the *Duke of Buccleuch* went Gibson's own letter to Paxton dated 5th February, and what an enthusiastic epistle it was too, enough to make Joseph Paxton and the duke put out the flags!

'You will be pleased to hear of my safe arrival at Calcutta,' it read, 'and I am happy to inform you that all the plants which accompanied me from Pondorah [Pandua] arrived in most splendid order notwithstanding the different conveyance by boats and the time it takes to perform the journey down. I do assure you that it gives me no little pleasure to say that nothing can be more perfect and more beautiful than the collection of plants which I have brought down and forwarded from the Khosea range of hills. I very truly remarked in one of my former communications that these hills form one of the richest flora in the world and of these you will have peculiar demonstration when you receive the plants intended for Chatsworth. I can assure you that although I have had the pleasure and honour of having sent all these novelties to this garden I am now surprised to see what an enormous quantity there are. They appear, now that they are all together, an unequalled variety of grandeur and novelty.'

Before the 18th of the month he assured Paxton twenty-eight chests would be on their way from Calcutta. He was not able to tell Paxton how they had been packed, but he had no reason to doubt that Masters had selected and packed as well as he would have done himself. He did differ from their methods in one or two respects, but said he would mention that later on. In the meantime he reminded his head gardener he had not said a single word about the collection which would accompany him home, 'but here I promise you that it shall be composed of the cargo which accompanied me from

Pondorah and the plants which I shall collect from the gardens; but before I proceed further allow me to inform you that two plants of Amherstia are now ready packed for Chatsworth, one I put in the chest myself yesterday, the other has been packed for some time. Depend upon having Amherstia dead or alive and, at the same time, I must say that no care or attention whatever shall be wanting on my part to keep these, the most noble of all plants, alive. Nothing can be more beautiful on earth than the plants in question.'

The next day he was to see Lord Auckland at Government House to settle the arrangements for homecoming and, as a concluding word of caution, probably prompted by Dr Wallich, he thought he had better mention something of the expense of the trip: 'This mission will be enormously expensive before everything is made straight. The freightage on the boxes themselves will amount to great sums besides my travelling expenses and every other necessary expense connected with the affair, but as nothing but real and necessary expenses have been incurred I cannot but flatter myself that it will meet with your and the Duke of Devonshire's most favourable approbation, particularly when you receive the splendid harvest which I have reaped and I do assure you that I have endeavoured, so far as lay in my power, to render everything satis-factory and nothing shall prevent me from continuing to do so. Nothing will repay me or give me greater pleasure than to have the honour of saying, when I return home, I have given my noble master satisfaction in this so critical an undertaking.'

The ship *Zenobia*, skippered by Captain Owen, seemed to be the ideal combination for the exacting job of taking a Bengal jungle's floral wealth to England's shores. Captain Owen had often taken plants to the home country for Dr Wallich and carried out the job conscientiously. He would ensure safety for this magnificent botanical cargo, Dr Wallich assured Gibson, the duke and Lord Auckland.

At this time the duke was being inundated with letters from the doctor, for on 13th February he wrote to him again to assure him that the twelve cases which had left were a more superb assortment of plants than had ever before left the country. Lord Auck-land himself had come across the river to look at them and had said how pleased he was with Gibson's harvest. At that very moment he was in negotiation with Captain Owen for a cabin between decks for Gibson and his 'hand plant luggage and for 10 or 12 cases on the poop'. All hands were feverishly busy at the gardens preparing for both present and future consignments for Chatsworth.

Lord Auckland took a hand in the correspondence, writing the duke to tell him of Gibson's triumphant Calcutta homecoming. 'I can truly say of him that throughout his voyage and sojourn in India he has conducted himself with excellent propriety and has laboured with much intelligence and indefatigable industry in your service. He has made a grand collection of plants.' He himself, he mentioned to the duke, had spoken for Gibson to have a good cabin so that 'he might be able to nurse and protect all the numerous seeds and roots which, in addition to plants on the poop, he will take in charge'.

February 23rd saw another letter from Dr Wallich to the duke, with the news that six more closed cases had gone by the *Duke of Northumberland* at three pounds a case, a total of eighteen pounds. All the details for Gibson's voyage had now been fixed, a roomy cabin with enough height for him to take in it four cases, several baskets of orchids and several large cases of dried specimens and insects and his collection of seeds. It had been decided that twelve cases, six small and six large, were to go on the poop at two pounds each, and Gibson's passage had been fixed at £120, making £144 in all; a large sum, remarked the doctor, but when he thought of the mass of rare plants waiting to go he did not hesitate.

Unfortunately Gibson had gone down with a bout of fever, but was now more alert and active than ever. There was just a little snag in all this staff work, for which Dr Wallich had to excuse himself to his noble patron—he had sent along a plant with Gibson for the Court of Directors of the East India Company. He now proceeded to explain that from the very beginning, although Gibson had never mentioned it in any letter home, he had made a bargain with the duke that he should have an amherstia for Chatsworth provided he (Gibson) would take one for his liberal masters, the Court, along with two cases of deodar seeds. It was all official and above board; he had reported it to the Governor-General, who in turn had reported direct to the Court that an amherstia was on its way for them. It had cost the duke two pounds and he asked forgiveness for blundering so. He made amends, however, by telling the duke a piece of exclusive news—amherstia was just coming into flower in the Calcutta Garden, and he could hardly say whether it was in its greatest beauty in that state or when ornamented with new leaves that were produced in such a constant succession and of a beauty which could not be described such was the graceful form, the elegant tint and pendulous direction of the young leaves and branches. 'Of all plants in the world this is the one which will grace the conservatory at home and I promise Your Grace it shall be introduced at Chatsworth, whatever be our success on the present occasion.'

With a last plea for another Gibson to collect in India Dr Wallich concluded his correspondence. He pitched his last appeal high; unheard of treasures could confidently be expected, the Calcutta Botanic Garden offered facilities for such a project not found anywhere else in India; why, they even had the benefit of free portage, a tremendous advantage as his grace would find out when large quantities of seeds and plants were to be handled from upcountry by either packet or letter mail. Gibson had already found that out.

And then on 4th March he and Masters on the garden moorings wistfully and with real sadness in their hearts waved their last goodbyes to the indefatigable gardener, Gibson. 'March 4th,' the Doctor wrote, 'the *Zenobia* passed by these gardens in fine style this morning at half past eight and it quite gladdened my heart to see from my verandah how finely the cases stood arranged on her poop.'

One hundred and forty days later from the *Zenobia* off Plymouth an overjoyed Gibson wrote thankfully and with heartfelt enthusiasm to the Duke of Devonshire. He had arrived and almost all was well; he had brought home safely a thousand tender exotics through innumerable hazards of tide, tempest and climate. His whole letter exulted, but let Gibson speak for himself as he was always able to do:

'I have the honour to embrace the earliest opportunity of informing Your Grace of my arrival in the English Channel from Calcutta with my valuable and magnificent collection and to state that these plants are in the most beautiful order and preservation.

'The collection of plants is very extensive occupying 15 glazed boxes and several open boxes; some of the plants in the latter were procured at the Cape of Good Hope, there are also a quantity of orchids attached to the branches of trees which have been suspended in my cabin during the whole voyage from India. I can enumerate upwards of 100 specie orchids independent of the other fine plants which comprise the collection and were not in England when I took my departure for India, but I hope some of them which have been sent in previous collections to Your Grace will now be well established and flourishing.'

But there was disastrous news to tell too, and Gibson with truly characteristic tact and discretion had overlaid it with his epistle of good tidings. It had to be told now. 'I have to inform Your Grace with the deepest regret of the death of the *Amherstia nobilis* which was presented by Dr Wallich to your grace.

'Dr Wallich on his presenting Amherstia, for some particular reason also wished one to be sent to the Honourable, the Court of Directors and desired that it might accompany me home.'

Unfortunate coincidence, for this plant he had the honour and chagrin to report 'is in a most lively and luxuriant state, but as I have been so unfortunate as to lose in one case this most splendid production, yet have succeeded in the other, it does not afford me the same satisfaction as though it was included in my own collection and it would grieve me much to see it separated from the rest'.

Already Gibson had a scheme which he introduced to his master to prevent this separation: 'The following plan might be adopted, and, I deem, with success.'

He was not known as the intelligent gardener for nothing, and he had the remedy for transforming failure into success already worked out. If the duke would make application to the directors for the living plant he had no doubt it would be complied with immediately, for, after all, the duke could well be considered to have the greatest claim on it; hadn't he been the means and the cause of its introduction to this country? That was logical to Gibson and he followed his theory with a practical one. If only the living plant could be taken to Chatsworth then the duke could agree to the condition that one, or even two plants, would be returned to the directors as soon as the plant could be propagated. His last argument was telling indeed: 'If this is not done I fear that Amherstia will not only be lost to us but also quickly lost to England also.'

He then gave more detail of losses which he assured his master were comparatively nothing. Some few of the minute orchids, as might be expected on so long a voyage from India, were dead. His collection of seed and dried specimens of plants was extensive and would, he hoped, be found to consist of many new and rare things. There were also some specimens of natural history, moths, animals, skins, etc., which he hoped would also serve to add interest and profit to his mission.

Worried throughout the long voyage with plants on the poop in all weathers always on his mind, with branches and seed bags swinging on the cabin rafters all around him, Gibson now had other worries; how to get this most amazing botanical hoard, the largest living collection ever brought into this country, to Chatsworth.

He had applied his mind and imagination to the problem ahead and was able to give the duke the benefit of this. He anticipated, he wrote, some difficulty in transporting the collection to Chatsworth as it would be dangerous to remove any of the plants from the glazed cabins before they were unpacked in the comparative climatic safety of his glasshouses at home. He could see that coach transport would be useless both for the time taken and the rough handling the cases would get on the rackety roads from London to Derbyshire.

There was another way though, he reminded the duke, which he suggested was the safest and quickest method of transport: 'I would have a fly boat at Pickfords and take everything at once by canal to Cromford from which they would be forwarded to reach Chatsworth the same day.'

That was a journey by fast narrow canal boat (with frequent changes of tow horses) of some 150 miles via the Thames, Brentford, through the Regent's Canal and the Grand Junction through the Midlands, passing Northampton, Leicester, then into the Derby Canal to Erewash, finishing at Cromford near Chesterfield, a matter of a few miles to Chatsworth and safety.

He asked for a decision before *Zenobia* finally tied up in St Katharine Dock, London river, and also asked for ducal influence to be brought to bear on that old bugbear of all travellers, the Customs. It was important, he said, that all his precious plants should be unshipped immediately *Zenobia* docked. He knew what he was doing when he asked 'Your Grace to order the means by which this can be executed as I am entirely unacquainted with the rules and regulations of the Customs with regard to importing plants, seeds, etc.'.

The very same day—it must have been a busy one for him—he sent another long, informative letter to his immediate superior, Joseph Paxton, to whom he gave a few more details of the voyage. They had touched at the Cape and sailed from there on 18th May, touched at St Helena on 1st June and then the sad, sad news of the demise of amherstia had to be told again. The plant in which he took the greatest pleasure, and to which he directed his sole, nay almost soul, interest was dead. It was with the deepest regret he had to give this unfavourable information. But now that was done, would Paxton write and press the duke to get in touch with the East India Company Court of Directors? 'Get Amherstia down to Chatsworth', he pleaded, 'or we'll lose it.' He repeated his fears about an overland journey and again put forward his canal project. He personally would take amherstia to the City Road warehouse of Pickford's where the fly boat, he advocated, would be waiting.

He had time now to think of the plants sent previously, without the supreme advantage of a Gibson's solicitude and care, and hoped that Paxton had received them in a flourishing condition, for, as he well knew, 'there are many things experienced on board ship which act in so many different opposite directions against vegetation that I am almost surprised at one of the plants thus surviving.'

The number of boxes, not counting his fifteen, was twenty-eight and six in the *Northumberland* which had left Calcutta seven days before *Zenobia*, and he longed to know how Chatsworth had received them all, dying, dead or living.

The passage, now he had time to remember something of the voyage, had been a fine one, but not quick. Fortunately the weather had been highly favourable during the greater part of it, to which he attributed his success with his cargo. There had been some bad weather—not what the sailors called bad: that meant the ship lost a mast or two, he told Paxton—but it had given him some anxious hours roping his poop cases, and covering them with tarpaulins.

A last stern direction for Paxton came from Gibson for his beloved amherstia; would he please see that the order for the redirecting of his tree was on board immediately they docked, for 'if I loose sight of it depend upon its destruction as no care whatever would be taken of it'. Perhaps it might be stowed in the Customs House for days and not noticed. He had asked for Mr Bailey, the duke's gardener at Chiswick, to meet him at the dockside.

London at last; everything was in confusion, people ran here and there, the docks seemed in one vast commotion, but what did Gibson care—he was home, 'filled', as he said, 'with joy at the sight of my native shores from which I shall never again take my departure, 'tis a feeling inexpressible'.

Prompted by Gibson's heartfelt literary efforts on behalf of his charges the wheels began to turn, the first set in motion by the duke, who wrote to Sir James B. Carnac, chairman of the East India Company, although he was unacquainted with that gentleman—hard times needed hard measures! The duke wrote with almost as much earnestness as Gibson, certainly more than could have been expected from a ducal personage. He excused himself for this because of his anxiety. He shortly outlined the story: 'About two years ago I was induced by the kindness of Dr Wallich to send a young gardener to Calcutta. A great object of his mission was to procure me a plant of Amherstia, which for want of care and superintendence on the voyage has hitherto been found impossible to bring alive to this country. Two plants from the Botanic Garden have now arrived in London under the care of my gardener. The one directed to me has died, the other directed to the Court of Directors is alive and will, with care, become flourishing.

'It is to supplicate for this plant that I venture to write to you and be assured there is not in England a gardener capable of rearing it and propagating it so sure as Mr Paxton, with the assistance of the young man who has nursed the plant during its long voyage. I have today been to India House and seen my friend Mr Fenton. It was necessary to remove the plant from the ship—I shall, however, be most ready to return the Amherstia whenever you demand me to do so.'

Then from Chatsworth, Paxton, in the act of sending to London the daily fruit, flower and vegetable box packed for Devonshire House, had been given Gibson's letter. 'I am in such a state of excitement', he told the duke, 'at its contents, particularly to that what relates to the Amherstia that I shall worry myself to death if I stay at Chatsworth. . . . If ever I lay my hands on Amherstia all the Directors in the world shall never make me let go till it reaches Chatsworth. I have therefore decided to leave Chatsworth by the coach for London. I cannot wait any more.'

There was a footnote—the *Duke of Northumberland*'s boxes had arrived in good condition.

A doubt had meanwhile arisen in London, a doubt which almost spelled tragedy, for the duke had heard that maybe amherstia was not unique after all. He wrote anxiously to the President of the Horticultural Society, probably the most knowledgeable man of his day on orchids and exotics, to know if this calamitous news were correct. Was amherstia growing in London?

A quick answer settled all the duke's apprehensions. 'No, no, no,' wrote Dr Lindley; 'there is no Amherstia in the King's Road. Your Grace was quite right in your opinion, the impostor is *Brownea grandiceps*. Instead of deriving his origin from the temple garden of Buddha he has had no more dignified birthplace than the bush round a Demerara sugar plantation. I am so happy to be able to assure you that your Amherstia is as yet the only Amherstia in Europe.'

On 31st July from the East India Honourable Court of Directors came the anxiously awaited reply from Sir James Carnac. He begged in the name of the Court of Directors to ask the duke to accept amherstia.

The long story ends with the last letter in the Chatsworth correspondence—a note from Chatsworth from the duke to Sir James: Gibson and his canal cargo had arrived. Everything had been unpacked and everything was well. Amherstia was in a flourishing state and he added his sincere thanks for the court's kindness.

A last vignette from this, the largest botanical expedition mounted up to that time in England, was the picture of the duke sitting in the famous painted dining-room at Devonshire House in London with *Amherstia nobilis* in riotous bloom in a place of honour, outrivalling the artistic glories of this beautiful room while the duke's friends paid court to her as to any beautiful lady.

9. The End of an Era

So THAT was that. The introduction of the Wardian case and steam power as applied to shipping put an entirely new complexion on the art and artifices of plant hunting and its so vital consequence, the safe and speedy transportation of the hunter's spoils to his own country.

By 1842 Loddiges, the great London nurserymen, could boast of having used five hundred cases to bring plants home successfully from all parts of the globe. 'Whereas', they reported, 'we used to lose 19 out of 20 cases during the voyage 19 out of 20 is now the average that survive.' Sir William Hooker, writing from Kew in 1856, was able to say: 'They' (the Wardian cases) 'have been the means in the last 15 years of introducing more new and valuable plants to our gardens than were imported during the preceding century.' Many of these plants must have been the new plaything, the new favourite of the noble gardeners, the orchid, and, despite Sir William's statement, it is a well authenticated fact that during the reign of George III, from 1760 to 1820, which covers almost the whole range of collectors in this work, without the advantages of the case and with all the disadvantages of travel under sail, on horseback or on foot, nearly seven thousand new exotics were introduced into this country.

A list painstakingly worked out by Loudon in 1825 showed that at that time there were growing in England nearly one-fourth of the estimated flora of the world. Reaching right back into the centuries he totalled up 13,140 'exotic species and botanists' varieties', whose countries of origin he listed as follows: Europe, 4,169; Asia, 2,365; Africa, 2,639; South America, 644; North America, 2,353; Unknown, 970.

From the catalogue of plants in their possession in 1826 Conrad Loddiges and Sons could 'venture to assert that such an assembly of plants was never brought together before by any individual either in this country or abroad. The total number of species exceeds 8,000'. They then went on to describe botanically 120 hardy trees, 2,644 shrubs, and of tender exotics—309 ericas, 25 ixias, 68 aloes, 33 passiflora, 38 disemma, 73 acacia, 25 bignonia, 17 gardenia and 31 eucalyptus, to mention some of the more well-known and favoured.

In their soaring palm houses at Hackney, London, they had growing in magnificent tropical confusion 107 different species and varieties of palms from 28 different countries or islands.

This then was the sum of the work of the pioneer collectors, who had either surmounted or succumbed to every evil and ill of exploratory foreign travel to bring back the floral and arboreal treasures of the world.

With the return of Gibson to Chatsworth a new era, a new world, opened out to the botanical traveller. Orchidomania broke out, and for most of the remainder of the century orchid hunters were everywhere tearing these fantastic beauties from their natural haunts in their thousands. Whole tracts of forests were mown to the ground to get at the epiphytal treasure. This over, then much of the lure of the tropical, subtropical and antipodean exotics had gone, mainly—and this is no exaggeration—because most of the desirable, transferable and growable plants had been collected.

Higher, hardier plants were now to be sought for to suit a new fashion in gardens and gardening, the William Robinson era, of hardy herbaceous and rockery plants, as the Farrers, Wilsons and Wards of this world travelled the mountainous Asiatic ranges.

There was, and still is, adventure, excitement and romance to be found in botanical travel. But as the reading of any recently written plant hunting book will show, when compared with the desperate do or die struggles of the pioneer plant hunters during the years 1740 to 1840, almost all the sheer physical drudgery, danger and derring-do have vanished with faster and easier communications by both sea and land. Scientific interest in the physical well-being of the hunter has resulted in processed canned foods, vitamins and medical supplies all prepared for easy travelling, and in well-designed weather-resistant clothing. And it is comparatively easy to get supplies, botanical and otherwise, in and out of what formerly were almost inaccessible areas.

Even as late as 1856 Philip Henry Gosse in his *A Stroll Around Kew Conservatories* could write with truth: 'The greatest difficulty, however, in transmitting specimens from distant and savage countries, especially if they be far from the sea, arises from the want of these facilities for intercourse which are so common at home that we use them daily without a thought. To send large packages such as those which contain growing plants over a thousand miles of country without roads or bridges or vehicles through tangled and trackless forests, over precipitous mountains, along rivers full of rocks, rapids, cataracts and thousands of dangers among concealed and vindictive savages and half barbarous whites, more suspicious and jealous still—this seems a hopeless task. Yet it is one which the indefatigable perseverance, skill and science of the Englishman are constantly encountering and as constantly overcoming.'

We cannot do better than end on this note in the hope that the great gardening public as they admire the beauties of the garden will not ignore, or forget to spare a thought for, the services of our great botanical collectors, men who must rank among the greatest of our nation's benefactors, and of whom it can be proudly written, as of Wren, 'If you would seek their monument, look around.'

BIBLIOGRAPHY

Allen, P., *History of the Expedition Under the Command of Captains Lewis and Clarke*, 1843.

Amherst, A., *History of Gardening*, 1895.

Anderson, A. W., *The Coming of the Flowers*, 1950.

Andrews, H. C., *The Botanical Repository*, volume 46.

Anonymous, *The Three Famous Voyages of Captain James Cook Round the World*, 1888.

Belcher, Lady, *Mutineers on the 'Bounty'*, 1870.

Blake, S. T., in *Proceedings* of the Royal Society of Queensland, 1955.

Bligh, W. A., *A Voyage to the South Seas*, 1792; *A Narrative of the Mutiny on Board H.M.S. 'Bounty'*, 1810.

Bretschneider, Emil, *History of European Botanical Discoveries in China*, 1898.

Brett, James N. G., *Life of Peter Collinson*, 1925.

Brewster, D. E., in *Edinburgh Journal*, 1827.

Cameron, H. C., *Sir Joseph Banks*, 1952.

Cottage Gardener, The, volume vi.

Cox, E. H. M., *Plant Hunting in China*, 1945.

Cox, Emily M., *Plants of the World*, 1865.

Cox, R., *The Columbia River*, 1832.

Curtis, W., *Botanical Magazine*, volumes 1–14, 1787–1800.

Dawson, W. R., *The Banks Letters*, 1958.

Dickinson, V., *Miss Eden's Letters*, 1919.

Don, George, *African Journal*: MSS., Lindley Library.

Douglas, D., *Journal* (North-west America, 1823–7), Royal Horticultural Society, 1914.

Eden, E., *Up the Country—Letters from India*, 1842.

Ellis, J., 'Directions for Bringing Plants from the East Indies and some Additional Observations on the Method of Preserving Seed from Foreign Parts', *Philosophical Transactions*, volumes 51, 58.

Empire Review, volume 19, 1910.

Evans, Pole I. B., *The Flowering Plants of South Africa*, 1925.

Field, B. (ed.), *New South Wales*, 1825.

Gardeners' Chronicle, 1842, 1881–3, 1885, 1891, 1900, 1926, 1928.

Gardeners' Magazine, The (ed. J. C. Loudon), 1826, 1830, 1835, 1836, 1840, 1842.

Gibson, John, Letters, 1836, MSS., Chatsworth Collection.

Gosse, P. H., *Wandering Through the Conservatories at Kew*, 1856.

Hadfield, M., *Pioneers in Gardening*, 1955.

Hawks, Ellison, *Pioneers of Plant Study*, 1928.

Hooker, Sir J. D., *Journal of the Rt. Hon. Sir J. Banks*, 1896; *Himalayan Journals*, volume ii, 1854.

Hooker, W., *Companion to the Botanical Magazine*, volume ii.

Horticultural Register, volume 63.

Jackson, B. D., *Guide to the Literature of Botany*, 1881.

Kew Bulletin, 1891.

King, J., *A Voyage to the Pacific Ocean*, volumes i, ii, iii, 1784.

Lambert, A. B., *A Description of the Genus Pinus*, 1832.

Lee, I., *The Coming of the British to Australia*, 1906.

Lees, O. and M., *Desert Plants*, 1959.

Lett, Canon, H. W., 'Botanists of Northern Ireland', *Irish Naturalist*, 1913.

Lettson, J. C., *Hortus Uptonensis*, 1781.

Lewis, Meriwether and Clarke, Capt., *Travels to the Source of the Missouri and to the Pacific Ocean*, 1804.

Liger, L., *The Retir'd Gardener;* translated by J. Carpenter, 1717.

Lindley, J., *Instructions for Collecting and Packing Seeds and Plants from Foreign Countries*, 1825.

Linnean Society, *Transactions*, volume xii; *Proceedings*, 1856.

Loudon, J. C., *Hortus Britannicus*, 1832; *Magazine of Natural History*, 1829–40; *Arboretum et Fruticetum Britannica*, 1838.

Maiden, J. H., *Sir Joseph Banks, Father of Australia*, 1909.

Masson, F., *Stapeliae Novae*, 1796.

Menninger, E. A., *What Flowering Tree is That?*, 1958.

Merrill, E. P., *Chronica Botanica*, volume 14, 1950–4.

Nicholson, J., *Anecdotes of the 18th Century*, 1812–15.

Overland Monthly, October 1883.

Parkinson, S., *A Journal of a Voyage to the South Seas*, 1773.

Philosophical Transactions, 1759–70.

Pritzel, G. A., *Thesaurus Literaturae Botanicae*, 2nd edition, 1872–7.

Queensland, Royal Society of, *Proceedings*, 1955.

Rees, A., *Encyclopaedia of Arts, Science and Literature*, 1819.

Rhind, W., *Rhind's Vegetable Kingdom*, 1868.

Royal Horticultural Society, *Transactions*, volumes i, ii, iii, iv, vi.

Royal Society, *Catalogue of Scientific Papers*, volume ii.

Sloane, Sir H., *Natural History of Jamaica*, 1707–25.

Smith, Edward, *The Life of Sir Joseph Banks*, 1911.

Smith, J. E., *Linnean Correspondence*, volume ii, 1821.

Smith, Lady, *Memoirs and Correspondence of Sir J. E. Smith*, 1832.

South African Botanical Society, *Journal*, 1958–9.

South African Philosophical Society, *Transactions*, volume 4.

Thunberg, C. P., *Travels in Europe, Africa and Asia*, volume ii, *circa* 1780.

Veitch, James, *A Manual of Orchidaceous Plants*, 1882–4.

Veitch, J. H., *Hortus Veitchii*, 1906; *A Manual of Coniferae*, 1881.

Wallace, A. R., *Island Life*, 1911.

Ward, F. Kingdon, *The Romance of Plant Hunting*, 1924.

Ward, N. B., *The Growth of Plants in Closely Glazed Cases*, 1842.

Weston, R., *Flora Anglicana*, 1775.

Wheatley, H. B. (ed.), *Evelyn's Diary*, 1906.

Wilson, E. J., *Vineyard Nurseries, Hammersmith*, 1961.

Index